STEMMING from original m. used in the Communications Development Training Program of the Bell Telephone Laboratories, this book discusses the fundamentals of modulation theory including recent progress in this and related fields.

In recent years the underlying philosophy of communication theory has been extended to include new factors, and a more general analysis points to possible savings from: (1) the statistical structure of the original message, (2) matching the information-bearing signals to the noisy channel, and (3) final destination and form of the message. Particular systems of modulation are treated here on a unified basis from the most modern information theory.

The first eight chapters are concerned with the pertinent general philosophy and provide a framework that permits one system to be compared with another on a rational basis and in the light of recent analytical advance. Such factors as non-surpassable ideals, the rate of receiving information, redundancy, band-width occupancy, threshold effects, signal-to-noise ratio, distortion, interchannel crosstalk, and probability of errors are used for comparison. The last twelve chapters contain theoretical treatments of particular modulation systems.

Only a knowledge of elementary calculus and some knowledge of Fourier methods are needed to benefit from this book. For help in grasping and retaining essentials, review questions and problems have been included.

MODULATION THEORY

PROBABILITY AND ITS ENGINEERING USES. *By* THORNTON C. FRY. Second Edition.

TRANSMISSION NETWORKS AND WAVE FILTERS. *By* T. E. SHEA.

ECONOMIC CONTROL OF QUALITY OF MANUFACTURED PRODUCT. *By* W. A. SHEWHART.

ELECTROMECHANICAL TRANSDUCERS AND WAVE FILTERS. *By* WARREN P. MASON. Second Edition.

POISSON'S EXPONENTIAL BINOMIAL LIMIT. *By* E. C. MOLINA.

ELECTROMAGNETIC WAVES. *By* S. A. SCHELKUNOFF.

NETWORK ANALYSIS AND FEEDBACK AMPLIFIER DESIGN. *By* HENDRICK W. BODE.

CAPACITORS—THEIR USE IN ELECTRONIC CIRCUITS. *By* M. BROTHERTON.

FOURIER INTEGRALS FOR PRACTICAL APPLICATIONS. *By* GEORGE A. CAMPBELL and RONALD M. FOSTER.

APPLIED MATHEMATICS FOR ENGINEERS AND SCIENTISTS. *By* S. A. SCHELKUNOFF. Second Edition.

EARTH CONDUCTION EFFECTS IN TRANSMISSION SYSTEMS. *By* ERLING D. SUNDE.

THEORY AND DESIGN OF ELECTRON BEAMS. *By* J. R. PIERCE. Second Edition.

PIEZOELECTRIC CRYSTALS AND THEIR APPLICATION TO ULTRASONICS. *By* WARREN P. MASON.

MICROWAVE ELECTRONICS. *By* JOHN C. SLATER.

PRINCIPLES AND APPLICATIONS OF WAVEGUIDE TRANSMISSION. *By* GEORGE C. SOUTHWORTH.

TRAVELING-WAVE TUBES. *By* J. R. PIERCE.

ELECTRONS AND HOLES IN SEMICONDUCTORS. *By* WILLIAM SHOCKLEY.

FERROMAGNETISM. *By* RICHARD M. BOZORTH.

THE DESIGN OF SWITCHING CIRCUITS. *By* WILLIAM KEISTER, ALASTAIR E. RITCHIE, and SETH H. WASHBURN.

SPEECH AND HEARING IN COMMUNICATION. *By* HARVEY FLETCHER. Second Edition.

MODULATION THEORY. *By* HAROLD S. BLACK.

SWITCHING RELAY DESIGN. *By* R. L. PEEK, JR., and H. N. WAGAR.

TRANSISTOR TECHNOLOGY, Volume I. *Edited by* H. E. BRIDGERS, J. H. SCAFF, and J. N. SHIVE.

TRANSISTOR TECHNOLOGY, Volume II. *Edited by* F. J. BIONDI.

TRANSISTOR TECHNOLOGY, Volume III. *Edited by* F. J. BIONDI.

PHYSICAL ACOUSTICS AND THE PROPERTIES OF SOLIDS. *By* WARREN P. MASON.

THE PROPERTIES, PHYSICS AND DESIGN OF SEMICONDUCTOR DEVICES. *By* J. N. SHIVE.

PRINCIPLES OF ELECTRON TUBES. *By* J. W. GEWARTOWSKI and H. A. WATSON.

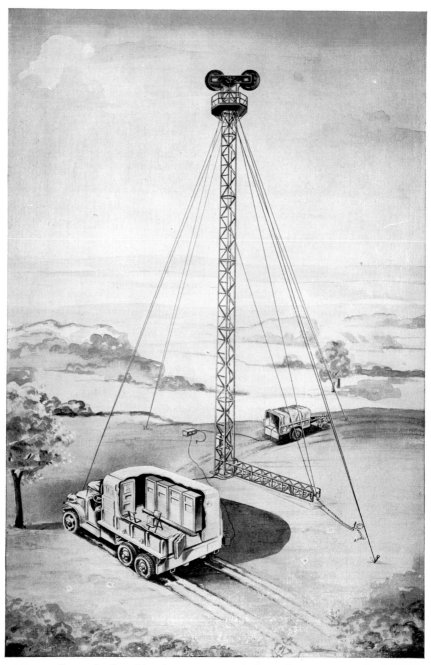

PLATE I Portable microwave transmitting and receiving installation

MODULATION
THEORY

HAROLD S. BLACK

Member of the Technical Staff
Bell Telephone Laboratories, Inc.

D. VAN NOSTRAND COMPANY, Inc.

PRINCETON, NEW JERSEY

TORONTO   NEW YORK   LONDON

D. VAN NOSTRAND COMPANY, INC.
120 Alexander St., Princeton, New Jersey (*Principal office*)
24 West 40th Street, New York 18, New York

D. VAN NOSTRAND COMPANY, LTD.
358, Kensington High Street, London, W.14, England

D. VAN NOSTRAND COMPANY (Canada), LTD.
25 Hollinger Road, Toronto 16, Canada

First Published August 1953

*Reprinted May 1956, November 1958, February 1960,
August 1962, January 1966*

PREFACE

This book discusses the fundamentals of modulation theory in the light of recent progress in this and related fields. It is addressed to advanced students and practising engineers.

In recent years the underlying philosophy of communication theory has been extended to include new factors. The more general analysis includes possible savings due to: (1) the statistical structure of the original message, (2) matching the information-bearing signals to the noisy channel, and (3) final destination of the message. Radical advances and outstanding practical applications of new systems of modulation have been made as a direct result of the clearer understanding and new points of view that the extended theory of communication affords. Considerable interest is also being shown in possibilities of further theoretical and practical advances.

Particular systems of modulation, some old and some new, are here treated on a unified basis consistent with modern information theory. The first eight chapters are concerned with the pertinent general philosophy. They provide a framework that permits the reader to compare one system with another on a rational basis and in the light of recent analytical advance. Comparison is from the standpoint of such factors as nonsurpassable ideals, the rate of receiving information, redundancy, band-width occupancy, threshold effects, signal-to-noise ratio, distortion, interchannel crosstalk, probability of errors, et cetera. The last twelve chapters are concerned with the theoretical treatment of particular modulation systems.

The text stems from a revision of material used for three successive years in the Communications Development Training Program of The Bell Telephone Laboratories. The experience of using the material in this program suggests that the text is suitable for individual study and reference as well as for classroom instruction. A reader needs to know elementary calculus and to have some knowledge of Fourier methods in order to benefit from the entire book. Except to illustrate a discussion or to promote understanding by dealing with concrete situations, the text does not discuss design techniques, methods of instrumentation, or specific applications. These topics have been covered elsewhere. Paper application of theory often helps readers of such a book as this to grasp and retain essentials. Review questions in the Appendix and problems at the ends

v

of certain chapters have been included for this purpose. However, a student is likely to benefit most by asking his own questions and formulating his own problems.

The author wishes to acknowledge the wholehearted cooperation and help of his many colleagues, particularly the suggestions of J. O. Edson, R. V. L. Hartley, H. Nyquist, R. K. Potter, and C. E. Shannon. Much credit is due J. G. Kreer, Jr., M. E. Mohr, and C. O. Mallinckrodt for their substantial contributions to the treatment of amplitude modulation, frequency modulation, and pulse modulation, respectively. The author is indebted to K. M. Collins for his interest and editorial assistance and to C. Hartley and H. P. Gridley for directing the production of the final plates and drawings, respectively. Commendation is due Mrs. Frances A. Richards for her meticulous care and accuracy in copying the manuscript.

H. S. BLACK

Murray Hill, New Jersey
January, 1953

CONTENTS

CHAPTER 1

HISTORICAL BACKGROUND

Boy winks at girl. Girl smiles. Here is an example of communication wherein messages are sent and received. Very often, the message itself is not in a form capable of being propagated over the transmission medium. Modulation is a process whereby the message is translated into information-bearing signals for purposes of transmission over the intervening medium. The receiver is waiting to be informed. This is accomplished by the arrival of a received wave, and modulation describes the process whereby the original message is recovered from the incoming information-bearing signals, a modulated light wave in the boy-meets-girl example. Moreover, as will be brought out in Chapter 2, modulation can be utilized for a wide variety of purposes.

In its broad aspects, modulation theory is closely related to efficient communication. Modulation is considered to include the general processing of the message, to the end that the message may be uniquely represented by signals that are appropriate for transmission to the receiver. At the receiver, by a process that, in some cases, is essentially remodulation (Chapter 10, p. 157), the wanted message is recovered by demodulating or decoding the noisy, incoming, information-bearing signals. Viewed analytically, the entire process of recovering the message is regarded as modulation. No matter how, when, or where we communicate, we usually encounter modulation.

The historical background of the basic concepts underlying present-day modulation theory deserves at least brief examination. Such a review can be helpful in relation both to new engineering applications and to extensions of the theory. Moreover, the historical background forms an interesting introduction to the philosophy of modulation. On first reading, however, it should be appreciated that, in this first chapter, technical terms and concepts have been freely used in advance of their later definition and development.

MEANING OF MODULATION

Before attempting a presentation of the historical background, let us first consider another illustration of the meaning of modulation. Fig-

1

ure 1–1 illustrates the application of the terms *message* and *information* to a complete system of communication and shows the modulation process as including all of the functions performed by the complete transmitter or receiver. This represents an *extension* of the customary definition of modulation. Although the extended definition includes the older and more familiar kinds of modulation, it is convenient to retain both the customary and extended definitions, particularly since no question will arise as to which usage is intended.

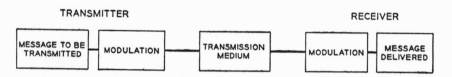

MESSAGE TO BE TRANSMITTED denotes a particular selection from among an aggregate of entities. An "entity" is regarded as anything which can be distinguished. The groups of entities which constitute possible selections from the aggregate and from among which a sender is free to choose, are subject to general and particular restrictions applicable to the occasion.

Each message has associated with it information peculiar to itself, determined as to its nature by the selection made by the sender, and as to its amount by statistics relating to the number and sort of different selections available to the sender within the existing restrictions.

At the transmitting end MODULATION is defined as the entire process whereby the message to be conveyed is uniquely specified and unambiguously represented by information-bearing signals. Two steps are necessary for efficient communication. First, use the most concise specification to represent the desired message. Second, use the optimal signal representation for transmission over the medium.

The TRANSMISSION MEDIUM may require repeaters. Provision for dropping and adding message channels; arrangements for branching and interconnecting systems; inter-system synchronization; alarms; telemetering; signaling; etc.: illustrate the types of situations that may be encountered at some of the repeaters.

Likewise regarded as MODULATION is the entire process at the receiving end whereby, in response to information-bearing signals, the original message is produced in the form desired and made available for delivery as the MESSAGE DELIVERED when and where it is wanted.

The over-all purpose is to deliver the message in whatever form desired, when and where it is wanted.

Fig. 1–1   Complete communication system

In communicating a message by electric signals (Fig. 1–1), one of the first steps is to represent the selected message by information-bearing signals. Redundancy is avoided only if the representation constitutes the most concise specification for uniquely distinguishing the selected message from all others of the class considered. From the standpoint of best over-all efficiency, the signal representation should be further transformed to an optimal representation which takes into account the probability that the signals will be disturbed by noise and other factors before reaching the receiver. Once information-bearing signals are generated, they may be moved about in frequency or otherwise altered by additional steps of modulation preparatory to their transmission over the medium, or as a preliminary step to multiplexing operations. Analogous examples of compound steps of modulation may be encountered either at the repeaters or at the receiving terminals.

Sometimes, as implied by Fig. 1–1, the receiver is called upon to make the information of the message available in some altogether different form from either the information-bearing signals or the original message. This is by no means unusual. For example, recording a received telephone message on a disk record means that the information which was received as an undulating electric signal is recorded and made available on the record as a continuously varying displacement in space. As another example, suppose the recipient be totally deaf. Then the receiver might display the message information as visible speech (Ref. 1).*

HISTORICAL NOTE

Although not formulated with mathematical rigor, some of the fundamental concepts of interest here are almost as old as the electrical transmission of telegraph messages. In particular, multiplexing by frequency and time division appeared at a very early stage in the history of this development. An early American invention by Moses B. Farmer, conceived in 1852 and patented in 1853, describes the transmission of a plurality of telegraph messages over a single line by the process of allocating independent intervals of time to the transmission of each message. To accomplish this, he utilized two rapidly revolving synchronous commutators, one at each end of the line. This is an example of multiplexing messages by time division.

Code transmission appeared even earlier and dates back to the first telegraph message on record, which was transmitted over a 10-mile line by Samuel F. B. Morse on January 24, 1838.

"In the latter part of the year 1832, Samuel F. B. Morse, an American artist, while on a voyage from France to the United States, conceived the idea of the electromagnetic telegraph. It was over ten years later, 1843 and 1844, that the first experimental line between Washington and Baltimore was constructed. The following year, 1845, telegraph lines began to be built over other routes." P. C. HOERNEL, "The Artificial Line," *Bell Laboratories Record*, New York, Vol. 1, October, 1925, pp. 51–60.

"On May 24, 1844 Samuel F. B. Morse telegraphed from Washington to Baltimore the historic sentence: 'What hath God wrought?' This was not, however, the first telegraph message on record. On January 24, 1838, at New York University where he was a professor of Fine Arts, Morse exhibited his invention to a company of invited guests. One of these wrote on a slip of paper, and Morse transmitted over a ten-mile wire the sentence: 'Attention, the Universe! By kingdoms, right wheel!' — a prophetic foreshadowing of the important part which electrical communications were to play in bringing nations into better understanding and closer cooperation." *Telephone Almanac*, New York, 1924, p. 9.

* The references cited are listed at the end of each chapter according to the number used in the text.

However, Morse was not first in this field.   Joseph Henry was the first (1831 and 1832) to construct an electric telegraph using an electromagnet as the receiving element and he demonstrated its operation over a line one mile long.   Henry's telegraph included a battery, a line, and a receiving device consisting of an electromagnet with a polarized armature so arranged as to strike a bell when reversals of current were sent.   He was the first to employ audible reception.   First to formulate rules for working over long lines, his use of an electromagnet for rapid signaling formed the basis of later commercial telegraph development, ocean cable systems and contained the principle of all telephone call bells.

Also, it is significant to note that representation of code characters by a multi-unit code where each code character in turn is represented by a particular sequence of on-or-off pulses was proposed independently by Shilling, Gauss and Weber, and Steinheil in the 1830's.   A five-unit code was used commercially by Whitehouse in 1853.   Gauss and Weber employed a single wire and a deflecting galvanometer to communicate with one another and concluded that combinations of only five code elements were sufficient for communication.   Viewed theoretically, this, too, is an example of time division because the five code elements constituting each code character are multiplexed by time division.

Looking further, we find a time-division electric telegraph system that goes back ten years earlier.   This older system used a plurality of time-division intervals, one for each letter.   This was an improvement on the use of a separate wire for each letter of the alphabet as proposed much earlier (1758) by a Scot named Marshall and often considered the first *practical* telegraphy scheme.   Another synchronous telegraph arrangement built by Ronalds in 1823 also deserves mention.   At each end of a wire, disks were revolved slowly in unison.   Around the periphery of the disks were the letters of the alphabet.   When a particular letter appeared in an aperture at the sending end, a key was closed and a spark at the receiver illuminated the same letter there.

Lloyd Espenschied called the writer's attention to another interesting recognition of fundamentals, appearing in a book on multiplex telegraphy published in 1885.   This book was by A. E. von Granfeld and entitled "Die Mehrfach-Telegraphic auf Einem Drahte."   In the Introduction and also on pages 252 to 258, von Granfeld not only uses the terms *time division* and *frequency division*, but also goes on to speculate as to the likelihood of their having a common root in time.

Hardly a generation following the transmission of the first words by telephone in 1875, it was demonstrated experimentally that speech messages could be multiplexed by time division.   The over-all performance was checked by demonstrating that simultaneous telephone conversations could be separated without serious mutual interference or noticeable impairment in quality. Early attempts to exploit the invention commercially were unsuccessful due to practical difficulties of instrumentation. The problems of high-speed mechanical switching, employed as the time-division means, were unsurmountable.

Apart from the requirements that time-division systems impose on the medium, there is a basic question to be answered about the rate at which each channel in turn is connected to the line. Namely, how fast do we have to commutate for proper simultaneous communication. Today we know from the sampling principle (Chap. 4) that for speech transmission each voice-frequency channel should be connected momentarily to the line at a rate in excess of twice the highest voice frequency to be transmitted. At the turn of the century, it was thought that a rate equal to the highest voice frequency was proper. This early conclusion was arrived at experimentally. As we know today, the interpretation of the results was in error because the frequency response of the telephone instruments used was only half as high as assumed.

These experiments are described in an article by Mr. Willard M. Miner in the *Electrical World and Engineer*, December 5, 1903, page 920. Miner was associated with Lieutenant Jarvis Patten who previously had invented a system of multiplex telegraphy. Miner acquired the patents and apparatus of Patten several years prior to 1903 and undertook to apply this apparatus to the development of a system of time division multiplex telephony, but he found that Patten's telegraph apparatus was commercially inoperative telephonically.

Thereupon Miner devised new apparatus and using his new embodiments found that switching rates corresponding to 1,000 to 2,000 samples per second per channel would not answer the purpose for ordinary telephony, but beyond 3,000 improved results were obtained which got markedly better at 3,500 or 3,600, the best result being obtained at about 4,320 samples per second per channel. Miner points out that the duration of contact (duration of the sampling interval) is not important and in U. S. Patent 745,734 (December 1, 1903) calls such a switch a distributor or "sunflower." Although not affecting the quality of the direct transmission, the duration of contact has an important bearing on interchannel crosstalk when the band width of the system is limited as shown by Carson and also Bennett. This is demonstrated in Carson's memorandum of May 25, 1920 which W. R. Bennett refers to on page 200 of his paper (Ref. 2) entitled "Time-Division Multiplex Systems."

What seems extraordinary in retrospect is the slow evolution of quantitative expressions concerning the above-described concepts. Not until 1920 does there appear to have been mathematical proof of the sampling principle as applied to communication. Then John R. Carson, in his unpublished memorandum, presented a mathematical treatment covering one special case of sampling. He also enumerated quantitative requirements for a commutator-type of time-division system, including a discussion of its signal-to-noise ratio and interchannel crosstalk as a function of the band width and certain other parameters. In particular, Carson demonstrated that, if a signal is sampled instantaneously at regular intervals and at a rate slightly higher than twice the highest signal frequency, the samples will contain all the information available in the original signal.

Time-division telephony was apparently set up experimentally at an earlier date than frequency division. In 1914 R. A. Heising constructed an experimental frequency-division system, providing two conversations over a single circuit. But two inventions, the vacuum tube and the electric wave filter, were needed to make frequency division attractive commercially in the fields where it subsequently found world-wide applications. Moreover, not until very recently has time division shown possibilities of challenging conventional methods in broad-band applications, especially in the wire plant where frequency space is at a premium.

When in 1922 Carson disproved the claim that frequency modulation could save some of the band width required by amplitude modulation, he noted that all of the schemes devoted to this end involved a misconception. Two years later the misconception was demonstrated rigorously by Nyquist (Ref. 3) when he showed that the number of telegraph signals per unit of time which can be transmitted over any line is directly proportional to line band width. A well-known practical application of this new principle occurred in 1927, when Gray, Horton, and Mathes (Ref. 4) gave the first comprehensive theoretical treatment of the relationship between band width and quality of television images. In this discussion they formulated the minimum band-width requirements for a high-definition television system years in advance of its practical realization. Also Nyquist in 1928 (Ref. 5) extended and elaborated upon his earlier treatment of the theory of telegraph transmission.

In 1928 Hartley (Ref. 6) generalized earlier results, and among his conclusions he stated: "The total amount of information which may be transmitted over a system whose transmission is limited to frequencies lying in a restricted range is proportional to the product of the frequency range which it transmits by the time during which it is available for transmission." Hartley's treatment represented a first step in the direction of measuring a message and the message-transmitting capacity of a system. His philosophy found ready acceptance and recognition as a fundamental concept of communication.

Before entering upon further theoretical discussion of some of the present-day basic concepts of modulation theory, it seems worth while to outline in more detail the particular results presented in the Nyquist and Hartley papers.

SPEED OF SIGNALING

Nyquist (Refs. 3 and 5) set forth certain theoretical results pertaining to telegraphy which are fundamental to the theory of the transmission of information-bearing signals by wave propagation. Expressed in terms of present-day nomenclature, these were that the required frequency band is directly proportional to the signaling speed, and the minimum band required for unambiguous interpretation is substantially equal to half the number of code elements per second. Furthermore, he showed that the latter is substantially independent of the number of quantized values which a particular code element can assume, provided the peak noise is less than half a quantum step. Speed of signaling will be defined as the number of code elements per second, and code element was defined as the contribution to the impressed signal ascribed to a given time unit. Shapes of successive code elements were postulated as usually the same, so that they differ only by a magnitude factor. The number of possible magnitudes depends upon the number of quantum steps. Reference should be made to Chapter 5 for exact definitions and discussion of these terms.

It could be reasoned that these results follow directly from the earlier statement of the sampling theory advanced by John R. Carson, noting in the telegraph case that the information is quantized. Moreover, by extending this reasoning, it would have been possible to deduce a generalized relationship between band width and signal-to-noise ratio. In fact, Nyquist did consider briefly the effect of noise, imperfections, and interference in limiting the amount of information that could be transmitted and, conversely, also pointed out that in a quantized system there is no object in reducing interference beyond the point where the signal can be deciphered with certainty and ease.

Nyquist also reviewed the dual aspect of the transmitted wave, both as a function of frequency, requiring the so-called steady-state method of treatment, and as a function of time requiring the so-called method of transients. He showed that in principle either method may be used to evaluate the response and behavior of a system.

Nyquist considered the optimum choice of code types to transmit maximum information with a given number of signal elements. Also, he suggested signal shaping to permit maximum speed of code transmission without undue interference. Starting with an assumption that the sum of noise and other interference approaches but is less than half a quantum step, he demonstrated that the measure of the amount of information transmitted per second is approximately proportional to: the logarithm of the number of values a code element may assume times the number of code elements constituting a code character times the number of code characters per second.

NYQUIST INTERVAL

If the essential frequency range is limited to B cycles per second, $2B$ was given by Nyquist as the maximum number of code elements per second that could be unambiguously resolved, assuming the peak interference is less than half a quantum step. This rate is generally referred to as signaling at the Nyquist rate and $1/2B$ has been termed a *Nyquist interval*. The full significance and importance of this interval are brought out in most of the chapters to follow, particularly Chapters 6 and 7.

HARTLEY'S EXPRESSION FOR INFORMATION CAPACITY

Hartley (Ref. 6) stated that the amount of information that can be transmitted is proportional to the product of the width of the frequency range and the time it is available. This principle is true if carefully interpreted, but it should be kept in mind that certain assumptions are implied and some factors have been neglected. In particular, it should be appreciated that in engineering applications it would not be economically practical to make use of the full physical possibilities of a system.

The foregoing relation about information capacity refers to forms of communication which are carried on by means of magnitude-*time* functions. In certain instances it has provided a ready means of checking whether claims for a complicated system lie within the range of physical possibility.

In the case of a disk phonographic record, the information is in the form of a magnitude-*space* function. In picture transmission, the information transmitted existed originally as a magnitude-*space* function. The analog of frequency in the alternating space wave is the number of complete cycles or waves executed in unit distance, and this is the reciprocal of its wave length. This reciprocal Hartley designated as "wave number." Consequently, the information transmitted is measured by the product of frequency-range by time when it is in electrical form and by the product of wave-number-range by distance when it is in graphic form. Hartley demonstrated that when a record is converted into an electric current, or vice versa, the corresponding products for the two are equal regardless of the velocity of reproduction. Similarly, if a picture is enlarged without changing its detail or fineness of intensity discrimination, the product of wave-number-range by distance remains unchanged.

To illustrate the application of the principle to television, Hartley considered the evaluation of the band width necessary to maintain a constant view of the distant scene. By obtaining the product of the wave-number-range by the distance exactly as for a still picture, one need only to multiply by the number of images per second to obtain the total band width for continuous viewing. Hartley points out that the duration of the interval necessary to prevent flicker is an important factor, that the tendency to flicker is a property of the particular method of transmission, and perhaps the total frequency range required would be less for a system more like that of direct vision.

Hartley's paper (pages 542 to 545) includes six additional principles that are significant and concepts that are fundamental to recent further extensions of the general theory of communication. Information content is equated to the total number of code elements multiplied by the logarithm of the number of possible values a code element may assume. Moreover, it is pointed out that the information content is independent of how the code elements are grouped. The concept of quantization is introduced along with the suggestion that, by quantizing, the continuous magnitude-time function used in ordinary telephony may be transmitted by a succession of code symbols such as are employed in telegraphy. Although the resulting quantized voice wave is an approximation to the original voice wave, it can be made, in theory, to approach the original as closely as desired by reducing the size of the quantum steps. The criterion for successful transmission is that in no case shall the interference exceed half a step. Especially significant is the additional statement that, to obtain the maximum rate of transmission of information, the signal elements need to be spaced uniformly.

CONTEMPORANEOUS DEVELOPMENTS

Recent pulse systems and other applications of new methods of modulation emphasize that we are extending our basic concepts of communication theory. As indicated by the preceding discussion, important papers by Nyquist and Hartley discussed certain basic principles and presented the underlying philosophy of communication theory. Building on this foundation, Shannon (Refs. 7 to 9) has developed a more general theory by extending the earlier concepts to include new factors, such as the regions of uncertainty due to noise, the savings possible due to the statistical structure of the original message, and the savings possible due to the final destination of the message. Related contributions and original ideas have been developed by Wiener (Ref. 10).

Radical advances and outstanding practical applications of new systems of modulation (Refs. 11 to 15) have been reported which are the direct result of the clearer understanding and new points of view that the extended theory of communication affords. It is recognized that these developments open up a new unexplored field, and so it is not surprising to find that considerable interest is being shown (Refs. 16 to 20) in the applications, implications, and significance of the extended theory as well as in the possibility of further theoretical and practical advance.

References

1. R. K. Potter, G. A. Kopp, and H. C. Green, *Visible Speech*, D. Van Nostrand Co., Inc., New York, 1947.
2. W. R. Bennett, "Time-Division Multiplex Systems," *The Bell System Technical Journal*, New York, Vol. 20, No. 2, April 1941, pp. 199–221.
3. H. Nyquist, "Certain Factors Affecting Telegraph Speed," *The Bell System Technical Journal*, New York, Vol. 3, No. 2, April 1924, pp. 324–346.
4. F. Gray, J. W. Horton, and R. C. Mathes, "The Production and Utilization of Television Signals," *The Bell System Technical Journal*, New York, Vol. 6, No. 4, October 1927, pp. 560–603.
5. H. Nyquist, "Certain Topics in Telegraph Transmission Theory," *Transactions of the American Institute of Electrical Engineers*, New York, Vol. 47, April 1928, pp. 617–644.
6. R. V. L. Hartley, "Transmission of Information," *The Bell System Technical Journal*, New York, Vol. 7, No. 3, July 1928, pp. 535–563.
7. B. M. Oliver, J. R. Pierce, and C. E. Shannon, "The Philosophy of PCM," *Proceedings of the Institute of Radio Engineers*, New York, Vol. 36, No. 11, November 1948, pp. 1324–1331.
8. C. E. Shannon, "A Mathematical Theory of Communications," *The Bell System Technical Journal*, New York, Vol. 27, No. 3, July 1948, pp. 379–423 and Vol. 27, No. 4, October 1948, pp. 623–656.
9. C. E. Shannon, "Communication in the Presence of Noise," *Proceedings of the Institute of Radio Engineers*, New York, Vol. 37, No. 1, January 1949, pp. 10–21.
10. Norbert Wiener, *Cybernetics*, John Wiley and Sons, Inc., New York, 1948.
11. H. S. Black, J. W. Beyer, T. J. Grieser, and F. A. Polkinghorn, "A Multichannel Microwave Radio Relay System," *Transactions of the American Institute of Electrical Engineers*, New York, Vol. 65, December, 1946, pp. 798–806.
12. B. Trevor, O. E. Dow, and W. D. Houghton, "Pulse Time-Division Radio Relay," *RCA Review*, New York, Vol. 7, December 1946, pp. 561–575.
13. W. M. Goodall, "Telephony by Pulse-Code Modulation," *The Bell System Technical Journal*, New York, Vol. 26, No. 3, July 1947, pp. 395–409.
14. H. S. Black and J. O. Edson, "Pulse-Code Modulation," *Transactions of the American Institute of Electrical Engineers*, New York, Vol. 66, 1947, pp. 895–899.
15. L. A. Meacham and E. Peterson, "An Experimental Multichannel Pulse-Code Modulation System of Toll Quality," *The Bell System Technical Journal*, New York, Vol. 27, No. 1, January 1948, pp. 1–43.
16. W. R. Bennett, "Noise in PCM Systems," *Bell Laboratories Record*, New York, Vol. 26, No. 12, December 1948, pp. 495–499.
17. C. B. Feldman and W. R. Bennett, "Band Width and Transmission Performance," *The Bell System Technical Journal*, New York, Vol. 28, No. 3, July 1949, pp. 490–595.
18. D. Gabor, "Theory of Communication," *Institution of Electrical Engineers Journal*, London, Vol. 93, Part 3, 1946, pp. 429–457.
19. D. Gabor, "New Possibilities in Speech Transmission," *Institution of Electrical Engineers Journal*, London, Vol. 94, Part 3, 1947, pp. 369–387.
20. C. W. Earp, "Relationship Between Rate of Transmission of Information, Frequency Band Width, and Signal-to-Noise Ratio," *Electrical Communication*, New York, Vol. 25, No. 2, June 1948, pp. 178–195.

CHAPTER 2

WHY MODULATE?

Practical reasons for modulating stem from the necessity of preparing the message for transmission over the medium and preparing the received signals for their destination. For these same reasons, modulation may be used at repeaters and at branching points to interconnect systems and to facilitate dropping and adding channels. Additional special reasons for modulating arise in the numerous applications of electronics in many diverse fields.

TO PREPARE THE MESSAGE FOR TRANSMISSION

At the transmitting end, the selected message is rarely produced in a form suitable for direct transmission over the medium. It usually contains redundant information and hence can be shortened by taking advantage of its statistical structure. Moreover, the form is not likely to be most appropriate for all the conditions of delivery, including when, where, and how delivery is desired. It is not uncommon, therefore, to encounter a modulation process at the sending end. A minimum requirement is to convert the message that is to be transmitted into a form suitable for propagation over the transmitting medium. In the following paragraphs, several examples will be cited where modulation prepares the message for transmission.

To Multiplex Channels

Modulation permits multiplex transmission over a common medium. Two common methods, which are illustrated by Fig. 2–1, are time division and frequency division.

Time division is the process of propagating a plurality of information-bearing signals over a common medium, allocating a different time interval for the transmission of each signal. When channels are multiplexed by time division, each channel utilizes the entire frequency spectrum occupied by the system and modulation is used to produce the desired amplitude and phase relations that are essential to the process.

Frequency division is the process of propagating two or more information-bearing signals over a common path by using a different frequency band

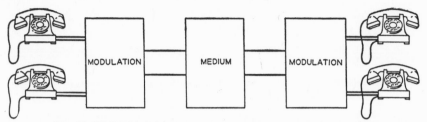

(a) GENERALIZED DIAGRAM OF TWO-CHANNEL CARRIER SYSTEM

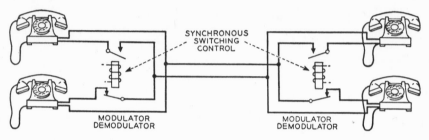

(b) AMPLITUDE MODULATION, TIME DIVISION

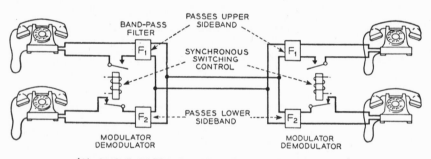

(C) SINGLE SIDEBAND MODULATION, FREQUENCY DIVISION

FIG. 2-1   Time-division, two-channel carrier system and frequency-division, two-channel carrier system

for the transmission of each signal. A good example is single-sideband modulation,* one of the older systems of modulation of widespread application. Single-sideband modulation translates the spectrum of the modulating wave in frequency by a specified amount, either with or without inversion. Thus, different channels can be translated to occupy different

---

* In 1925 the Morris Liebmann Prize was awarded to John R. Carson by the Institute of Radio Engineers for his discovery of the "single-sideband" method of carrier transmission by wire and radio.

frequency bands which clearly permits multiplexing channels by frequency division. Familiar examples are modern carrier systems.

To Shift Frequencies to Their Assigned Location

Modulation permits changing the frequencies of the information-bearing signals so that they fall in the particular band allocated or desired for purposes of propagation. For systems transmitting electric signals, the medium might be free space and the path of the transmission might be the path followed by a radiated beam or by guided transmission along an open-wire line. For many applications, however, it is preferable that the path be completely confined as in a coaxial cable or wave guide. In any event, if along the route the propagation characteristics are altered as, for example, by transferring from an open-wire line to cable, modulation again permits changing the frequencies as required.

To Increase Band-Width Occupancy and Transmitted Power

In translating the frequencies of the information-bearing signals, the modulation process may intentionally increase the frequency-space occupancy and increase the power, all for the purpose of simplifying the instrumentation. Amplitude modulation, widely used in radio broadcasting, affords a familiar example of the latter. High power is transmitted to permit simplification of the home receiver. High power is also emphasized in certain radar applications, and maximum pulse power and extreme range are often obtained by directly modulating the oscillator.

To Increase Frequencies for Ease in Radiation

Radio. If energy is to be radiated, the wave lengths corresponding to the radiated frequencies should be sufficiently short to permit the design of reasonably small and efficient radiators. To accomplish this, the information-bearing signals are often modulated up to high radio frequencies.

Voice Transmission Over an Air Path. Nature deals with an acoustic radiation problem in speech transmission in a similar fashion. This is doubly fortunate because the *modulating* wave is too low in frequency to be heard effectively by the human ear. The waves upon which modulations are imposed include buzz-like tones, generated by oscillation of the vocal cords, and hiss-like sounds that result when breath is forced past teeth or lips. The former are called "voiced" sounds and the latter, "unvoiced." These carriers are modulated by changes in tension of the vocal cords and changes in shape of the mouth cavities. Such changes are a result of muscular actions that occur at rates of the order of 10 cycles per second. In final speech the effects of modulation are evident in such things as the syllabic structure and frequency shifts that we recognize as inflections. Thus, information-bearing signals, at a low frequency of several cycles a second, are modulated upon much higher audio frequencies and these become the sounds of speech we hear.

To Balance Band-Width Occupancy and Sensitivity to Noise

At the transmitting end, preferably after the minimum specification necessary to represent the desired message has been determined, modulation may be used for the further purpose of either *increasing* or *decreasing* the band width of the spectrum of the information-bearing signals so as to obtain an economic balance between band-width occupancy and sensitivity to noise, interference, and other imperfections either of the transmission medium or other parts of the system. It is possible by an appropriate modulation process to trade extra band width for improvement in other system characteristics. One of the early and most widely used systems for capitalizing on the advantage of this exchange is the frequency-modulation system (Ref. 1)* proposed by Major Edwin H. Armstrong. The effectiveness of the process depends upon the peak value of the interference being less than the peak signal. Although frequency modulation is a well-known example, some of the more recent systems, for example, pulse-code modulation, afford possibilities of even more striking improvements.

To Translate Frequencies for Ease in Meeting Transmission Requirements

As might be expected, various situations are encountered in which, by shifting the frequency band occupied by the transmitted signals, it becomes easier to meet the over-all transmission requirements. For example, many types of messages (high-quality music, video television signals, et cetera) originally occupy many octaves of frequency. Transformers and equalizers designed to compensate for the delay distortion and attenuation characteristics of open-wire lines and cable pairs represent examples in which the complexity tends to be directly proportional to the number of octaves. Consequently, by translating the frequency band upwards by a modulating process, the range of frequencies considered in terms of octaves is reduced with the result that it becomes easier to satisfy the over-all transmission requirements of the system.

Another example appears in cable carrier systems. Over the frequency range used by existing types of cable carrier systems, the variation in attenuation is approximately proportional to frequency. Modulation at each repeater point by a method that inverts or pivots the transmitted band about its mid-point tends to equalize the loss over the signal band. The transmission loss of an even number of like spans is made substantially

* The references cited are listed at the end of each chapter according to the number used in the text.

independent of frequency, thereby permitting longer repeater spans and a great simplification of equalization and regulation.

TO TRANSLATE SIGNALS FROM ONE MEDIUM TO ANOTHER

To translate information-bearing signals from one medium to another is an additional reason for modulating. Clearly, this involves modifying conditions in the new medium according to those existing in the originating medium. In fact, the use of devices in which modulation changed the signal medium actually preceded (Ref. 2) the widespread and presently better-known use of modulation for the purpose of shifting signals from one location to another in the electrical frequency spectrum. In the paragraphs to follow, several examples will be mentioned.

Ordinary Telephony by Voice-Frequency Methods

In ordinary telephony by voice-frequency methods, the fluctuating sound intensities produced by the spoken word are usually regarded as the information-bearing signals to be conveyed. Each word or sound, if it is to carry information, must necessarily occupy a nonzero band of frequencies. Moreover, it will have its own aurally recognizable amplitude versus frequency and time pattern. This pattern contains the information which all ordinary voice-communication systems are called upon to transport. When received and detected by the human hearing mechanism, experience shows that satisfactory speech requires a band from about a hundred cycles per second to several thousand cycles per second.

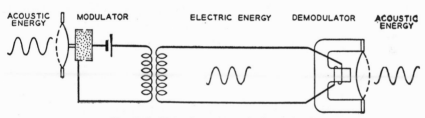

FIG. 2-2 Voice-frequency telephone circuit

In ordinary speech, we modulate sound energy as we talk. In telephony (Fig. 2-2), modulated sound signals impinge upon a telephone transmitter and produce modulated electric signals. In this process, the voice waves falling on the diaphragm of the telephone transmitter change the resistance of carbon particles through which unidirectional current is transmitted. Thus, the telephone transmitter acts as a converter or modulator. An ideal transmitter or microphone would change the fluctuating sound intensities to electric waves of identical frequencies, identical phases, and proportional amplitudes. When a signal modulates direct current, as previously described, the modulated electric signal in the output of the transmitter may be regarded as a single sideband of an amplitude-modulated carrier wave of zero frequency.

At the receiving end, after propagation over the line, demodulation in the telephone receiver results in changing the signals back to pressure waves in the air.

Radiant Beam Telephone

There is another example in the early experiments of Alexander Graham Bell. Some three years after he transmitted the first complete sentence of speech over wires on March 10, 1876, he experimented with the modulation of visible light. During these experiments he talked over a sharply focussed beam of light, giving the world its first *radiant beam telephone*. As in the previous example, modulation served to translate signals from one medium to another.

Telegraphy, Teletypewriter Systems, Facsimile, Telautograph, Telephotography, and Television

Other examples are available in telegraphy and teletypewriter systems. If we regard the mechanical operation of telegraph instruments and teletypewriter keys as messages, these are translated into electric signals by direct modulation. In television, telephotography, facsimile, and some telautograph systems, the original message to be conveyed is in the form of light signals. It is disposed in space-time for the television case and in space for picture, facsimile, and telautograph systems. The light signals are converted by modulation to electric signals of much lower frequency. At the receiving end, the equivalent of an inverse operation also represents a step of modulation which sometimes is termed "demodulation"; and, in all of the examples cited, this results in changing the signals back to the original medium.

TO PREPARE THE RECEIVED SIGNALS FOR THEIR DESTINATION

No physical communication link is noise-free. Consequently, the incoming signals will always be accompanied by unwanted but ever-present noise. One design objective is accurate interpretation of incoming signals in the presence of noise. In order to interpret this information under such adverse conditions, the receiver may utilize certain additional knowledge which need not be transmitted. For example, the kind of system is usually known and something is known about the type of message to be conveyed, such as whether it is a television message or an ordinary telephone message. In an efficient system of communication, the receiver makes full use of all such pertinent knowledge which, once conveyed, does not reappear in each message. Thus, in an efficient system, the receiver and transmitter conspire to conserve band width and signal power. In any event, modulation is usually required in the receiver in order to make either the original message, or information pertaining to the original message, available in the form desired and for delivery when and where the message is wanted.

TO CONVEY MESSAGES FROM ONE POINT IN SPACE–TIME TO ANOTHER

In previous examples, emphasis has all been upon the transmission of the message from one point in space to another at substantially the same time. Of course, delivery of the message was delayed unavoidably by the time of transmission over the medium and by additional intrinsic delays introduced by instrumentation. It is equally important, however, to be able to accept a message at one time and deliver it at another time later. Among the earliest systems of communication were those wherein information was impressed upon either a stone tablet or a sheet of parchment. This was done often for the purpose of conveying messages to descendants or others at some future time. Here we have an example of a system capable of transporting information from one point in space-time to another. A much more modern equivalent of the ancient method is provided by automatic recording and playback. Automatic means for recording and playing back signals may be utilized to provide delay. Signal delay may be thought of as the introduction of phase shift in amounts directly proportional to frequency of signal components and to delay duration.

Arrangements for the storage and delivery of signals are widely used in the newer types of modulation systems. Thus used, they may be called upon to satisfy a variety of requirements concerning storage capacity, permissible number of playbacks, permanence of the record, ability to add, remove, erase or transfer portions of the recorded information, ability to play back at different speeds, et cetera. Exact requirements may vary considerably in different applications.

Modulation plays an important part in recording and playing back. For example, one way to record a voice pattern is on a phonograph disk where the significant ups and downs in air pressure are neatly carved upon the disk surface. In this instance, the recorded voice signals vary as a function of their position in space. They have been converted from a magnitude-time function to a magnitude-space function. The conversion is the result of modulation and, in this instance, the recorded information signals are distributed in space in direct relation to their original position in time.

References

1. E. H. Armstrong, "A Method of Reducing Disturbances in Radio Signaling by a System of Frequency Modulation," *Proceedings of the Institute of Radio Engineers*, New York, Vol. 24, May 1936, pp. 689–740.
2. F. A. Cowan, "Modulation in Communication," *Transactions of the American Institute of Electrical Engineers*, New York, Vol. 66, 1947, pp. 792–796.

CHAPTER 3

KINDS OF MODULATION

Many kinds of modulation are possible, but a characteristic common to all involves change. To get the message through, something about the incoming signal at the receiving end has to change, and change in a way that the receiver cannot predict. Thus, in many systems of modulation the procedure is to cause the message wave to change some parameter of the carrier. However, it has been appreciated that the modulated wave will be deformed by transmission over a noisy channel. Accordingly, it is not surprising to find that, in the more recent kinds of modulation, the modulating wave is caused to change the carrier in such a way that the modulated wave will be less susceptible to noise, interference, and distortion. This is accomplished by utilizing a wave form such that the unpredictable perturbations which cannot be avoided will affect, to a considerable extent, only characteristics that the receiver chooses to ignore. Systems of code modulation are even more effective: first, because the message is quantized and, second, because the coding process affords a convenient opportunity for a more elaborate processing of the message.

AMPLITUDE MODULATION

The familiar definitions of amplitude modulation (and also angle modulation) require three concepts: namely, modulated wave, modulating wave, and carrier. First, a *modulated wave* is defined as a wave, some parameter of which varies in accordance with the value of the modulating wave. Second, *modulating wave* is defined as a wave which carries the specification of the message and varies the parameter of the wave that is modulated. Third, the wave to which modulation is subsequently applied is known as the *carrier*.

Amplitude modulation (AM) is modulation in which the amplitude of a wave is the parameter subject to variation.

Amplitude Modulation of a Sinusoidal Carrier

As implied by the three examples depicted in Fig. 3–1, it is not necessary to transmit the carrier continuously. Amplitude modulation of a sinusoidal carrier, which is further illustrated by Fig. 3–2, is one of the oldest

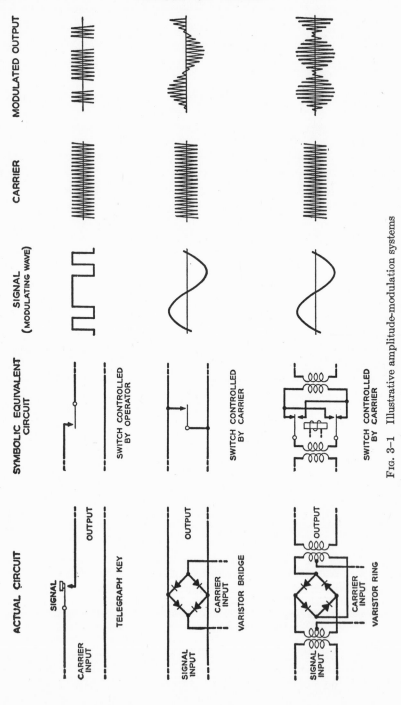

Fig. 3–1 Illustrative amplitude-modulation systems

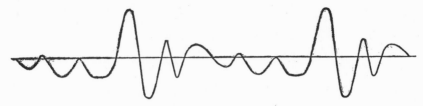

MODULATING WAVE

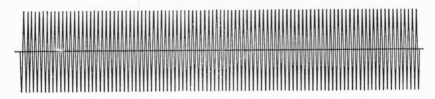

CARRIER

MODULATED WAVE

FIG. 3-2 Amplitude modulation of a sine-wave carrier by a voice-frequency modulating wave: typical wave forms

and most familiar systems of modulation. Thus, if $A_c \cos (2\pi f_c t + \Phi_c)$ is the sinusoidal carrier where A_c is the amplitude, f_c the frequency, and Φ_c the phase of the carrier, and if $V(t)$ is the modulating wave, then

$$A_c[1 + kV(t)] \cos (2\pi f_c t + \Phi_c) \qquad (3-1)$$

is the resulting modulated wave. In Chapter 9, this wave will be shown to be composed of the transmitted sinusoidal carrier which conveys no information and of the familiar (Ref. 1)* upper and lower sidebands which convey identical and, therefore, mutually redundant information. In (3-1), the greatest absolute value of $kV(t)$ multiplied by 100 is referred to

* The references cited are listed at the end of each chapter according to the number used in the text.

as the percentage modulation, that is, the modulation factor expressed in per cent.   If $|kV(t)| > 1$, the sinusoidal carrier is said to be over-modulated.   An example of over modulation is displayed in Fig. 3–3.

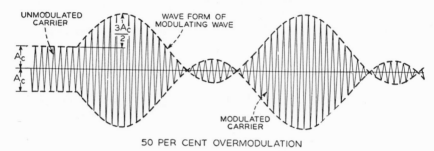

50 PER CENT OVERMODULATION

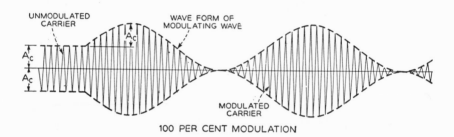

100 PER CENT MODULATION

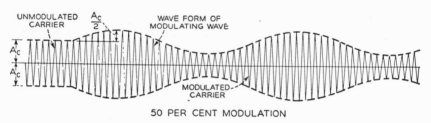

50 PER CENT MODULATION

FIG. 3–3   Amplitude modulation of a sine-wave carrier by a sine-wave signal: over-modulation, 100 per cent modulation, and 50 per cent modulation

In an amplitude-modulation system, the spectra of Fig. 3–4 further illustrate that it is not necessary to transmit the carrier in order to convey the information of the message and, moreover, for many purposes, it is sufficient to transmit only a single sideband.   Systems that take advantage of this fact, without regard to whether the carrier is transmitted or suppressed, such as single-sideband modulation (Refs. 2 and 3) and vestigial-sideband modulation (Refs. 4 to 6), will be regarded as examples of ampii-tude modulation.   *Vestigial sideband* is a term that was suggested by Nyquist, and the requirements for this method of transmission are discussed in Appendix 5 of Reference 4.   The amplitude and phase require-

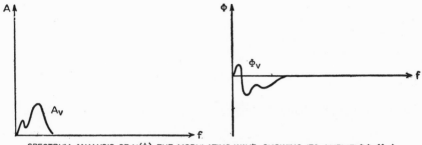

SPECTRUM ANALYSIS OF v(t), THE MODULATING WAVE, SHOWING ITS AMPLITUDE (A$_v$) AND PHASE (Φ$_v$) DISTRIBUTION AS A FUNCTION OF FREQUENCY

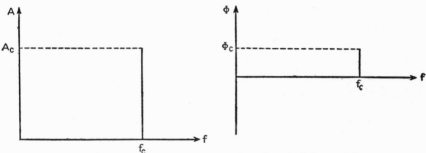

SPECTRUM ANALYSIS OF THE SINE–WAVE CARRIER [A$_c$cos(2π f$_c$t+Φ$_c$)] WHOSE AMPLITUDE–FREQUENCY AND PHASE–FREQUENCY SPECTRA ARE REPRESENTED BY LINES

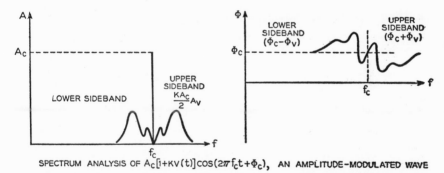

SPECTRUM ANALYSIS OF A$_c$[1+Kv(t)]cos(2π f$_c$t+Φ$_c$), AN AMPLITUDE–MODULATED WAVE

Fig. 3–4   Amplitude modulation: spectrum analysis showing amplitude-frequency and phase-frequency spectra of modulating wave, carrier, and modulated wave

ments to be satisfied in a time-division system using vestigial-sideband modulation are considered by Bennett in Reference 5 on pages 212–214. The filter requirements for vestigial-sideband transmission are presented by Bode in Reference 6 on pages 333–334.

There are several forms of modulation that are not strictly amplitude modulation but are so closely related to it that they are usually classified as special cases of amplitude modulation. Single sideband is one of these. Although this is amplitude modulation in which the carrier and one sideband have been eliminated from the modulated wave, it is commonly referred to as single-sideband modulation. It seems reasonable to follow this practice even though it is recognized that the practice seems unscientific. A similar convention, open to a similar objection, will be followed in speaking of vestigial-sideband modulation.

Single-Sideband Modulation

In single-sideband modulation, as demonstrated and elaborated upon in Chapters 9 and 11, the frequency spectrum of the modulating wave is translated in frequency by a specified amount either with or without inversion. These translations are illustrated by the amplitude-frequency and phase-frequency spectra depicted by Fig. 3–4. For example, in the case of an amplitude-modulated sine wave, the spectrum of the upper sideband $(C + V)$ is the spectrum of the modulating wave (voice or other information-bearing signals) displaced without inversion by an amount equal to the carrier frequency. On the other hand, the spectrum of the lower sideband $(C - V)$ is the spectrum of the modulating wave also displaced by an amount equal to the carrier frequency but with inversion. That is, a zero-frequency component of the modulating wave corresponds to the carrier, and any other frequency component of the modulating wave appears at a frequency lower than the carrier by a frequency difference equal to the frequency component of the modulating wave.

Vestigial-Sideband Modulation

Vestigial-sideband systems transmit one sideband and a portion of the other sideband which lies adjacent to the carrier frequency. In attempting to produce a single-sideband system, if the signals constituting the modulating wave contain significant frequencies down to and including zero frequency, then in the neighborhood of the carrier frequency, it becomes impossible (because of physical limitations on obtainable filter characteristics) to separate the two sidebands. In vestigial-sideband systems, residual portions of both the wanted and unwanted sidebands are transmitted in such proportions that the required filters can be physically realized and the desired final output can be obtained. Thus, vestigial-sideband systems are like single-sideband systems, except in a restricted region around the carrier frequency.

USAGE OF THE TERMS "SINUSOIDAL WAVE" AND "SINE WAVE"

Either sinusoidal wave or sine wave will be used in place of the older phrase "harmonic function" to signify any function that can be expressed as the sine of a linear function of independent variables which constitutes

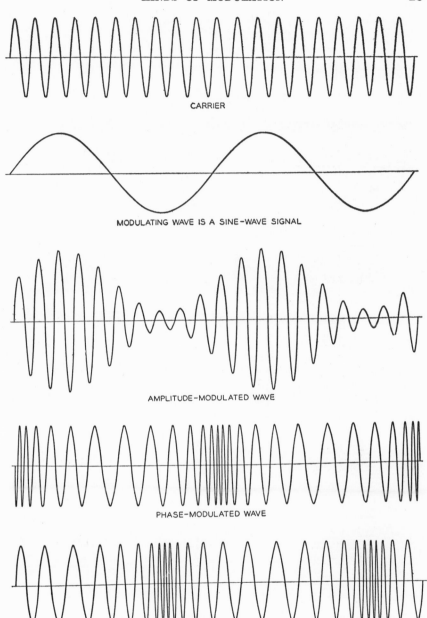

FIG. 3-5 Amplitude, phase, and frequency modulation of a sine-wave carrier by a sine-wave signal

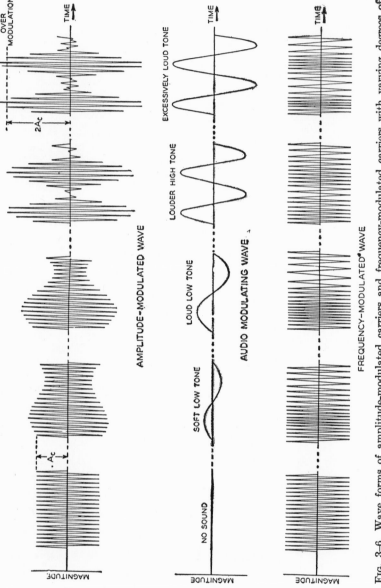

FIG. 3-6 Wave forms of amplitude-modulated carriers and frequency-modulated carriers with varying degrees of modulation

its argument. The term "harmonic" will be used to mean a harmonic of the fundamental frequency of any periodic wave. For example, if sin x represents a wave the fundamental frequency of which is proportional to x, sin $2x$ would be referred to as the *second* harmonic.

EXTENSION OF THE MEANING OF AMPLITUDE

At this point it is worth noting that the term *amplitude modulation* implies that we have extended the original meaning and definition of amplitude to include the concept of instantaneous amplitude. First, we recall that amplitude and value (instantaneous value) are not synonymous. In fact, for many years amplitude has been used to express the crest value of a simple harmonic function or, more generally, any parameter that when changed merely represents a change in scale factor. Accordingly, in $A \cos (\omega t + \Phi)$, A is the original meaning and definition of the amplitude of this simple harmonic function which is a cosine wave.

Thus, in our terminology, the harmonic function $A_c \cos (\omega_c t + \Phi_c)$ will be referred to indiscriminately either as a sinusoidal wave or as a sine wave. However, when the sine-wave carrier is amplitude-modulated, we replace A_c by a function of time, namely, $A_c[1 + kV(t)]$, and by so doing have departed from the original meaning of amplitude as applied to a sine wave. Although $A_c[1 + kV(t)]$ varies with time and we are concerned with its instantaneous value, nonetheless we will continue to speak of it as the amplitude.

ANGLE MODULATION

Angle modulation is modulation in which the angle of a sinusoidal carrier is the parameter subject to variation. If we write the expression for the sinusoidal carrier as $A_c \sin (\omega_c t + \Phi_c)$, the whole argument of the sine function is defined as the *angle*. Phase and frequency modulation, depicted in Figs. 3–5 and 3–6, are particular forms of angle modulation (Ref. 7).

Phase deviation, frequency deviation, and modulation index are terms often used in descriptions of systems of angle modulation, and the definitions given follow the Institute of Radio Engineers standards on modulation systems. *Phase deviation* is the peak difference between the instantaneous angle of the modulated wave and the angle of the carrier. *Frequency deviation* is the peak difference between the instantaneous frequency of the modulated wave and the carrier frequency. *Modulation index* is the ratio of the frequency deviation to the frequency of the modulating sine wave.

Phase Modulation

Phase modulation (PM) is angle modulation in which the angle of a sinusoidal carrier is caused to depart from the carrier angle by an amount proportional to the instantaneous value of the modulating wave. If $A \cos (2\pi f_c t + \Phi)$ is the sinusoidal carrier and $V(t)$ the modulating wave, then

$$A_c \cos [2\pi f_c t + \Phi_c + KV(t)] \tag{3-2}$$

is the resulting phase-modulated wave.

Frequency Modulation

Frequency modulation (FM) is angle modulation in which the instantaneous frequency of a sinusoidal carrier is caused to depart from the carrier frequency by an amount proportional to the instantaneous value of the modulating wave. Here, it should be noted, we will find it necessary to extend our definition of frequency. Mathematically the term "frequency" applies, strictly speaking, only to infinite wave trains, and the phrase "changing frequency" presents a contradiction in terms. In this connection, Carson introduced in 1922 the concept of *generalized frequency* (Ref. 8), which in 1937 he extended (Ref. 9) with Fry under the name *instantaneous frequency*. *Instantaneous frequency* is the time rate of change of the angle of a sine function the argument of which is a function of time. If the angle is measured in radians and the time in seconds, the frequency in cycles per second is the time rate of change of the angle divided by 2π. If $A_c \cos (2\pi f_c t + \Phi_c)$ is the sinusoidal carrier and $V(t)$ the modulating wave, then

$$A_c \cos \left[2\pi f_c t + K_1 \int^t V(t)\, dt + \Phi_c \right] \tag{3-3}$$

is the resulting frequency-modulated wave. The reason for omitting the lower limit of the definite integral and its interpretation are discussed in Chapter 12.

PM AND FM ARE NOT ESSENTIALLY DIFFERENT

There has in the past been considerable discussion concerning the essential difference, if any, between phase modulation and frequency modulation. Consequently, it seems worth while at this point to spend some time analyzing the two.

It should be noted that when we apply our definition

$$\text{(angular frequency)} = \frac{d}{dt} \text{(angle)}$$

to (3-3), we get

$$\frac{d}{dt} \left[2\pi f_c t + K_1 \int^t V(t)\, dt + \Phi_c \right] = \omega_c + K_1 V(t). \tag{3-4}$$

Treating (3–2) similarly, that is, differentiating its argument with respect to time,

$$\frac{d}{dt}\left[2\pi f_c t + \Phi_c + KV(t)\right] = \omega_c + KV'(t). \tag{3-5}$$

From (3–4) we conclude: in a frequency-modulation system, the deviation $[K_1 V(t)]$ of the instantaneous frequency from its unmodulated value is proportional to the magnitude of the modulating wave but is independent of its frequency.

From (3–5) we conclude: in a phase-modulation system the deviation $\left[K\dfrac{d}{dt}V(t)\right]$ of the instantaneous frequency from its unmodulated value is proportional to the magnitude of the *derivative* of the modulating wave.

This illustrates that, although phase modulation and frequency modulation are particular forms of angle modulation, nevertheless they are not essentially different. In fact, PM and FM are inseparable in the sense that any variation of the phase of a sinusoidal carrier is accompanied by a frequency variation and, similarly, any frequency change necessarily involves a phase change. Thus, the terms "phase modulation" and "frequency modulation" merely indicate which parameter is made proportional to the modulating wave and represent two cases of the same type of modulation.

Although both names were very often used in the past as if to represent different systems, and although current practice still employs both terms, it should be noted that in recent years frequency modulation has also come to connote angle modulation. Clearly, the lack of any essential difference between phase and frequency modulation may be traced to the equivalence of angular frequency and time-rate of change of phase.

The close relationship between phase and frequency modulation may also be illustrated by physical examples. If an equalizer having an output wave form that is directly proportional to the time integral of its input wave form precedes a phase modulator, the combination is a frequency modulator. If such an equalizer follows a frequency detector, the combination is a phase detector. Similarly, a differentiating network followed by a frequency modulator is equivalent to a phase modulator, and likewise a phase demodulator followed by a differentiator is equivalent to a frequency demodulator. (A differentiator is a network which multiplies each frequency component of the signal by $i\omega$ and an integrator is one which divides by $i\omega$.)

In fact, the outputs of most FM broadcast transmitters vary across the program frequency band from almost pure phase modulation to almost pure frequency modulation, and in between is a mixture of both. This result is obtained by a pre-equalizer and is commonly referred to as pre-emphasis. The inverse operation, usually performed by a network at the receiver, is known as de-emphasis and restores the pre-emphasized frequency spectrum to its original form.

PULSE MODULATION

Pulse-modulation systems sometimes use a high ratio of peak to average power for more efficient operation of the transmitter, and in these instances the pulses are separated in time one from another and show little tendency to overlap. Alternatively, however, the pulses, without losing their theoretical identity, may overlap to such an extent that the resultant array is a continuous wave. In either instance, for all practical purposes, the power associated with a particular pulse differs essentially from zero only over a limited interval; and within the limited interval there is no nonzero subinterval in which it is continuously zero. Information is conveyed by modulating some parameter of the transmitted pulses, for example, by varying the amplitude, duration, exact position in time, or shape of the pulse. If a system represents a continuously varying modulating wave by discrete signals (code symbols), the process is known as pulse-code modulation, and systems of this kind will be treated separately.

Pulse-modulation and pulse-code-modulation terminology has not been standardized except to a degree, and many of the terms already in use are redundant. For example, one encounters various names such as pulse-amplitude modulation, pulse-duration modulation, pulse-length modulation, pulse-width modulation, pulse-position modulation, pulse-time modulation, pulse-frequency modulation, pulse-number modulation, pulse-epoch modulation, pulse-bracket modulation, pulse-code modulation, pulse-maze modulation, et cetera. Figure 3–7 illustrates three types.

Meaning of Pulse Carrier

In pulse-modulation systems, the unmodulated carrier is usually a series of regularly recurrent pulses. Each pulse is characterized by the rise and decay in time or space, or both, of a quantity the value of which is normally constant. In this sense, we choose not to regard a radio-frequency pulse as a pulse but instead to view it as the result of modulation where the modulating wave is a pulse. For example, a spurt from a radio-frequency oscillator would be regarded essentially as the sidebands of a radio-frequency sinusoidal carrier, amplitude-modulated by a pulse. Our *pulse carrier*, therefore, might be described as a series of d-c pulses having a wave form that depends upon the pulse repetition rate and upon the band width and response of the system.

Pulse-Amplitude Modulation

In *pulse-amplitude modulation* (PAM) the amplitude of a pulse carrier is varied in accordance with the value of the modulating wave as depicted

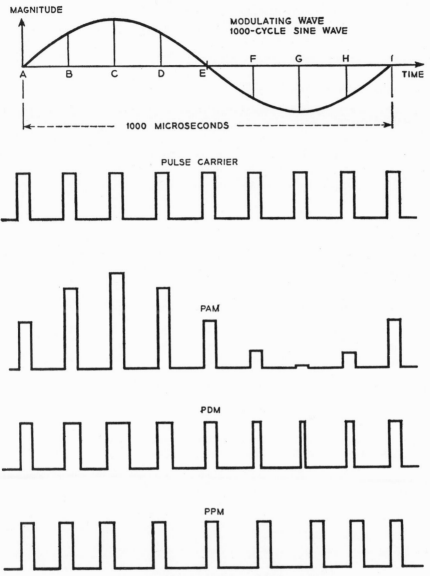

FIG. 3-7 Examples of pulse-modulation systems

in Fig. 3-7. It is sometimes convenient to regard PAM as simultaneous amplitude modulation of all of the Fourier components of the pulse carrier. More often, it is convenient to look upon PAM as modulation in which the value of each instantaneous sample of the modulating wave is caused to modulate the amplitude of a pulse. This point of view will be elaborated upon in Chapters 15 and 16; it stems from the sampling principle (Chap. 4) which specifies the least number of values per second necessary to determine uniquely the value of the sampled wave at all times. Thus, although the modulating wave is assumed to be arbitrary (except that the frequency range it occupies is essentially limited) and takes on an infinite number of different values during any nonzero interval of time, nevertheless it can be reproduced exactly from a knowledge of its samples, provided the number of instantaneous samples per second exceeds twice its significant band-width occupancy in cycles per second. Simple commutator types of time-division systems afford examples of PAM (Refs. 5 and 7 to 11). Reference 5 is a fundamental and very complete discussion by W. R. Bennett. As applied to telephony, Willard M. Miner (Ref. 10) in 1903 patented a commutator-type of time-division system.

Pulse-Time Modulation

Pulse-time modulation (PTM) is modulation in which the values of instantaneous samples of the modulating wave are caused to vary the time of occurrence of some parameter of a pulse carrier. Pulse-duration modulation and pulse-position modulation are particular forms of pulse-time modulation.

Pulse-Duration Modulation. Sometimes designated pulse-length modulation or pulse-width modulation, *pulse-duration modulation*, PDM (Refs. 11 to 14), is modulation of a pulse carrier in which the value of each instantaneous sample of a modulating wave is caused to vary the duration of a particular pulse (Fig. 3–7). The modulating wave may vary the time of occurrence of the leading edge, the trailing edge, or both edges of the pulse.

Pulse-Position Modulation. In *pulse-position modulation*, PPM (Refs. 15 to 17), the value of each instantaneous sample of a modulating wave is caused to vary the position in time of a pulse relative to its unmodulated time of occurrence (Fig. 3–7).

Characteristic Properties

The different pulse-modulation systems have different characteristic properties which are described in more detail in Chapters 15 to 18. Ease of multiplexing channels and, for PTM, valuable noise-reducing properties are outstanding characteristics.

Each of the systems, PAM, PDM, and PPM, readily permits multiplexing channels by time division. For example, application of the sampling principle permits the reduction of a continuous voice-frequency speech signal to about 8,000 discrete samples per second, and the information of each sample is carried by a modulated pulse. Consequently, if the pulses are short so that a single pulse can be sent in a small fraction of the 125-microsecond (1/8,000-second) interval between the successive pulses associated with a particular channel, the clear time may be occupied by other pulses from other voice channels, thus permitting multiplex operation with many channels.

Like FM, PTM has the property that, by using extra band width, some of the over-all performance characteristics of a PTM system can be improved, provided the peak interference is less than the peak signal. A feature of PPM is that, for fixed average power out of the transmitter, the peak power can be increased as the pulse duration is reduced. This is in contrast to conventional FM where, over a path of specified attenuation, the requirement that the peak interference be less than the peak signal represents a limitation on the signal-to-noise improvement obtainable with a given amount of average transmitter power.

Like AM, PAM theoretically is not helped by the use of wider frequency bands. With a fixed average transmitter power and noise that has a uniform power density spectrum over the acceptance band but is random in phase, a greater frequency range theoretically affords no improvement in signal-to-noise ratio. At the same time, it need not cause degradation.

PULSE–CODE MODULATION

Pulse-code modulation, PCM (Refs. 18 to 24), is a radically new type of pulse system and represents a major contribution to the communications art. As in the earlier pulse systems (Fig. 3–8), each modulating wave is sampled periodically at a rate somewhat in excess of twice its highest frequency component. Unlike the continuously variable samples used in PAM, PDM, and PPM, in PCM the samples are quantized (Chap. 5) into discrete steps. The individual steps may be alike, or in logarithmic relation, or they may vary otherwise, depending upon the characteristic properties of the modulating wave.

In addition, each quantized sample is assigned a particular code pattern, the code pattern assigned being uniquely related to the magnitude of the quantized sample. This gives rise to various possible patterns of coded pulses. For example, if amplitude is the parameter quantized, there may be: patterns of on-or-off pulses; or patterns of three-value code elements, namely, values of $+S$, O, and $-S$, as in the familiar case of submarine cable telegraphy; or, in general, patterns of N code elements, in which each code element will assume one of q distinct amplitude values. At the receiving end, each code pattern is identified, decoded, and caused to produce a voltage proportional to the original quantized sample. From a succession of such samples, the original wave is approximated. By making each quantum step sufficiently small, theoretically the original wave may be approximated as closely as desired.

Pulse-code modulation has two outstanding properties: first, it affords

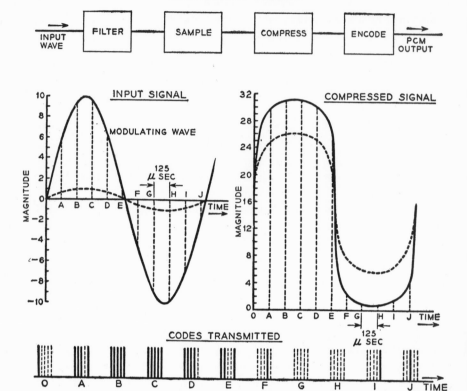

Transformation of voice to code pulses. The input signal, represented as a sine wave at the left above, is compressed logarithmically to give the curve shown at the right. Samples are taken every 125 microseconds, and each sample is converted to a five-pulse binary code as shown in the lower line. A solid vertical line is used to represent a pulse, and a dotted line, the absence of a pulse.

FIG. 3–8 Pulse-code modulation: how the sampling and quantizing principles permit a voice-frequency wave to be transformed to a sequence of various patterns of code pulses

marked freedom from noise and interference; and, second, it permits repeating the signals again and again without significant distortion. For example, consider the code patterns formed by on-or-off pulses. At each regenerative repeater, as long as each incoming pulse can be correctly identified in the presence of accumulated noise, interference, and distortion, a new and correct code pattern can be generated and started out afresh to the next repeater.

TOPICS NOT TREATED

A branch of modulation theory which we shall neglect is the *unwanted* generation of what has been termed *products of modulation* due to non-linear response as, for example, either in a nearly linear amplifier or in a common-channel modulator. This is not modulation at all within the present meaning of the term, and perhaps the proper term is *nonlinearity*. Another topic which we shall neglect is the theory of the design of modulator and related types of nonlinear circuits. Although these topics are important from the standpoint of instrumentation, it is thought best to confine the treatment of the text to other aspects of the theory. The literature on these topics is extensive. References 25 to 37 are cited as representing a short list of selected publications.

References

1. R. V. L. Hartley, "Relations of Carrier and Sidebands in Radio Transmission," *The Bell System Technical Journal*, New York, Vol. 2, No. 2, April 1923, pp. 90–112.
2. E. H. Colpitts and O. B. Blackwell, "Carrier Current Telephony and Telegraphy," *Transactions of the American Institute of Electrical Engineers*, New York, Vol. 40, February, 1921, pp. 205–300.
3. H. A. Affel, C. S. Demarest, and C. W. Green, "Carrier System on Long-Distance Telephone Lines," *Transactions of the American Institute of Electrical Engineers*, New York, Vol. 47, No. 4, October 1928, pp. 1360–1387.
4. H. Nyquist, "Certain Topics in Telegraph Transmission Theory," *Transactions of the American Institute of Electrical Engineers*, New York, Vol. 47, April 1928, pp. 617–644.
5. W. R. Bennett, "Time-Division Multiplex Systems," *The Bell System Technical Journal*, New York, Vol. 20, No. 2, April 1941, pp. 199–221.
6. Hendrik W. Bode, *Network Analysis and Feedback Amplifier Design*, D. Van Nostrand Co., Inc., New York, 1945, pp. 333–334.
7. Prof. B. van der Pol, "The Fundamental Principles of Frequency Modulation," *The Journal of the Institute of Electrical Engineers*, London, Vol. 93, Part III, 1946, pp. 153–158.
8. J. R. Carson, "Notes on the Theory of Modulation," *Proceedings of the Institute of Radio Engineers*, New York, Vol. 10, February 1922, pp. 57–64.
9. J. R. Carson and Thornton C. Fry, "Variable-Frequency Electric Circuit Theory with Application to the Theory of Frequency Modulation," *The Bell System Technical Journal*, New York, Vol. 16, No. 4, October 1937, pp. 513–540.
10. Willard M. Miner, United States Patent 745,734, 1903.
11. "Pulse-Width Modulation — The Basic Principles Described," *Wireless World*, London, Vol. LI, No. 12, December 1945, pp. 361–362.
12. "Multichannel Pulse Modulation — Details of Army Wireless Set No. 10," *Wireless World*, London, Vol. LII, No. 6, June 1946, pp. 187–192.
13. S. C. Kleene, "Analysis of Lengthening of Modulated Repetitive Pulses," *Proceedings of the Institute of Radio Engineers*, New York, Vol. 35, No. 10, October 1947, pp. 1049–1053.
14. R. A. Heising, United States Patent 1,655,543, January 10, 1928, assigned to Western Electric Company, Inc.
15. H. S. Black, J. W. Beyer, T. J. Grieser, and F. A. Polkinghorn, "A Multichannel Microwave Radio Relay System," *Transactions of the American Institute of Electrical Engineers*, New York, Vol. 65, December, 1946, pp. 798–806.

16. B. Trevor, O. E. Dow, and W. D. Houghton, "Pulse Time Division Radio Relay," *RCA Review*, New York, Vol. 7, December 1946, pp. 561–575.
17. R. D. Kell, United States Patent 2,061,734, November 24, 1936, assigned to Radio Corporation of America.
18. W. M. Goodall, "Telephony by Pulse-Code Modulation," *The Bell System Technical Journal*, New York, Vol. 26, No. 3, July 1947, pp. 395–409.
19. H. S. Black and J. O. Edson, "Pulse-Code Modulation," *Transactions of the American Institute of Electrical Engineers*, New York, Vol. 66, 1947, pp. 895–899.
20. L. A. Meacham and E. Peterson, "An Experimental Multichannel Pulse-Code Modulation System of Toll Quality," *The Bell System Technical Journal*, New York, Vol. 27, No. 1, January 1948, pp. 1–43.
21. R. W. Sears, "Electron Beam Deflection Tube for Pulse-Code Modulation," *The Bell System Technical Journal*, New York, Vol. 27, No. 1, January 1948, pp. 44–57.
22. C. B. Feldman, "A 96-Channel Pulse-Code Modulation System," *Bell Laboratories Record*, New York, Vol. 26, No. 9, September 1948, pp. 364–370.
23. Paul M. Rainey, United States Patent 1,608,527, November 30, 1926, assigned to Western Electric Company, Inc.
24. A. H. Reeves, United States Patent 2,272,070, February 3, 1942, assigned to the International Standard Electric Corporation. Also French Patent 853,183, October 23, 1939.
25. H. J. van der Bijl, "Theory of the Thermionic Amplifier," *Physical Review*, New York, Vol. 12, September 1918, pp. 171–198.
26. H. J. van der Bijl, "Theory and Operating Characteristics of the Thermionic Amplifier," *Proceedings of the Institute of Radio Engineers*, New York, Vol. 7, April 1919, pp. 97–128.
27. J. R. Carson, "Theoretical Study of the Three-element Vacuum Tube," *Proceedings of the Institute of Radio Engineers*, New York, Vol. 7, April 1919, pp. 187–200.
28. H. J. van der Bijl, "On the Detecting Efficiency of the Thermionic Detector," *Proceedings of the Institute of Radio Engineers*, New York, Vol. 7, No. 6, December 1919, pp. 603–635.
29. J. R. Carson, "The Equivalent Circuit of the Vacuum Tube Modulator," *Proceedings of the Institute of Radio Engineers*, New York, Vol. 9, June 1921, pp. 243–249.
30. R. A. Heising, "Modulation in Radio Telephony," *Proceedings of the Institute of Radio Engineers*, New York, Vol. 9, August 1921, pp. 305–352.
31. J. R. Carson, "Notes on the Theory of Modulation," *Proceedings of the Institute of Radio Engineers*, New York, Vol. 10, February 1922, pp. 57–64.
32. F. B. Llewellyn, "Operation of Thermionic Vacuum Tube Circuits," *The Bell System Technical Journal*, New York, Vol. 5, No. 3, July 1926, pp. 433–462.
33. Eugene Peterson and Clyde R. Keith, "Grid Current Modulation," *The Bell System Technical Journal*, New York, Vol. 7, No. 1, January 1928, pp. 106–139.
34. W. R. Bennett, "New Results in the Calculation of Modulation Products," *The Bell System Technical Journal*, New York, Vol. 12, No. 2, April 1933, pp. 228–243.
35. E. Peterson and L. W. Hussey, "Equivalent Modulator Circuits," *The Bell System Technical Journal*, New York, Vol. 18, No. 1, January 1939, pp. 32–48.
36. R. S. Caruthers, "Copper Oxide Modulators in Carrier Telephone Systems," *The Bell System Technical Journal*, New York, Vol. 18, No. 2, April 1939, pp. 315–337.
37. W. R. Bennett, "Cross Modulation Requirements on Multichannel Amplifiers Below Overload," *The Bell System Technical Journal*, New York, Vol. 19, No. 4, October 1940, pp. 587–610.

CHAPTER 4

THE SAMPLING PRINCIPLE

The sampling principle specifies the least number of discrete values (samples) of an unknown function necessary for its complete and unambiguous definition. Since our discussion will be limited to physical systems, we will assume that the unknown function is a real function of a real variable, single-valued, finite, continuous, and everywhere possessing a derivative. As we shall discover, these discrete values of information (samples) need not necessarily be values of the function. They can be values of significant parameters such as derivatives of various orders, integrals, et cetera. Moreover, the samples need not be uniformly distributed. For example, if the unknown function is a magnitude-time function, the instantaneous samples of the magnitude of the function need not be uniformly spaced in time.

SPECIAL STATEMENT OF THE SAMPLING PRINCIPLE

A restricted but widely used form of the sampling principle states:

If a signal that is a magnitude-time function is sampled instantaneously at regular intervals and at a rate slightly higher than twice the highest significant signal frequency, then the samples contain all of the information of the original signal.

In practical applications of the sampling principle, we are usually called upon eventually to reconstruct, from a knowledge of discrete instantaneous samples, the values of an unknown magnitude-time function for all significant times. If an arbitrary wave is plotted, it can be reproduced in all its detail from the values of a set of ordinates erected at equally spaced intervals, provided the spacing of the sampling ordinates is less than half the period of the highest significant frequency component of the original wave.

Similarly, if a voice wave is passed through a low-pass filter having a cutoff frequency that is below 4,000 cycles per second, all of the information necessary for its distortionless reconstruction is contained in a set of very short samples of the voice wave taken at regular intervals at the rate of 8,000 per second. Since the highest significant signal frequency is less than 4,000 cycles per second, no intrinsic distortion is involved.

Significance

Since the sampling principle specifies substantially the *least* number of discrete values necessary to reproduce a changing magnitude-time function, application of the sampling principle reduces the communication problem to one of transmitting a finite number of values.

SAMPLES OF NONZERO DURATION

Although we have mentioned instantaneous sampling, it is realized that instantaneous sampling never can be realized because the operation of a physical circuit, however fast, still requires a nonzero interval of time. Moreover, samples are often lengthened intentionally for convenience in instrumentation.   In the two typical examples to follow, certain significant properties of samples of nonzero duration will be indicated.

Ordinary Samples

As a simple illustration we shall consider that the sampling mechanism merely extracts successive portions of pre-determined duration taken at regular intervals from the sampled wave.   Again considering a voice-frequency wave as in ordinary telephony, in practical applications the voice signal usually is passed through a low-pass filter, as shown in (a) of Fig. 4–1, to attenuate to negligible values all frequencies above an upper limit that is less than half the sampling frequency, f_c.   After filtering, the resulting magnitude-time function is designated V.   In (b) of Fig. 4–1, V indicates the instantaneous value of a short portion of a voice signal which might have passed the low-pass filter.

Another magnitude-time function is the unit sampling wave, which is shown in (c) of Fig. 4–1 with the designation U.   Mathematically, as indicated in (f) of Fig. 4–1, U can be regarded as equal to a d-c term plus the sampling frequency, f_c, plus harmonics of the sampling frequency.

In this example, U will be used to sample the voice input at regular intervals T, and the duration of each sample will be t_0.   The interval between pulses, T, is equal to $1/f_c$.   The ratio of the pulse duration to the interval between pulses is designated k; k equals t_0/T.

When U is multiplied by V, the product UV is an analytical description of a process for sampling the voice input.   The result is shown as a series of positive and negative pulses in (d) of Fig. 4–1. U is either one or zero. When U is one, the product UV is equal to V; when U is zero, the product UV is zero.

Because UV is similar in appearance to amplitude-modulated pulses, it is not surprising to find that, upon performing the indicated multiplication UV, one obtains an attenuated replica of V simply by passing UV through a low-pass filter as shown in (e) of Fig. 4–1.   In the process of sampling and filtering, V is reduced by a factor k. We shall neglect for the present the delay and distortion introduced by the low-pass filter. Amplifying by a factor $1/k$ restores V to its original value.

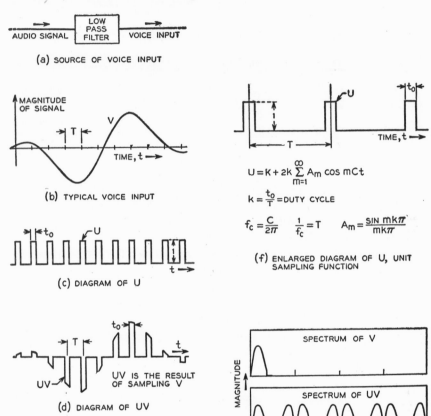

(a) SOURCE OF VOICE INPUT

(b) TYPICAL VOICE INPUT

(c) DIAGRAM OF U

$$U = K + 2k \sum_{m=1}^{\infty} A_m \cos mCt$$

$$k = \frac{t_0}{T} = \text{DUTY CYCLE}$$

$$f_c = \frac{C}{2\pi} \qquad \frac{1}{f_c} = T \qquad A_m = \frac{\sin mk\pi}{mk\pi}$$

(f) ENLARGED DIAGRAM OF U, UNIT SAMPLING FUNCTION

(d) DIAGRAM OF UV

UV IS THE RESULT OF SAMPLING V

(e) PASSING UV THROUGH A LOW-PASS FILTER AND AMPLIFIER TO OBTAIN V

(g) SPECTRUM ANALYSIS OF V AND UV

FIG. 4–1 Properties of ordinary samples

We may show more concretely that passing UV through a low-pass filter yields the original signal. In (g) of Fig. 4–1 is a spectrum analysis showing the magnitude of V, and also UV, as a function of frequency. The upper diagram is the spectrum of V. After sampling, V becomes UV. The spectrum of UV is the spectrum of V, small but exact, together with upper and lower sidebands about f_c and harmonics of f_c. Figure 4–2 represents symbolically the spectrum of UV for a sampled audio band. It shows the separation of components when the sampling frequency exceeds twice the top audio frequency.

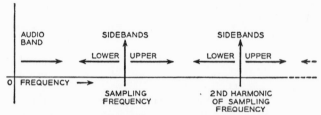

FIG. 4–2 Spectrum of a sampled audio band, illustrating separation of components when the sampling frequency is more than twice the top audio frequency

Flat-Top Samples

As a second example, imagine $V \equiv V(t)$ is sampled as before, except that the sampling is instantaneous. Also imagine that the duration of each sample is lengthened to T. Finally, assume that the resultant array of flat-top pulses is passed through a low-pass filter that substantially rejects all frequencies above an upper limit less than $f_c/2$; this filter, however, has substantially no effect on the in-band frequencies. Under these conditions, if $V(t) = \sum A_v \cos (\omega_v t + \theta_v)$, one obtains (Ref. 1)*

$$\sum_v \left[\frac{\sin \omega_v \dfrac{T}{2}}{\omega_v \dfrac{T}{2}} \right] A_v \cos \left[\omega_v \left(t - \frac{T}{2} \right) + \theta_v \right] \tag{4–1}$$

in the output of the low-pass filter.

If now, in this example, each sample is lengthened only to t_0 instead of T, (4–1) becomes

$$\sum_v k \left[\frac{\sin \omega_v \dfrac{t_0}{2}}{\omega_v \dfrac{t_0}{2}} \right] A_v \cos \left[\omega_v \left(t - \frac{t_0}{2} \right) + \theta_v \right], \ 0 < t_0 \le T, \tag{4–2}$$

a relationship derived in Chapter 16 in the section entitled *Double-Polarity, Flat-Top Pulses.* Thus, the output of the low-pass filter is given by (4–2) which corresponds to kV in the first example. This shows that, by using flat-top samples, we have introduced distortion as well as a delay of $t_0/2$. However, the distortion can be corrected by an equalizer. Now say that we ignore the delay and assume that the low-pass filter is followed by an

* The references cited are listed at the end of each chapter according to the number used in the text.

equalizer. Let K represent a constant factor of proportionality such that the frequency characteristic of the equalizer is given by

$$K\left[\frac{\omega \dfrac{t_0}{2}}{\sin \omega \dfrac{t_0}{2}}\right].$$

Then if we amplify the resulting attenuated but undistorted signal by an amplifier that has an amplification factor of $1/kK$, we recover V where V (it will be remembered) is an arbitrary magnitude-time function the highest frequency component of which lies within the pass band of the low-pass filter.

To recapitulate, if a signal that is a magnitude-time function is sampled instantaneously at regular intervals and at a rate slightly higher than twice the highest significant signal frequency, and if each sample is clamped for a time t_0, $(0 < t_0 \le T)$; then after rejecting all frequencies in excess of the highest significant signal frequency, a delay of $t_0/2$ will have been introduced along with a certain amount of attenuation and distortion. However, independent of the spectral content of the signal within its allotted frequency range, there need be no intrinsic deformation of the reconstructed signals because the distortion and attenuation can be compensated for by a fixed equalizer and fixed-gain amplifier. This may be interpreted as illustrating a particular scheme for reconstructing the magnitude-time function from a knowledge of its instantaneous samples, the samples being taken at regular intervals and at a high enough rate.

MORE GENERALIZED SPECIAL STATEMENT OF THE SAMPLING PRINCIPLE

At this point the previous statement of a special form of the sampling principle will be generalized slightly:

If a signal is a magnitude-time function, and if time is divided into equal parts forming subintervals such that each subdivision comprises an interval T seconds long where T is less than half the period of the highest significant frequency component of the signal; and if one instantaneous sample* is taken from each subinterval in any manner; then a knowledge of the instantaneous magnitude of each sample plus a knowledge of the instant within each subinterval at which the sample is taken contains all of the information of the original signal. (Ref. 2.)

Significance

The foregoing statement implies that the exact timing of the samples may be an involved function of time. This need not, however, necessarily

---

* When the chosen instant of sampling falls at one extremity of a subinterval, that instant is excluded from the adjacent subinterval in order to insure $1/T$ distinct instants of sampling as well as one sample from each subinterval.

increase the band-width requirements. In an efficient system of communication, either the instants at which samples are taken represent information which the receiver is assumed to know, or, if this information has to be transmitted, no significant extra band width should be required. Otherwise band width is wasted unnecessarily. In any event accurate timing is important. Lack of precision in defining each instant of sampling will contribute to inaccuracy in the subsequent reconstruction of the message and will manifest itself as extra noise.

PPM with Natural Sampling

Let us envision a PPM system and consider two cases. Case I will employ uniform sampling and is, therefore, another example of the special statement of the sampling principle previously treated. Case II, however, will employ what has been called *natural sampling* and will illustrate the more generalized special statement of the sampling principle which we are considering.

In a PPM system (Fig. 4–3), the information of each channel is conveyed by varying the exact position in time of the channel pulses. Suppose the channels are all ordinary telephone channels. With no voice input, the pulses associated with a particular channel might occur 8,000 times a second, or every 125 microseconds. When the channel is busy, a pulse occurs earlier or later as the magnitude of the voice wave is plus or minus. The exact displacement of a pulse from its unmodulated position is directly proportional to the magnitude of the voice wave at the time of sampling.

In Case I, the sampling is at uniform intervals; and a knowledge of this and of the modulated pulses, at the receiver, is sufficient to reconstruct the original voice wave.

In Case II, by contrast, the time of sampling coincides with the time of appearance of the position-modulated pulse. Here too, theoretically we have the necessary information to reconstruct the original voice wave without using extra band width. Actually, in a multichannel system, the maximum swing, or variation in exact position in time from the mean, is small. Consequently, the distortion introduced in each of the channels of a PPM system using natural sampling (Case II) as a result of using a method of reception appropriate to uniform sampling (Case I) would be small, at least for ordinary telephony. From an engineering standpoint, PPM systems using either uniform sampling or natural sampling provide commercial telephone channels with equal success and with equal ease of instrumentation. In both types of sampling, it is practical to disclose the time of sampling to extraordinary precision; and in most practical applications there need be no appreciable impairment in the derived message due to lack of sufficiently precise knowledge of the exact time of sampling.

PPM with Longer Interval between Pairs of Samples

As another example of a multichannel PPM system in which the samples are not uniformly spaced, let us imagine a system in which each message channel is examined only 4,000 times a second, that is, at regular intervals of 250 microseconds. During each examination, *two* nearly instantaneous

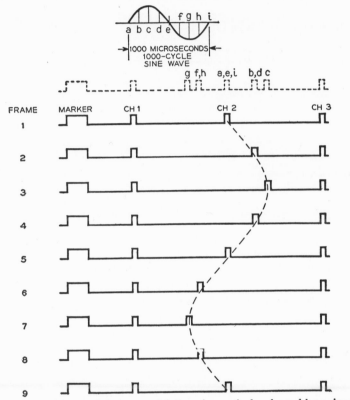

FIG. 4–3 Pulse position modulation: modulation of a particular channel by a sine wave

samples are taken which are separated in time by a comparatively brief interval. As in the other examples, no intrinsic distortion is involved. With regard to practical embodiments, a particular arrangement for the reconstruction of the voice wave at the receiver was devised which proved to be only slightly more complicated than for Case I or Case II of the previous illustration. Considering a particular pair of samples, the first sample to occur is a measure of the magnitude of the sampled wave at the instant of sampling, and this information is transmitted. If the first and second samples happen to be very closely spaced, their difference is approximately proportional to the first derivative. In any event, it is a displacement proportional to the difference that is transmitted. Knowledge of these magnitudes, the repetition rate, and the spacing between samples is enough to permit exact reconstruction of the message. A careful study of this method of sampling showed that, for the transmission of ordinary speech, the over-all signal-to-noise ratio was only slightly different than with uniform sampling.

GENERALIZED TREATMENT OF THE SAMPLING PRINCIPLE

Although the treatment to follow is limited to simple magnitude-time functions of the type previously defined, the results are applicable to other single-valued functions. Moreover, they are capable of extension to functions of more than one variable.

Introductory Discussion of Theoretical Limitations

If the magnitude-time function is always zero within either an open or closed nonzero interval of time, its spectrum theoretically includes component frequencies larger than any arbitrarily assigned number, however large, although, of course, the magnitudes of the very-high-frequency components may be small. This clearly follows from the fact implied for most such functions that a derivative of at least some order (including zero) is not everywhere continuous. For the narrow class of functions that are identically zero over a nonzero interval but still do not have a discontinuous derivative of any order, the proof is still possible but includes some rather abstract reasoning from Fourier theory. A good example is a signal, everywhere finite, continuous, and possessing a derivative the value of which is and remains zero until a particular time t_0, that is, from $t = -\infty$ to $t = t_0$. No finite number of samples can define such a signal, except approximately, without additional knowledge of its wave form. Similarly, in a system having a finite band width, transients theoretically endure forever. Practically, of course, factors of this sort may not be important at all if the significant margins are liberal. However, these factors cannot be neglected in detailed theoretical investigations and may play a part in certain practical situations.

As another example, suppose a low-pass filter freely passed all frequencies up to and including B cycles per second and utterly failed to transmit all higher frequencies. As is well known, in response to an applied input, a signal would appear in the output at earlier times than the earliest input signal. This absurdity arises because the amplitude and phase response characteristics of physical networks are not independent, and their implicit relation to one another may be formulated explicitly by demanding zero response prior to the time that the input is applied. Thus, the amplitude and phase characteristics previously implied in defining an idealized low-pass filter are not compatible in a physical network.

Although an ideal filter is nonphysical, theoretically it can be approximated by physically realizable elements to within a specified accuracy: first, by including an equalizer sufficiently elaborate to correct to the accuracy desired for any attenuation and delay distortion (which would be introduced by an unequalized network) as a function of frequency up to frequencies approaching cutoff; and, second, by the use of a large enough number of sections to introduce what can be regarded as sufficient loss to all out-of-band frequencies. However, the closer the approximation of the physical filter to the ideal, the longer the delay or time of propagation from input to output and, also, the longer the duration of substantial transients in the output in response to frequency components approaching cutoff. In the final analysis, tolerance to delay, tolerance to the deformation of the sampled wave in the output due to transients, and the required precision of resolution, all are factors which of necessity affect the conservation of band width.

Periodic Sampling of a Magnitude-Time Function and Related Band-Width Restrictions

Thus, in the special statements of the sampling principle, the assumptions made were impossible of exact physical realization. For example, the band width was assumed nonzero, and the highest significant signal component was assumed to be within the pass band of the system. Although this implied that all higher frequencies were unimportant, they never can be zero. Consequently, depending upon the manner and extent to which the highest frequency components of the sampled wave exceed B, the $2B$ samples per second fail to define precisely the arbitrary wave being sampled.

This shows that, even when a channel has a certain band width starting with zero frequency and including all frequencies less than B cycles per second, close scrutiny is necessary to determine just what frequency range is being utilized. For example, suppose we are free to use such a channel for a certain period of time T_0. Although this of itself implies that we can use any signal functions of time, provided they are confined to T_0 and provided their spectra lie entirely within B, actually, as explained previously, it is impossible to fulfill both of these conditions exactly. We may keep the spectrum substantially within the band B in the sense that the out-of-band components can be regarded as having been made sufficiently small; and, in addition, we can arrange to have the magnitude-time function arbitrarily small outside T_0. However, all of this will involve delaying the message and reducing, no matter by how little, the theoretical message capacity of the channel.

This means that with a limited band width there is uncertainty in our evaluation of the signal wave by physical means. By properly and carefully controlling the transmission, although only at the expense of delaying the message, the uncertainty can be made, in theory, arbitrarily small. However, when we sample close to the minimum instead of at a moderately

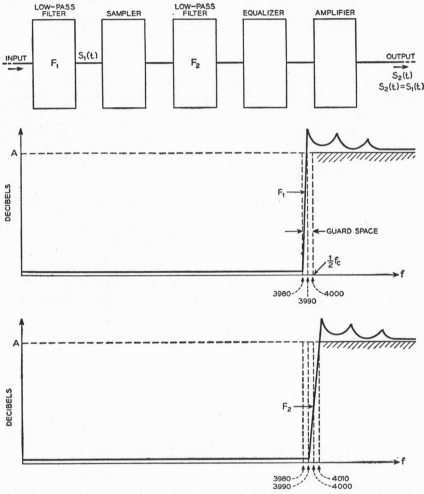

FIG. 4–4 Theoretical limitations of the sampling principle

higher rate, the transmission requirements tend to become unreasonably difficult, and for some applications the resulting delay could not be tolerated.

To illustrate these matters further (Fig. 4–4), suppose we consider an ordinary telephone channel and undertake to sample an arbitrary voice-frequency wave at regular intervals 8,000 times a second. The question is: How wide a frequency range can we handle? Naturally, the highest frequency component of the sampled wave must be less than 4,000 cycles per second, because otherwise the samples do not uniquely determine the wave that is being sampled. Next, suppose we allow a guard space of 20 cycles per second, divide this guard space by two, and allot the first half to F_1 (Fig. 4–4). Then filter F_1 is called upon to pass all frequencies from 0 to 3,980 with uniform attenuation and uniform delay, and it is also called upon to attenuate all frequencies above 3,990 by A decibels. Thus, the frequency range from 3,980 to 3,990 cycles per second clearly represents a transition range.

Accordingly, it is assumed that F_1 also includes equalizers to insure that the in-band transmission distortion and in-band phase distortion are each independent of frequency to within prescribed limits. These limits can be made sufficiently small so that the deformation of the wave form of the transmitted signal due to these factors will about equal the deformation caused by a limited instead of an infinite out-of-band loss. This means that the required out-of-band attenuation A must be sufficient to make the unwanted frequency components of the input wave unimportant compared with the accuracy of resolution needed to define the wanted component of the sampled wave.

The wave at the output of the filter F_1, designated as $S_1(t)$, is the wave to be sampled. Because $S_1(t)$ is assumed to have been filtered adequately by F_1, it can be described as having no significant frequency components in excess of 3,990.

After sampling, the samples are filtered by another similar low-pass filter, F_2, which passes all frequencies from 0 to 3,990 and attenuates frequencies above 4,010 by A decibels (Fig. 4–4). Filter F_2 also is supposed to include in-band equalization and, outside of its pass band, is called upon to attenuate all unwanted switching or sampling sidebands, as in Fig. 4–2 and (g) of Fig. 4–1, to the extent dictated by the resolution sought. Depending upon the nature of the samples, the output of the filter F_2 is further equalized and amplified as required, and then will be found to yield $S_1(t)$ to the precision specified.

If the samples are ordinary (continuous) samples (Fig. 4–1), no additional equalizer following F_2 is needed. If, however, the samples are, for example, flat-top samples, then the required characteristic of the equalizer will be that of the aperture equalizer mentioned previously in the discussion of flat-top samples. It should be noted that filter F_2 (Fig. 4–4) is required to pass all frequencies from 0 to 3,990 in order to transmit uniformly all of the frequency components capable of passing F_1 with an attenuation less than A; and, of course, F_2 must also attenuate by A decibels all frequencies above 4,010 (see Fig. 4–2 and (g) of Fig. 4–1).

Clearly, in the absence of noise, interference, and nonlinear distortion, and at the expense of delaying the message, $S_1(t)$ can be recovered with as high an accuracy as we wish to specify. This is because the inherent distortion in the recovered wave depends only upon adequate suppression of all frequency components of the sampled wave which are greater than or equal to half the sampling rate, and which, therefore, can be controlled by A, the out-of-band loss.

Equally important is the fact that the recovery, or reconstruction, of the sampled wave is entirely unaffected by the particular times at which the samples are taken just so long as they are taken at perfectly regular intervals and at a fast enough rate. That is to say, merely advancing or delaying the sampling times need not advance, delay, or otherwise affect the recovered wave. To prove this, note that the result is true for any sine-wave input with a frequency that is less than half the sampling rate. Then, since superposition holds, the result is true in general to the extent that the spectrum of the sampled wave does not include frequencies as high as half the sampling rate.

Consequently, the result proved for the idealized case can be made to hold in a practical situation to within an arbitrary error, however small, by providing a large enough value of A (Fig. 4–4). But, before continuing, let us consider a contrary example in the neighborhood of half the sampling frequency. In this instance the proper precautions will not be taken. Suppose $\cos 2\pi\,3999t$ is sampled beginning with $t = 0$ at regular intervals of 125 microseconds (1/8,000 second). The result for the first few dozen samples will be samples each of magnitude of the order of unity. Again, suppose $\cos 2\pi\,3999t$ is sampled beginning with $t = 1/15{,}996$ second also at regular intervals of 125 microseconds. The result for the first few dozen samples will be samples each of magnitude of the order of zero. Clearly, the response of F_2 (Fig. 4–4) to these two sets of samples will be entirely different instead of almost the same. The explanation is that the spectrum of the sampled wave contains frequencies above 4,000 cycles per second, as can be easily shown.

To recapitulate, reference to Fig. 4–4 will show that no physical measurement which we can make will detect any difference in the wave forms of $S_1(t)$ and $S_2(t)$ other than the delay introduced by the filters and the deformation due to imperfect in-band transmission and finite out-of-band loss. Moreover, this result will be unchanged either by advancing or retarding the samples. It is enough that the samples be uniformly spaced, provided they are taken at a fast enough rate. Consider an utterly impractical case merely for purposes of illustration. Say that $A = 240$ decibels and that each filter is equalized to within 10^{-13} decibel. If the delay distortion in seconds as a function of frequency is less than about $\dfrac{0.28 \times 10^{-13}}{f}$ (where f is the in-band frequency in cycles per second), then $S_2(t)$ (Fig. 4–4) ordinarily might be expected to differ from $S_1(t)$ roughly by less than 2×10^{-13} of the magnitude of $S_1(t)$.

Using methods originated by H. Bode (Ref. 3), an estimate prepared by E. N. Gilbert of the approximate theoretical lower bound to the delay (Fig. 4–4) is 0.14 second for F_1 and 0.07 second for F_2. Therefore, according to this estimate the delay due to both filters must exceed 0.21 second. If a delay of only two milliseconds were tolerable, either A would have to be less than about 2.3 decibels or else the guard space would have to be at least 1,200 cycles per second for F_1 and 2,400 cycles per second for F_2. Limiting A limits the resolution and hence, as will be shown presently, limits the maximum message capacity of the channel. Increasing the guard space increases the band-width occupancy and consequently reduces the message capacity of the medium.

In any physical system of communication, the signal wave which we finally elect to pass must occupy of necessity an essentially limited band. Consequently, as we attempt to reduce band-width occupancy by approaching rather close to the practical minimum, we find that other parameters are affected. For example, the delivery of the message will be delayed. In a program distribution network, a radio broadcasting system, or a one-way television system, fairly substantial delay, compared to the performance of present conventional systems, might be admissible. On the other hand, for a long-distance, two-way, ordinary telephone channel, delays appreciably longer than several milliseconds per link would be questionable, even with speed-of-light transmission over the medium. If we are to avoid serious service impairment, very little additional delay is admissible in each of the several multilink circuits that make up most present-day circuits as long as 4,000 or 5,000 miles. Such delays tend to interrupt the exchange that occurs in normal conversation. Thus, the minimum band width that is practical will depend upon the service or, as we shall term it, upon the destination of the message. Likewise, as already mentioned, when the guard space or frequency interval separating a region of low loss from a region of high loss is made smaller and smaller, the over-all transient response to frequency components approaching cutoff becomes a substantial factor over longer and longer times; and, consequently, the output wave becomes correspondingly quite altered. As a result, in practical situations, factors of this sort rather than the actual size and cost of complex networks may control the permissible minimum guard space (Fig. 4–4).

To summarize, the intrinsic band width required is the width of the signal spectrum that must be preserved in order to make the signal wave being sampled sufficiently undistorted. In addition, because of the response characteristic of physical networks, additional frequency range or guard space is also required. Consequently, the total frequency space assigned to a channel includes the entire band, namely, the intrinsic band width plus guard space. This means that the minimum band-width occupancy occurs when any further band limitation operates to delay and impair the signal beyond tolerable limits, assuming adequate signal power.

Generalized Statement of the Sampling Principle

From the preceding discussion we see that we can confine our attention to a simple magnitude-time function. We also may say that its significant frequencies include all frequencies less than B. Nyquist (Ref. 4) pointed out that, if the function is substantially limited to the time interval X, $2BX$ values are sufficient to specify the function, basing his conclusions on a Fourier series representation of the function over the time interval X. This gives BX sine and $(BX + 1)$ cosine terms up to frequency B in the series expansion. Usually X is large and we speak of $2BX$ values.

The $2BX$ instantaneous samples need not be equally spaced as in the foregoing derivation. More generally, any set of $2BX$ independent numbers associated with the function may be used to define it completely and uniquely.

It is not surprising to find that derivatives and integrals of any order are appropriate for any of the independent numbers because these are operations that can be simulated by equalizers. If the independent numbers are bunched to a substantial extent, the values must be known with extraordinary precision to afford accurate reconstruction of the function.

As an example, let us consider groups of instantaneous samples bunched together and, therefore, separated by substantial intervals of time compared to $1/2B$. Consider an ordinary speech channel that normally would be sampled at uniform intervals of $1/8,000$ second. The physical interpretation of bunched samples can be thought of as depending upon the persistence of the transient response of a low-pass filter to the bunched samples. It is evident that, if the interval between bunches is long enough, the information to be used will become lost in the noise. Using the noise values normally associated with a speech input channel, it was found by the writer that the bunches could be separated by intervals as long as about one-tenth of a second before encountering theoretical difficulty on the score of noise. This means that theoretically we could keep away from the message circuit for periods as long as one-tenth of a second and still not lose significant knowledge of the message. Practically, if there is appreciable bunching, the samples have to be known to extraordinary precision for reasonably good reconstruction of the message.

Of course, infrequent examination of the wave to be sampled delays the delivery of the information to its destination. Moreover, bunching the samples or the even more generalized representation of a sampled wave by any set of independent numbers implies complicated reconstruction processes.

In general, the arbitrary sampled wave can be represented by any set of $2BX$ independent numbers associated with the function, and this in turn represents the least number of values capable of completely and uniquely defining the function. The total number necessary per period of time X is fixed. It is the same as when the samples are spaced uniformly.

ADDITIONAL THEOREMS PERTAINING TO PERIODIC SAMPLING OF SIGNALS

We have shown previously that, on a classical basis and in the absence of noise, there is a unique relationship between an arbitrary signal occupying the band of all frequencies less than B and the instantaneously sampled values of the signal taken uniformly at the rate of $2B$ samples per second. If we are given the signal wave, we can determine the samples; and if we are given the samples we can determine the signal wave.

These results and the theorems to follow are equally applicable to any set of sampling points spaced $1/2B$ second apart. That is, the results are independent of the exact times of sampling, provided only that the samples are taken at regular intervals of $1/2B$ second.

THEOREM I: *Given samples at the rate of 2B samples per second of a signal wave having a highest frequency component that is less than B; given unit impulses* centered about the sampling instants; multiply each unit impulse by its coincident sample and divide by the rate of sampling; and apply the resulting array of impulses to an ideal low-pass filter of cutoff frequency B: the response of the filter will be the signal wave.* (Ref. 5.)

Suppose we multiply $V \cos 2\pi f_v t = V \cos \omega_v t$ by a succession of short rectangular pulses of unit height and duration t_0 centered about what eventually are to become the sampling instants. If the sampling rate is f_c, we obtain (Fig. 4–1) simple (continuous) samples of duration t_0. Writing $2\pi f_c = \omega_c$, $\dfrac{1}{f_c} = T$ and $\dfrac{t_0}{T} = k$, we have

$$F(t) = V \cos \omega_v t \left[k + 2k \sum_{m=1}^{\infty} \frac{\sin mk\pi}{mk\pi} \cos m\omega_c t \right]$$

$$= \frac{t_0}{T} V \cos \omega_v t + \frac{t_0}{T} V \sum_{1}^{\infty} \frac{\sin m \frac{t_0}{T} \pi}{m \frac{t_0}{T} \pi} [\cos(m\omega_c + \omega_v)t + \cos(m\omega_c - \omega_v)t].$$

$$(4\text{–}3)$$

* Unit impulses are infinitesimally narrow pulses each of infinite height to give unit area. Infinitesimally short pulses have a flat frequency spectrum, whereas pulses of finite duration do not.

A unit impulse has zero duration, infinite height, and unit area. Hence, we may write an expression for $\delta(t)$, periodic unit impulses at regular intervals T, namely,

$$\delta(t) = \lim_{t_0 \to 0} \left[\frac{1}{T} + \frac{2}{T} \sum_{1}^{\infty} \frac{\sin m \frac{t_0}{T} \pi}{m \frac{t_0}{T} \pi} \cos m\omega_c t \right]$$

$$= f_c \left[1 + 2 \sum_{m=1}^{\infty} \cos m\omega_c t \right]. \tag{4-4}$$

A train of samples in which each sample is multiplied by a unit impulse is

$$[V \cos \omega_v t] \, \delta(t) = f_c V \left[\cos \omega_v t + \sum_{1}^{\infty} \cos (m\omega_c + \omega_v)t + \cos (m\omega_c - \omega_v)t \right]. \tag{4-5}$$

Each component of $V(t)$, the wave being sampled, will be represented by a term proportional to that component plus a series of additional cosine terms each of appropriate amplitude, phase, and frequency. Since the system is linear, the principle of superposition may be applied to the composite signals which comprise $V(t)$. If the highest frequency component of $V(t)$ is less than B, if $f_c = 2B$, and if we neglect frequencies in excess of B, then, on the assumption that there is no delay in the filter, the filtered train of impulses will be $f_c V(t)$, which, upon dividing by f_c, is the theorem.

THEOREM II: *Given samples at the rate of 2B samples per second of a signal wave containing frequency components greater than B; given unit impulses centered about the sampling instants; multiply each unit impulse by its coincident sample and divide by the rate of sampling; and apply the resulting array of impulses to an ideal low-pass filter of cutoff frequency B: the response of the filter will be a new signal wave with frequencies confined to the band from zero to B and yielding the same sampled values as the original signal wave.* (Ref. 5.)

The theorem follows from Theorem I.

THEOREM III: RELATION BETWEEN SIGNAL AND MEAN SQUARES OF ITS SAMPLES. *If the average of the squares of the instantaneous samples of a magnitude-time function, $f(t)$, approaches a limiting value as the number of samples is indefinitely increased; the limiting value is equal to $\overline{f^2(t)}$, the mean square of the function (except where $f(t)$ itself contains a discrete component of finite amplitudes of frequency mB or two discrete components of finite amplitude and frequencies f_1 and f_2 such that $|f_1 \pm f_2| = 2mB$, $m = 1, 2, 3,$ ...).* (Ref. 5.)

Let the samples be taken at nT where $n = 0, \pm 1, \pm 2, \pm 3, \ldots$ and $f(t)$ be the sampled wave. Then $f^2(nT)$ is an expression for the squared samples. This we may equate to another expression for the squared samples which we may write as a limit of the product of the squared signal, $f^2(t)$, and a periodic switching function of infinitesimal contact time. This function is merely the limit approached by the unit sampling function (Fig. 4–1) as t_0 is caused to approach zero. Thus,

$$U = \lim_{t_0 \to 0} \left[\frac{t_0}{T} + 2 \frac{t_0}{T} \sum_{m=1}^{\infty} \frac{\sin m \frac{t_0}{T} \pi}{m \frac{t_0}{T} \pi} \cos m\omega_c t \right]. \qquad (4\text{–}6)$$

The mean square value of the samples is the limit of the average value of $f^2(t)U$ taken over the contact intervals of duration t_0. The average value of $f^2(t)U$ taken over all time, including the blank intervals, is in the limit a fraction t_0/T of the average over the contact intervals only. Therefore,

$$\overline{f^2(nT)} = \frac{T}{t_0} \overline{f^2(t)U} \qquad (4\text{–}7)$$

or

$$\overline{f^2(nT)} = \overline{f^2(t)} + 2 \sum_{1}^{\infty} \overline{f^2(t) \cos 2m\pi f_c t}. \qquad (4\text{–}8)$$

Clearly, the long time average of $f^2(t) \cos 2m\pi f_c t$ vanishes unless $f^2(t)$ contains a component of frequency mf_c. This only happens if $f(t)$ contains a component of frequency $\dfrac{mf_c}{2}$ or two components f_1 and f_2 such that

$$|f_1 \pm f_2| = mf_c.$$

When no such relation of dependency exists,

$$\overline{f^2(nT)} = \overline{f^2(t)}, \qquad (4\text{–}9)$$

which is the theorem.

THEOREM IV: *The mean square value of the response of an ideal low-pass filter to a train of unit impulses multiplied by instantaneous samples occurring at double the cutoff frequency is equal to the square of the rate of sampling multiplied by the mean square value of the samples. The mean square value of the samples will be equal to the mean square value of the sampled wave, provided the sampled wave does not contain a discrete component of finite amplitude of frequency equal to half the sampling frequency, or any pair of discrete components of finite amplitudes and frequencies such that the absolute value of the sum or difference of their frequencies is equal to the sampling frequency.* (Ref. 5.)

In the treatment of flat-top samples of short duration, it was demonstrated that passing the samples through an ideal filter followed by an amplifier yields the original signal. This assumes that $f(t)$, the original signal, contains no frequencies as high as $B = f_c/2$, one half the sampling rate.

Theorem II shows that, if $f(t)$ contains frequencies exceeding B, the response of the filter-amplifier is $\varphi(t)$, where $\varphi(t)$ is confined to the band 0 to B and yields the same samples as $f(t)$, that is,

$$\varphi(nT) = f(nT). \tag{4-10}$$

Applying Theorem III to $\varphi(t)$ gives the result,

$$\overline{\varphi^2(nT)} = \overline{\varphi^2(t)}, \tag{4-11}$$

subject to the restrictions of the theorem.

Using $\varphi(nT) = f(nT)$, it follows that $\varphi^2(nT) = f^2(nT)$. Replacing $\varphi^2(nT)$ by $f^2(nT)$, the previous result becomes

$$\overline{f^2(nT)} = \overline{\varphi^2(t)}, \tag{4-12}$$

which completes the theorem. Moreover,

$$\overline{\varphi^2(nT)} = \overline{f^2(nT)} = \overline{\varphi^2(t)} = \overline{f^2(t)}. \tag{4-13}$$

THEOREM V: *If we are given the samples, the signal wave is given by multiplying* $\left(\dfrac{\sin 2\pi Bt}{2\pi Bt}\right)$ *pulses by the samples.* (Ref. 6.)

A pulse or signal element of this type is placed at each sampled point and its amplitude is adjusted to equal the value of the instantaneous sample. Since the spectrum of an aperture pulse is constant within the band and zero outside, each product satisfies the conditions on the spectrum and, furthermore, passes through the sampled points. Consequently, the sum of these pulses is the signal wave, because there is one and only one function with a spectrum limited to B and passing through given values at sampling points spaced $1/2B$ second apart.

In other words, the signal can be represented as the sum of elementary signal elements of the form $\dfrac{\sin 2\pi Bt}{2\pi Bt}$ centered at sampling points and each having a peak value equal to the signal at the corresponding sampling point. Likewise, to reconstruct the signal, we merely need to generate a series of $\dfrac{\sin 2\pi Bt}{2\pi Bt}$ signal elements proportional to the samples and add the ensemble.

It is worth noting that the energy in a pulse of the form $V_r \dfrac{\sin 2\pi Bt}{2\pi Bt}$ is

$$V_r^2 \int_{-\infty}^{\infty} \frac{\sin^2 2\pi Bt}{4\pi^2 B^2 t^2} \, dt = \frac{V_r^2}{2B}, \tag{4-14}$$

which is the same as the energy of a rectangular pulse of magnitude V_r and duration $1/2B = 1/f_c = T$. This result is consistent with Theorem III. Conversely, Theorem III implies the value of the foregoing integral.

THEOREM VI: FUNDAMENTAL THEOREM OF APERTURE EFFECT IN SAMPLING. *The frequency characteristic introduced by lengthening the sample or otherwise changing the shape of the sample (wave form of the pulse) is calculated by determining the steady-state admittance function of a network that converts impulses to the actual pulses used. The general formula for this admittance when a unit impulse input is converted into an output pulse $g(t)$ is*

$$Y(i\omega) = f_c \int_{-\infty}^{\infty} g(t)e^{-i\omega t}\, dt,$$

where f_c is the rate of sampling and ω is the angular frequency of the signal. (Ref. 5.)

Infinitesimally short pulses have a flat frequency spectrum, whereas pulses of finite duration do not. The relation to be proved is similar to the variation in transmission with frequency caused by the finite size of the scanning aperture in television and telephotography. Hence, it has become customary to use the term "aperture effect" in the theory of restoring signals from samples.

If we sample $V \cos \omega_v t$ at a rate f_c, we have from the last equation in Theorem I the expression for a train of samples in which each sample has been multiplied by a unit impulse, namely,

$$\frac{V}{T} \cos \omega_v t + \frac{V}{T} \sum_{1}^{\infty} \cos (m\omega_c + \omega_v)t + \cos (m\omega_c - \omega_v)t. \qquad (4\text{-}15)$$

Suppose this train of samples is applied to a linear electrical network having a response $g(t)$ when the input is a unit impulse. The steady-state admittance of the network is given by (Ref. 7) as

$$Y_0(i\omega) = \int_{-\infty}^{\infty} g(t)e^{-i\omega t}\, dt, \qquad (4\text{-}16)$$

and $I(t)$, the response of the network to the train of samples, is

$$I(t) = \frac{V}{T} |Y_0(i\omega_v)| \cos [\omega_v t + \text{phase of } Y_0(i\omega_v)]$$

$$+ \frac{V}{T} \sum_{m=1}^{\infty} |Y_0(i[m\omega_c + \omega_v])| \cos [(m\omega_c + \omega_v)t + \text{ph } Y_0(i[m\omega_c + \omega_v])]$$

$$+ |Y_0(i[m\omega_c - \omega_v])| \cos [(m\omega_c - \omega_v)t + \text{ph } Y_0(i[m\omega_c - \omega_v])], \qquad (4\text{-}17)$$

where phase is abbreviated ph. If the signal frequency f_v is less than $f_c/2$, an ideal low-pass filter with cutoff at $f_c/2$ responds only to the first component of $I(t)$. In this case the "aperture effect" or variation of transfer admittance with signal frequency is given by

$$Y(i\omega_v) = \frac{1}{T} Y_0(i\omega_v) = f_c Y_0(i\omega_v), \qquad (4\text{-}18)$$

which is the theorem.

THEOREM VII: ENCIPHERMENT AND DECIPHERMENT. *At the sending end, the magnitude of each sample may be varied in an arbitrary manner without increasing the frequency range of the samples. Furthermore, provided the transformation follows a law that is fully known by the receiver, the original values of the samples may be determined.*

For example, if continuously varying signal elements are enciphered with the aid of a key, and if the enciphered signal elements are not perturbed, the receiver can decipher the signal elements and recover the original information, provided the receiver has knowledge of the key.

Similarly, if the samples are compressed in accordance with an arbitrary but known law, and the receiver expands them by an exactly inverse operation, the wanted information can be recovered. This example illustrates that the use of an instantaneous compandor theoretically need not imply extra band width and, furthermore, in the absence of noise, need not of itself perturb the final output of the receiver.

The reason, of course, is that no more band width is needed to transmit the samples after they have been compressed than before. Therefore, even when applied to a continuous wave, such a companding process requires no extra band width between the compressor and expandor. Of course, as the band is narrowed, the over-all requirements imposed upon the quality and stability of transmission become increasingly severe.

THEOREM VIII: *If the polarity of alternate samples is reversed, the spectrum of the samples consists of the lower and upper sidebands of the sampled wave around carrier frequencies of B, $3B$, $5B$, ...*

This follows directly by considering the spectra of the even- and odd-numbered samples and reversing the polarity of one of the two groups. Alternatively, if we use the general method previously followed in the treatment of ordinary samples of finite duration, a complete expression may be written for the train of samples.

THEOREM IX: *Periodic sampling at intervals $1/2B$ of a wave the spectrum of which is confined to all frequencies less than B cycles per second produces upper and lower sidebands of $2B$ and of each harmonic of $2B$. If any one of these sidebands is selected and sampled at the same instants, it will be found to produce the same set of samples as does the original wave.*

We note that the theorem is true for any single frequency of $f(t)$. Since superposition holds, the theorem is true generally.

THEOREM X: *When sampling a band of frequencies displaced from zero, the minimum sampling rate f_r for a band of width B and highest in-band frequency f_2 is $2f_2/m$ where m is the largest integer not exceeding f_2/B.* (Ref. 8, pp. 594–595.) *Obviously, not all higher rates are necessarily usable.*

Often a signal band does not include zero frequency.   By standard modulation techniques a band extending from f_1 to $f_1 + B$ can be translated to the range 0 to B, sampled at a rate $2B$, and restored to the original range by an inverse translation.   These techniques, however, include modulators (in the restricted sense), carrier generators, and band-separating filters, as well as amplifiers to make up the inevitable losses.   For simplicity a direct sampling process which avoids shifting the band would be preferred.

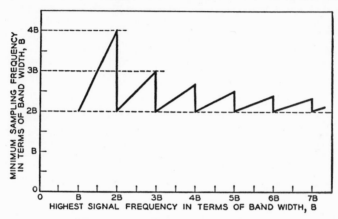

FIG. 4–5   Minimum sampling frequency for band of width B

For uniformly spaced samples the minimum sampling rate (Fig. 4–5) is not in general twice the highest frequency in the band but is

$$f_r = 2B\left(1 + \frac{k}{m}\right) \tag{4–19}$$

where $k = f_2/B - m$.

Thus, k varies between 0 and 1.   When the band is located between adjacent multiples of B, $k = 0$ and $f_r = 2B$ independent of f_2.   As k increases from 0 to 1, the sampling rate increases from $2B$ to $2B(1 + 1/m)$. The highest rate is required when $m = 1$ and k approaches 1.   This corresponds to a signal band extending from $(B - \Delta f)$ to $(2B - \Delta f)$ with Δf small.   The required rate is $2(2B - \Delta f)$, which approaches $4B$ as Δf approaches 0.   When $\Delta f = 0$, we change to the case of $m = 2$, $k = 0$, and $f_r = 2B$.   The next maximum is $3B$ and is approached when f_2 approaches $3B$.   As f_2 increases, the successive maxima decrease asymptotically toward $2B$.

The theorem may be verified from steady-state modulation theory by noting that the first-order sidebands on harmonics of $2B$ do not overlap the signal when the equation is satisfied.

References

1. H. Nyquist, "Certain Factors Affecting Telegraph Speed," *The Bell System Technical Journal*, New York, Vol. 3, No. 2, April 1924, pp. 324–346.
2. Augustin-Louis Cauchy, "Mémoire sur Diverses Formulaes dé Analyse," *Comptes Rendus*, Paris, France, Vol. 12, 1841, pp. 283–298.
3. Hendrik W. Bode, *Network Analysis and Feedback Amplifier Design*, D. Van Nostrand Co., Inc., New York, 1945, p. 318.
4. H. Nyquist, "Certain Topics in Telegraph Transmission Theory," *Transactions of the American Institute of Electrical Engineers*, New York, Vol. 47, April 1928, pp. 617–644.
5. W. R. Bennett, "Spectra of Quantized Signals," *The Bell System Technical Journal*, New York, Vol. 27, No. 3, July 1948, pp. 446–472.
6. C. E. Shannon, "Communication in the Presence of Noise," *Proceedings of the Institute of Radio Engineers*, New York, Vol. 37, No. 1, January 1949, pp. 10–21.
7. G. A. Campbell, "The Practical Application of the Fourier Integral," *The Bell System Technical Journal*, New York, Vol. 7, No. 4, October 1928, pp. 639–707.
8. C. B. Feldman and W. R. Bennett, "Band Width and Transmission Performance," *The Bell System Technical Journal*, New York, Vol. 28, No. 3, July 1949, pp. 490–595.

Problems

1. Two components of frequencies 3,900 and 4,100 are present in such relationship that they just cancel when sampled at the instants $t = 0, T, 2T, \ldots$ where $T = 1/8,000$ second.

   (a) If one of these components is given by

   $$a \cos \left[2\pi 3,900t + \frac{\pi}{2} \right]$$

   and the other by

   $$\alpha \cos [2\pi 4,100t + \varphi],$$

   find α and φ.

   (b) With the values thus found, change the sampling instants to $t = T/2, 3T/2, 5T/2, \ldots$. Determine how near the components now come to canceling.

2. How many values of y for arbitrarily chosen values of t are necessary and sufficient to determine uniquely and for all times the sine wave, $y = A \sin (\omega t + \varphi)$? Assume $\omega \leqslant \omega_o$ and that the arbitrarily chosen values of time are restricted to an interval of time that is less than π/ω_o.

CHAPTER 5

QUANTIZATION, CODE TRANSMISSION, AND MULTIPLEXING

Quantization, code transmission, and multiplexing are important basic concepts of modulation. With the introductory treatment of the preceding chapters as a background, these topics may now be treated in greater detail. Quantization naturally follows sampling (Chap. 4). Code transmission is closely associated with the concepts of sampling and quantization. Particularly in a code transmission system, the concepts of code structure, message, information, and translation are closely bound up with those of quantization and sampling. Methods of multiplexing are, of course, equally applicable to quantized or continuously varying signals.

QUANTIZATION

Quantization means that each of a set of small ranges into which a larger range may be divided is assigned a single discrete number. This number may be that corresponding to the mean of the range.

Quantization permits the approximate representation of a continuously varying function by a set of discrete values. Graphically, the process of quantization means that a straight line representing the relation between input and output in a linear continuous system is replaced by a flight of steps, as shown in (a) of Fig. 5–1. A *quantum* is the difference between

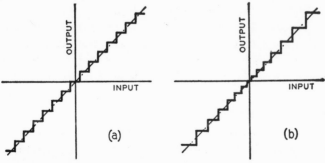

FIG. 5–1   Relation between input and quantized output, with quantization uniform in (a) and tapered in (b)

59

two adjacent discrete values. Thus, in the figure, the mid-points of the tread fall on the straight line, and the height of the step is the quantum. Clearly, the greatest error inherent in quantization amounts to half a quantum step. By reducing the size of each step and using enough steps to cover the total range, the deformation in the quantized signal may be made arbitrarily small.

Granularity in the quantized signals is measured by the difference between the input and output signals, as shown in (a) of Fig. 5–2. We see that the maximum instantaneous value of the error is half a step, and the total range of a particular error is from minus half a step to plus half a step. In (b) of Fig. 5–2 is shown a typical variation of the error as a function of the input signal, and (c) of Fig. 5–2 shows a typical variation of the error as a function of time.

Provided there is a large enough number of small steps, the error signal resembles a series of straight lines with varying slopes, s, but nearly always extending over the vertical interval between minus and plus half a step. Exceptional cases occur when the signal goes through a maximum or minimum within a step. The limiting condition of closely spaced steps enables us to derive quite simply an approximate value for the mean square error. (Ref. 1.)* Write

$$e = st, \quad -\frac{S_0}{2s} < t < \frac{S_0}{2s}, \tag{5-1}$$

where e is the error, S_0 is a full step, and t is the time referred to the midpoint as the origin. Then the mean square error is

$$\overline{e^2} = \frac{s}{S_0} \int_{-\frac{S_0}{2s}}^{\frac{S_0}{2s}} e^2 \, dt = \frac{S_0^2}{12}, \tag{5-2}$$

or one-twelfth the square of the step size.

The error may be considered to result from a nonlinear process in which the component frequencies of the original signal are applied to the nonlinear staircase characteristic. Nonlinear products of a higher order may have frequency components remote from those in the original signal, and these can be excluded by a filter passing only the signal band. If the original signal is a simple sine wave, these many products may be identified individually. For speech or other complex signals they merge into an essentially flat band of noise which sounds much like resistance noise due to thermal agitation.

Quantized Speech Samples

It is quite apparent that some distortion or granularity is inherent in the application of the principle of quantization to samples of an electric

---

* The references cited are listed at the end of each chapter according to the number used in the text.

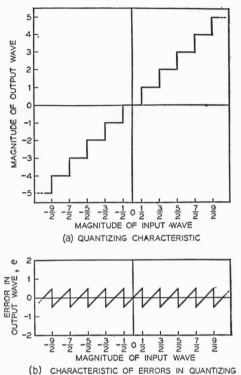

(a) QUANTIZING CHARACTERISTIC

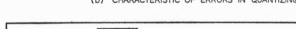

(b) CHARACTERISTIC OF ERRORS IN QUANTIZING

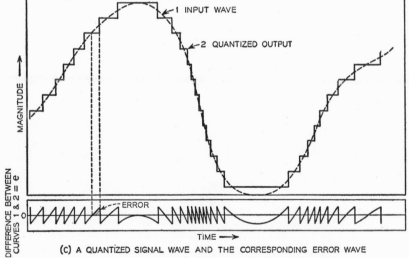

(c) A QUANTIZED SIGNAL WAVE AND THE CORRESPONDING ERROR WAVE

FIG. 5-2   Illustration of the quantizing principle

signal carrying the information of the spoken word. The greater the range assigned to a given quantum step and the fewer steps used, the greater will be this granularity. In ordinary telephony, the problem is to determine the smallest number of steps into which voice signals may be quantized without serious distortion, and what the size of each step should be.

The range of voltages covered by voice signals, from the peaks of loud talk to the weak passages of weak talk, is of the order of a thousand to one. If the range of voltages assigned to each quantum step were small enough to keep the granularity within desired limits for the weaker passages, and if the range assigned to each step were the same, thousands of steps would be required. By making most of the steps vary logarithmically, a nearly uniform percentage precision is obtained throughout the greater part of the range and far fewer steps are needed. It has been found experimentally that from 64 to 128 logarithmic steps introduce so little granularity that the speech wave is reproduced to a high degree of fidelity as judged by experienced observers.

When logarithmic steps are used, as in (b) of Fig. 5–1, the degree of step subdivision is fine enough to care adequately for the low-magnitude sounds including background noise. Although the precision expressed in per cent is independent of talker volume in the case of logarithmic steps, the performance for loud talk is somewhat less favorable than for the case of linear steps. Effects of higher granularity on the high peaks are not fully offset by lower granularity elsewhere.

Consider now the more general problem of optimum tapering for particular types of signals. The number of steps and the size of each step for least granularity will depend entirely upon signal characteristics. For example, if the signal is derived from a multichannel frequency-division system, many steps would be used because of the uniformly severe linearity requirements which such a system imposes; and in addition, the steps would be uniform rather than tapered.

CODE TRANSMISSION

Systems of code transmission capable of handling a continuously varying message stem from two findings. One is that a continuously varying signal may be represented by a definite number of samples per unit of time. The other is that, by the principle of quantization, the sequence of samples which are of continuous variation may be approximated as closely as desired by a sequence of quantized samples. Thus, the specification of a particular message to be conveyed is limited to a discrete set of values. Any plan for representing each value of the discrete set as a particular arrangement of discrete events is an example of code transmission. In this sense, the transmission of the quantized samples themselves as quantized pulse-amplitude modulation is an example of code transmission.

An early example is a proposal of P. M. Rainey (Ref. 2) for transmitting pictures. The proposed system transmitted a predetermined code combination of electric impulses for each elemental area of the picture. At the receiving end it utilized these telegraphic code combinations to vary the intensity of a light beam, and then caused that beam to reproduce a likeness of the original picture.

Definitions

Before discussing code transmission generally, we need certain definitions which imply additional concepts. A *code* is any plan for representing each of a discrete set of values as a particular arrangement of discrete events. *Code element* is one of the discrete events in a code, such as the presence or absence of a pulse or of a dot or dash or space as used in a Morse code. *Code character* is a particular arrangement of code elements used in a code to represent a single value. *Binary code* is a code in which each code element may be either of two distinct kinds or values, for example, the presence or absence of a pulse. In a *ternary code*, each code element may be any of three distinct kinds or values; in an *N'ary code*, each code element may be any one of N distinct kinds or values. *Regenerative repeatering* is a process in which each code element is replaced by a new code element of specified timing, wave form, and magnitude.

It is worth noting that an important concept implied in the definition of code element is that, in identifying a particular code element, nonsignificant differences are ignored. For example, a *code element* is one of a group of entities having the following property: the group is capable of division into subgroups such that each member of any subgroup is like every other member of that subgroup with respect to each of certain characteristics, which we choose to recognize, and differs distinguishably from members of all other subgroups with respect to at least one of these characteristics. In identifying a particular code element, differences in other characteristics are ignored.

In these terms, a *code* is any plan of representing each of a limited number of values as a particular arrangement of either code elements or code characters composed of code elements. Although the number of plans is definitely known, the selection of any particular plan is subject to certain restrictions. Such restrictions may apply generally or may be characteristic of the particular occasion. In typing a telegram, two letters which differ in shape and so constitute different symbols may not both be selected if they are alike with respect to position. This is a general restriction. The limitation of the selection to ten words is a particular one. Particular limitations also may be self-imposed by the sender.

A *message* is a particular selection from among the symbols or code elements constituting a code which has been made in conformity with the restrictions applicable to the occasion.

Each message has associated with it *information* peculiar to itself, determined as to its *nature* by the selection made by the sender, and to its *amount* by statistics (Chap. 6) relating to the number and sort of different selections available to the sender within the existing restrictions. It is the latter, if we ignore the conceptual meaning and interpretation of the message, that determines the complexity of the specification that uniquely describes the message. With a simple N'ary code, if all quanta are equally probable and the probability of any code element is independent of preceding code elements, the amount of information is proportional to the number of code elements comprising the message multiplied by the logarithm of N.

A specification capable of uniquely defining any particular message can be chosen in many ways and is transmitted directly or is transformed or acted upon in some manner so as to produce unambiguous information-bearing signals which are suitable for transportation. Applications are encountered in which the specification may be the same as the message itself, whereas in other instances the specification may be either simpler or more complex than the message it defines.

The *translation* of a message consists of the replacement of its code elements by those of a second code, the symbols of which correspond to those of the first in such a way that a message in the first code uniquely determines one in the second. Translation is of itself an example of modulation, although at the same time it may be but a part of a more involved modulation process.

A *signal element* is a code element of a form which is suitable for transmission over the medium.

Transmitter

At the transmitting end, a coder is called upon to set up a particular pulse-code combination for each quantized signal value. Obviously, a great many codes are conceivable; in practice, however, codes which allow simplicity in the operations of encoding and decoding are usually selected. An example is the use of on-or-off pulses to represent digits of the binary number system. A system with instrumentation that permits rapid coding obviously is desirable since this will allow more channels to be handled in time division by common equipment.

Band-Width Occupancy

In code transmission (PCM), if band width is conserved, the code elements may overlap in time to such an extent that, upon casual inspection, the resultant signal array may show little evidence of discrete signal elements.   The extent to which adjacent code elements are separated in time depends upon the speed of signaling as well as the wave form of the code elements and the over-all transient response of the system.   With slow enough signaling the code elements will be widely separated in time.   With high-speed signaling approaching the Nyquist rate ($2B$ elements per second if the band width is B) the code elements will overlap to such an extent as to produce a continuously varying wave.

Parameters such as band width, statistical structure of the specification defining the message, destination of the message, statistical structure and nature of the interference and noise, all are functionally related, and their relative importance will depend upon the specific application.   In practice, the optimum band width represents the most useful compromise in efforts to reduce noise and interference and to increase signal.

Regenerative Repeaters

When the peak interference is less than half a quantum step, a code element may be identified without error.   Consequently, if each quantized signal element can be identified successfully at a regenerative repeater, and if the signal elements are regenerated so that they occur at precisely the right relative time and have the right wave form and right value, then the new signal, except for delay, is exactly the same as the signal originally transmitted.   In a long system having many repeater points, regeneration has to be practiced at spans short enough to permit the elimination of noise and distortion before it reaches the noise threshold, namely, half a quantum step.   Thus, in a code transmission system, transmission impairments have to be considered only for the distance between regeneration points.   When these impairments are kept below threshold, they are not carried over from one span to the next.

Receiver

At the final receiver, the regenerated code elements are operated upon to re-create as closely as possible the original signal (provided it is the original signal that the receiver is called upon to deliver) by operations complementary to those at the transmitter.   Unfortunately, however, no process at the receiver can undo the effects of quantization which remain as noise.   Therefore, the quanta must be made small enough from the beginning so as to permit a satisfactory reproduction of the wanted message.

Synchronization

Because precise timing is involved in identifying the signal elements, some scheme of synchronization is required, assuming the objective is

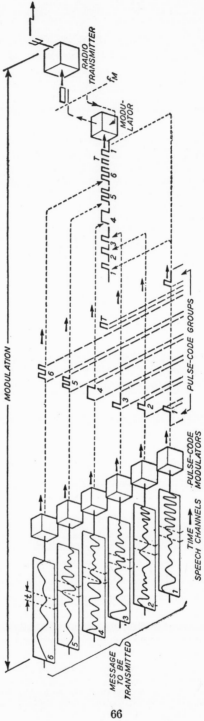

FIG. 5-3 In a time-division, multichannel telephone system, the entire frequency band is used for transmitting each voice wave

conservation of band width and signal power as well as essentially error-free identification. Provision for synchronization usually need not encroach seriously upon the band width in most practical systems. In time-division systems, for example, synchronization may be common to many channels.

METHODS OF MULTIPLEXING

As mentioned in Chapter 2, channels may be multiplexed by arranging them in time sequence or by arranging them along the frequency scale. In addition to time division and frequency division, there is a third type called *phase discrimination*.

Upon occasion, channels may be multiplexed by assigning different modes of transmission to different channels. For example, two copper-wire pairs may be made to yield a third path by the familiar process of phantoming and, in theory, we may phantom a pair of phantoms and so on. Over a suitable radio path, cross polarization yields two independent channels even though each channel uses the same frequency range. Similarly, in a wave guide, a plurality of different modes of transmission may be supported simultaneously and afterwards separated without serious mutual interference.

Methods of multiplexing that in practical applications intrinsically do not afford a high degree of separation between channels become attractive when applied to some of the latest schemes of communication since certain of these new methods are relatively insensitive to interference.

Time-Division Multiplexing

In time-division multiplexing, many channels (represented by independent information-bearing signals) are propagated over a common medium by allocating different time intervals for the transmission of each signal. Each channel utilizes the entire frequency spectrum of the system. Alternatively, time-division multiplex may be regarded as a kind of phase discrimination (Ref. 3) wherein the information-bearing signal of a particular channel is modulated on harmonic carriers. These carriers are so phased as to balance out interchannel crosstalk during time intervals allotted to that channel.

Figure 5-3 illustrates a time-division multiplex arranged to provide six voice-frequency telephone channels. Very short samples of the speech wave in each channel are taken successively and transmitted. After one set of samples of all the channels has been transmitted, another set is taken and transmitted, and so on continuously, set after set (frame after frame). At any one instant, therefore, only one of the speech wave trains is displayed by the transmitted signal. As indicated in Fig. 5-3, the samples taken successively of each channel need not be transmitted in the form they are taken. In the diagram they are converted into code characters and these, in turn, modulate a radio transmitter.

Frequency-Division Multiplexing

In frequency-division multiplexing, a plurality of channels (different information-bearing signals) is propagated simultaneously over a common path by using different frequency bands for the transmission of each signal.

This means that a band of relatively high frequencies is divided into a number of narrower bands, each of which serves as a channel. Figure 5–4 is a diagrammatic representation of a six-channel, carrier-telephone system. In the composite band, frequencies representing all of the channels may be present all of the time. The name *frequency-division multiplex* comes from the assignment of each of the multiple speech wave trains to one of the number of equal divisions of the allotted frequency band.

Phase-Discrimination Multiplexing

In phase-discrimination multiplexing (Ref. 3), N different information-bearing signals or channels, each of which is modulated simultaneously on $N/2$ carriers with a different set of carrier phases provided for each channel, are propagated simultaneously over a common path, and a homodyne detection process is used at the receiver for channel selection.

If N is odd we may imagine a system employing sidebands on zero frequency and the next $(N-1)/2$ harmonics of the switching, that is, sampling frequency. In any event, the carriers are of proper numbers and phases to the end that the resulting combination of the numbers and phases of the corresponding sidebands will permit subsequent interchannel separation with maximum economy of band-width occupancy.

A familiar example is the quadrature carrier system (Refs. 4 and 5) which is capable of yielding two channels for each double sideband of frequency range occupancy. In true phase discrimination, there need be no separation of channels in either time or frequency. By requiring a homodyne detection process, the necessary precision of instrumentation is in general more difficult to achieve than with either frequency division or time division. Still, in certain situations, phase discrimination offers engaging prospects for maximum economy of band width for maximum transmission advantage. Like amplitude modulation and vestigial sideband, the method has the important advantage of being capable of transmitting low modulating frequencies including zero frequency.

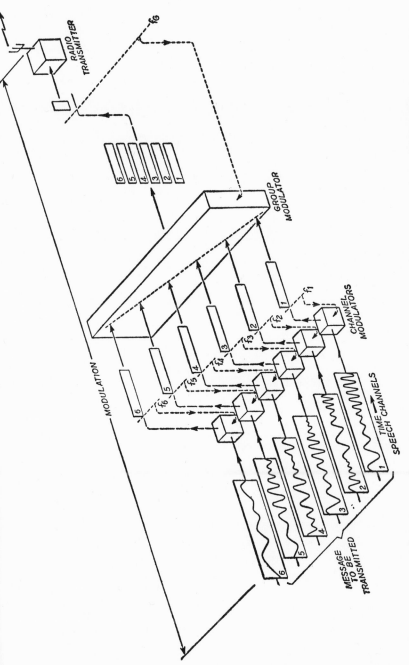

FIG. 5–4 In frequency-division, multichannel telephone systems, all the voice waves are transmitted continuously, but each uses only a small part of the total frequency band

References

1. W. R. Bennett, "Spectra of Quantized Signals," *The Bell System Technical Journal*, New York, Vol. 27, No. 3, July 1948, pp. 446–472.
2. Paul M. Rainey, United States Patent 1,608,527, November 30, 1926.
3. W. R. Bennett, "Time-Division Multiplex Systems," *The Bell System Technical Journal*, New York, Vol. 20, No. 2, April 1941, pp. 199–221.
4. H. Nyquist, "Certain Topics in Telegraph Transmission Theory," *Transactions of the American Institute of Electrical Engineers*, New York, Vol. 47, April 1928, pp. 617–644.
5. A. V. T. Day, United States Patent 1,885,010, October 25, 1932.

CHAPTER 6

EFFICIENT SYSTEMS OF COMMUNICATION

Crude systems of communication certainly must have existed before the dawn of civilization. From primitive beginnings to the modern high-speed and far-flung communication networks of today we certainly have come a long way. Theory and invention, development and research, improved techniques and new instrumentalities — these and a host of other factors have made valuable contributions. An ultimate dominating factor has been theory, and in no place in the art of communications is this more evident than in the evolution of efficient systems. Outstanding improvements in efficiency if not accompanied by undue complexity might be expected to simplify problems of switching, multiplexing, and repeatering, and to permit the exchange of band width and signal power to the extent that both are utilized to best advantage.

Accordingly, realization of efficient systems usually involves modulation. Conversely, problems of modulation generally start with questions of system efficiency. The two are so interdependent that a discussion of modulation theory must consider at least some aspects of system efficiency. This is the purpose of the present chapter.

At the transmitting end of a communication system two steps are necessary for good efficiency: first, use the minimum amount of information to represent the desired message; and, second, use the optimal signal for transmitting this information to the receiver. In practical applications these two steps may coalesce. At the receiving end we encounter companion steps: first, efficient execution of the inverse operations; and, second, realization of possible savings due to considerations of when, where, and how the message is to be delivered.

SUMMARY

Most of this chapter is concerned with the contributions of information theory to efficient systems of communication. Here we find that modern theory, as developed by C. E. Shannon, derives and makes available theorems on ideal, nonsurpassable performance and develops quantitative criteria for comparing the merits of different systems. This affords an opportunity to compare well-known existing types of systems with the

71

theoretical ideal and, of course, stimulates the search for new systems having capabilities that more closely approach ideal, nonsurpassable performance. Another contribution has been the application of advanced mathematical concepts and methods to communication problems. Ultimately this may prove to be of great importance.

Shannon's central theorem in information theory deals with the transmission of a channel having a band width B, mean signal power S, and mean resistance noise power N. The theorem states that a method of coding exists whereby C binary digits per second may be transmitted with arbitrarily small frequency of error where C is given by

$$C = B \log_2 \left(1 + \frac{S}{N}\right), \tag{6-1}$$

and *no higher rate can be so transmitted.* No method of encoding to accomplish the ideal rate is exhibited, although it is demonstrated that, as the ideal rate is approached, the statistics of the message resemble those of noise.

Applied to the transmission of discrete or quantized values, the ideal performance derived by Shannon is appreciably better than well-known codes of reasonable complexity. More interesting, however, is its application to continuous message waves.

A continuously variable quantity can assume an infinite number of values; and if all these values were distinguishable, the amount of information contained in even the shortest sample would be unlimited. Actually the minimum recognizable difference between two magnitudes in a physical communication system cannot be made arbitrarily small. For practical purposes, therefore, it should always be possible to replace a continuously varying source by a discrete source sufficiently fine-grained to represent all observable variations. The only question is how such equivalents should be quantitatively specified.

Ground work for the reduction of the continuous to the discrete case was adequately formulated in the early papers by Nyquist and Hartley. Both Nyquist and Hartley showed what must indeed have been commonplace knowledge from the earliest days of telegraphy, namely, how the number of distinct signal values available to a signal element is limited by the relative magnitude of the interference.

Like Nyquist, Hartley did not neglect noise in deriving his formula. He postulated a particular detector system and assumed that the signal elements were of adequate power and were spaced sufficiently far apart so as to override noise and intersymbol interference and thus prevent errors in transmission. Shannon assumed a finite probability of error and obtained a statistical result. In comparing Hartley's formula with Shannon's it is necessary to remember that they do not represent the same transmission performance: one is essentially error-free; the other is error-free only in the statistical sense that the average rate of errors can be made arbitrarily small.

Hartley reduced telephony to telegraphy by substituting a stepped approximation for the continuously varying signal. Shannon has proposed various "fidelity evaluation functions" for a quantitative measure of the difference between transmitted and received waves. Actual calculations are rather intricate.

Information theory could be expected to instigate suggestions for removing a great part of the redundancy and superfluous matter from our everyday communications, thereby permitting substantial savings in band width, signal power, and time. So far this expectation has not been realized to any important degree.

Recent work by B. M. Oliver (Ref. 30)* on the application of prediction to the transmission of television signals may be cited as a scientific approach to the reduction of redundancy. The objective is to make a statistical analysis of the message at its source and to transmit enough information so that a similar analyzer at the receiver can reconstruct the original message. With an ideal analyzer only a minimum of information need be transmitted.

In effect, linear prediction turns out to be quite similar to ordinary preemphasis, although the networks are very different from what would be expected from a conventional steady-state analysis.

Nonlinear prediction introduces entirely new possibilities. At the transmitter, Oliver uses an automatic computer that compares the actual message data with a multi-entry table of probabilities, and sends out only the deviations from the most probable values. A complementary computer at the receiver uses the deviation data to obtain the original information from an identical table. If the prediction is good, very little data need be sent. Over a short period of time, if the prediction becomes badly wrong, the temporary heavy load of information is partially stored and fed out gradually during the ensuing calmer interval.

INTERFERENCE THRESHOLD AS A FUNCTION OF BAND WIDTH

For the past twenty years there has been considerable development and an ever-increasing application of new systems of modulation such as frequency modulation, pulse-position modulation, and pulse-code modulation. These have the interesting property that it is possible to exchange band width for signal-to-noise ratio. This means, in effect, that we can transmit the same information in the same time with less signal power, provided we are willing to use more band width.

* The references cited are listed at the end of each chapter according to the number used in the text.

If and only if the signals are quantized, as in pulse-code modulation, is the converse true. That is, as explained on pages 75 to 77, we can use less band width at the expense of more signal power. Before the advent of PCM (pulse-code modulation which, in effect, substitutes a stepped approximation for a continuously varying signal), it was seldom appreciated that, to all practical intents and purposes, a signal covering a given band of frequencies could be transmitted over a communication channel capable of handling only a narrower band of frequencies. As Hartley showed, if the signal varies continuously with time, this is impossible unless the narrower band of frequencies is occupied for a correspondingly longer time. In fact, it was the development of these newer systems that prompted a re-examination of the foundations of communication theory. By the same token it will be advantageous to examine systems of this type from the standpoint of signal power and band-width occupancy before passing to the more general case.

Interference Threshold

If it can be guaranteed that the peak interference is less than half a quantum step, a code element theoretically can be identified without error. For simplicity, we intentionally ignore the possibility of correct identification in the presence of larger values of interference, and we regard half a quantum step as the noise threshold for error-free operation. Let q be the number of quantum steps per code element. The optimum arrangement for propagation over the transmitting medium is one of equal steps.

When the steps are equal, $(q - 1)$ is the ratio of peak-to-peak signal to peak-to-peak interference at the threshold of error. The interference may be noise. If at the instants of sampling, S' and N' denote peak-to-peak signal and noise respectively,

$$\frac{S'}{N'} = q - 1, \qquad (6\text{-}2)$$

or expressed in decibels,

$$\text{Interference threshold} = 20 \log_{10} (q - 1). \qquad (6\text{-}3)$$

If no avoidable delays are permitted, interference threshold is a measure of the signal-to-noise requirement for virtually error-free operation. Other things being equal, the signal-to-noise requirement is a measure of the necessary signal power. In a practical system the signal power must exceed the theoretical threshold to allow for operating margins, et cetera.

Law Governing the Exchange of Band Width for Signal Power

As pointed out by Nyquist, information capacity is measured by the logarithm of q and is proportional to the number of code elements. If we encode without delay and signal at the Nyquist rate, namely, $2B$ code elements per second in a band B cycles wide, we may write, using (6–2)

$$C = 2B \log_2 \left(1 + \frac{S'}{N'}\right), \qquad (6\text{–}4)$$

an expression for the law governing the exchange of band width for signal power in the type of error-free system under discussion. The relationship is best understood by considering a particular example.

Illustrative Example. Suppose we are concerned with the transmission of speech signals which are confined to frequencies below 4,000 cycles per second. Assume that short samples of the signal are taken at the rate of 8,000 per second and each sample is quantized into one of 64 possible discrete values. In practice the steps would be properly tapered as explained in Chapter 5 so as to minimize the effect of granularity in the quantized signals.

On this basis the resulting samples constitute an array of 64'ary code elements in which the quantum steps are tapered. For transmission, equal steps are wanted. By translation (Chap. 5), the array with tapered steps is replaced by another array of 64'ary code elements in which the quantum steps are equal.

After translation the signals are transmitted over a band 4,000 cycles wide. The interference threshold (6–3) is $20 \log_{10} (64 - 1) = 36$ decibels. With perfect transmission and instrumentation, peak noise will have no effect on transmission, *provided* it is always 36 or more decibels below the maximum wanted signal.

If it is desired to make the system even more immune to interference, we could represent each sample of the message wave by a binary code composed of six elements (noting that $2^6 = 64$). Since code elements theoretically can be transmitted at the Nyquist rate, namely, $6 \times 8,000 = 48,000$ per second, the band-width occupancy would be 24 kilocycles per second. Under these conditions the operation theoretically will be error-free, provided the peak interference is less than the peak signal.

These matters are illustrated in more detail in (a) of Fig. 6–1. The numbers adjacent to the plotted points represent the number of magnitudes available to each code element. The point designated $64 \times 64 = 4,096$ refers to a system wherein a code element can assume any one of 4,096 possible values, and each code element represents the magnitudes of two successive samples of the speech wave.

The 4,096 possible values assigned to each code element are assumed to be divided into 64 groups, each containing 64 values. The group into which a received signal falls represents the magnitude of the first sample of speech, and the element value within the group indicates the value of the second sample. This, of course, makes the decibel threshold of interference for the first sample of the pair 36 to 72.2 decibels, depending upon the magnitude of the second sample, and for the second sample of the pair, 72.2 decibels. The latter value is the one plotted in (a) of Fig. 6–1.

The number of different ways in which the foregoing code-element values may be related to the samples of the speech wave is equal to the number

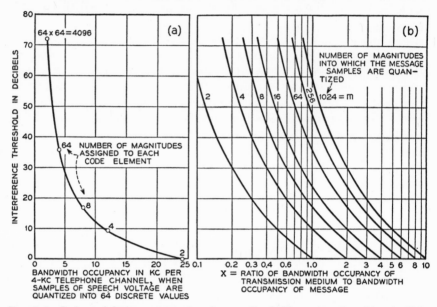

FIG. 6–1 Code-modulation systems: interference threshold as a function of band width
(a) Number of discrete values some one of which is assumed by a code element
(b) Number of discrete values some one of which is assumed by an m'ary message sample

of different permutations that can be formed with 4,096 things, or 4,096!. In other words, in carrying out this translation there are 4,096! different codes, any one of which is capable of uniquely representing the two quantized magnitudes of successive samples of a sampled speech wave. Even in a much simpler situation, different codes may display different properties as regards over-all transmission performance and ease of instrumentation.

It should be noted that the time required to put the information content of the message on the transmitting medium was increased by an amount equal to the extra time required to get two samples instead of one, namely, 125 microseconds. On the assumption that no unnecessary time is wasted at the receiver, this delay in putting the information-bearing signals on the transmitting medium represents the only extra delay theoretically necessary in the delivery of the message to its destination. The extra delay increases as we divide the band-width occupancy by a larger factor. Some entirely different scheme of encoding and decoding might not introduce this delay.

In the foregoing example, had we been dealing with a two-channel system, we could have sampled both speech messages simultaneously at periodic intervals of 125 microseconds, and, if no time were wasted, incur no delay in putting the information on the line. Although (a) of Fig. 6–1 shows discrete points, similar reasoning applied to a multichannel system with a large enough number of channels will show that band-width occupancy can be made to fall anywhere on the curve drawn between the points.

It should be emphasized that Fig. 6–1 depicts the interference threshold and performance of idealized systems. Imperfections in instrumentation, in the transmission medium, and so forth, all act to prevent these results from being completely realized in practical applications.

General Case. Assume that the message wave is confined to frequencies below B cycles per second, that it is sampled $2B$ times per second, and that m is the number of possible magnitudes available to each quantized sample. Assume further that Bx is the band width in cycles per second of the transmitting medium, and that q'ary code elements having equal quantum steps are transmitted at the Nyquist rate, namely, $2Bx$ elements per second. Then translation (Chap. 5, page 64) from the m'ary to the q'ary code with no unavoidable delay and error-free operation requires what might be termed an equal number of symbols in each alphabet, viz.;

$$m^{2B} = q^{2Bx}. \tag{6-5}$$

From (6–2)

$$\frac{S'}{N'} = m^{\frac{1}{x}} - 1. \tag{6-6}$$

From (6–3)

$$\text{db interference threshold} = 20 \log_{10} (m^{\frac{1}{x}} - 1). \tag{6-7}$$

From (6–4)

$$C = 2Bx \log_2 (1 + m^{\frac{1}{x}} - 1) = 2B \log_2 m. \tag{6-8}$$

Equation (6–7) is portrayed in (b) of Fig. 6–1, which shows the interference threshold as a function of x, the ratio of band-width occupancy of the transmitting medium to band-width occupancy of the message. The variable parameter is m, the number of possible magnitudes available to each quantized sample of the message wave.

Either (6–5) or (6–8) illustrates that, for continuous reception, the transmitted signal must convey information at the rate it is produced.

EFFICIENT SYSTEMS OF COMMUNICATION

Even taking into account the important theoretical advances made by Nyquist and Hartley in the 1920's, the treatment of the preceding section goes about as far as one can go without additional theoretical background. Fortunately, advances have been made.   By basing the general philosophy of communication on probability concepts, Shannon and Wiener (Refs. 1 and 2) have succeeded in recent years in extending and generalizing the theory.

Many workers have contributed to the recent advances, and some of the literature relating to this work is included in References 3 to 33.   The treatment to follow deals briefly with selected topics of the theory and resorts to a minimum of mathematics.   For more complete and precise treatments the reader should consult the source articles, particularly Reference 1. Attention here will be largely focused on the transmitter and transmitting channel, having in mind that the principles are equally applicable both to the inverse operation at the receiver and the matter of taking into account the destination of the message.

Meaning of Information

The fundamental problem of communication is for the receiver to select exactly or approximately a message selected at the transmitter.   The basic concept is that the actual message is one *selected* from a set of possible messages.   The system must operate for each possible selection, and the signal transmitted must be a specification of the particular message chosen at the sending end.   If and only if an unambiguous specification is transmitted can the receiver hope to re-create the original message.   Furthermore, from the viewpoint of modern information theory, whether the selected message has meaning or makes sense is regarded as quite irrelevant to the communication problem of transmitting the information.

Measure of Information

Following Nyquist and Hartley, we use a logarithmic measure of information.   From the standpoint of communication, information measure must be correlated with the notion of choice from a set of possibilities. The simplest is a choice from two possibilities each with probability 0.5. It is convenient to use the amount of information associated with such a choice as the basic unit.   We term the basic unit a "binary digit" or "*bit.*"

Fundamental to the concept of measure of information is the notion that the more uncertain we are about the composition of a message, the greater will be the amount of information we acquire when reception has completely removed the uncertainty as to what message was sent.   If the receiver could predict the message in advance, it would not be a message at all and no new information would be acquired.

If there are m possibilities all equally likely,

$$H = \log_2 m, \tag{6-9}$$

where H is the number of bits of information involved in the selection. If m is 8, the first bit corresponds to a choice of which half of the 8 possibilities is chosen, the second bit to a choice between the first and second pair of the selected half, and the last bit to a choice between the first or second member of the chosen pair. Thus 3 (or $\log_2 8$) bits of information determine the selection, and this is the amount of information acquired when the specification of the choice has been received. When $m = 1$, the outcome is certain and we have, from (6-9), $H = 0$, which is the appropriate result.

Thus we see that a logarithmic measure agrees with our intuitive feeling that, other things being equal, if a telephone conversation is twice as long, or if we have two channels instead of one, the amount of received information has been doubled. Another fundamental point to note is that, if an unfinished message is long enough, the task of finishing it, aided only by the part received, is virtually impossible.

The base to which the logarithms are taken is a matter of convenience and amounts to a definition of the unit of measure. When the logarithms are taken to the base 10 as is commonly done, the unit is termed a *Hartley*. One Hartley has the information value of 3.3219 bits since $\log_2 10 = 3.3219$.

When the uncorrelated probabilities ρ_i are not equal, the amount of information produced by a single choice (Ref. 1) is

$$H = - \sum_1^m \rho_i \log_2 \rho_i. \tag{6-10}$$

If the production of the message consists of a sequence of choices (as, for example, the letters of printed text or the elementary words or sounds of speech), the amount of information produced per symbol or per second can be calculated by an application of (6-10).

To illustrate, first regard (6-10) with like ρ's as a generalization of (6-9). Suppose we choose letters of the alphabet at random with equal probability. The information value of any letter, that is, a single selection, is $\log_2 26$. But on the average any one letter such as A appears $1/26$ of the time. Thus, in a sense, the information value of A is $1/26 \log_2 26$, or $-1/26 \log_2 1/26$. This we can write as $-\rho \log_2 \rho$ where ρ is the probability of A. In this example the information value of B is the same. Similarly, the total information value of all 26 letters is $-\sum_1^{26} \rho \log_2 \rho = \log_2 26$, which agrees with (6-9).

Now let ρ_A, ρ_B, et cetera, be the actual probabilities of A, B, et cetera. We might again say the contribution of A to the information is $-\rho_A \log_2 \rho_A$ and so on. That is,

$$H = - [\rho_A \log_2 \rho_A + \rho_B \log_2 \rho_B + \cdots \rho_Z \log_2 \rho_Z]$$
$$= - \sum_{i=A}^{Z} \rho_i \log_2 \rho_i$$

which is (6–10).

As another example, suppose the probabilities are 1/8, 1/8, 1/4, and 1/2. This is like an 8-letter alphabet, A, B, C, D, E, F, G, H, having equal probabilities in which we replace C and D by X and the last four letters by Y. One bit would distinguish between Y and the rest. Half a bit more distinguishes between X and AB, this being 0.5 instead of one because we only have to make this distinction half the time. Similarly, 0.25 bit more picks A or B. This adds up to 1.75 bits. To verify that (6–10) gives the right answer in this special case, we write

$$H = - \left[\frac{1}{8} \log_2 \frac{1}{8} + \frac{1}{8} \log_2 \frac{1}{8} + \frac{1}{4} \log_2 \frac{1}{4} + \frac{1}{2} \log_2 \frac{1}{2} \right] = 1.75.$$

If we have a 26-letter alphabet and select letters at random with equal probability, the amount of information is given by (6–9) and is

$$H = \log_2 26 = 4.7 \text{ bits per letter.} \tag{6–11}$$

Reference 34 contains a table of letter frequencies. If we take into account the probability of occurrence of each letter (Ref. 1),

$$H = - \sum_{i=1}^{26} \rho_i \log_2 \rho_i = 4.14 \text{ bits per letter.} \tag{6–12}$$

This means that the sequence of letters could be shortened by the ratio $4.14/4.7 = 0.88$ by encoding it in an alphabet in which the 26 letters occurred with equal probabilities. Since the antilog$_2$ 4.14 = 18 approximately, the unequal letter probabilities in English when used to produce text in this way reduce its powers to those of an 18-letter alphabet in which the letters are equally likely.

This illustrates a very important property of H. The quantity H is a maximum and is equal to ($\log_2 m$) when all of the possibilities are the same, that is, $1/m$. A second important property is the fact that the addition of new statistical correlations between parts of a message always tends to reduce its information value. Maximum uncertainty exists when there is no correlation between symbols and all symbols are equally likely.

Choice, Uncertainty, and Entropy

Up until this point the use of the word *entropy* has been avoided. As stated by Shannon (Ref. 1): "Quantities of the form $H = - \sum \rho_i \log \rho_i$ play a central role in information theory as measures of information, choice, and uncertainty. $H = 0$ if and only if all the ρ_i's are zero but one, and this one probability is unity. Only when we are certain of the outcome does H vanish. Otherwise H is positive." As is characteristic of entropy, we note that, for extreme unlikelihood of events or for practical certainty, H approaches $0 \log 0$ or $1 \log 1$. Either limit leads to small uncertainty and little information; and, as already mentioned, the uncertainty is a maximum when all the probabilities are equal. Similarity of its mathematical form makes the name inevitable. Resemblance, in fact, goes further than similarity of mathematical form (Ref. 1), for the entropy of thermodynamics actually is a measure of uncertainty of our knowledge concerning dynamical coordinates.

Calculation of Entropy from the Statistical Structure of the Message

The simplest case of all is when the symbols are chosen independently and all m symbols are equally likely. As already mentioned, under this condition the entropy is a maximum, and a measure of this maximum uncertainty is $\log_2 m$, the information value of a symbol in bits.

Next we may consider the case where all symbols are chosen independently, but all symbols are not equally likely. Unequal probabilities are found to reduce the entropy, the uncertainty now being measured by $-\sum \rho_i \log_2 \rho_i$, the information value of a symbol expressed in bits.

We now take up the case where successive symbols are not chosen independently. The simplest case of this type is a choice that depends on only the preceding symbol and not on earlier ones. That is, the probability with which each symbol is chosen is the probability that it follows the preceding symbol. The uncertainty of a new symbol is never increased by knowledge of the preceding symbol. Let

$$\rho(a) = \text{probability of choice } a$$
$$\rho_a(b) = \text{probability, having } a, \text{ that } b \text{ follows}$$

and

$$\rho(a, b) = \text{probability of } a, b$$

so that

$$\rho(a, b) = \rho(a)\,\rho_a(b).$$

Also,

$\rho(a, b)$ will be termed the probability of digram a, b.

The proper expression for the entropy, which is a measure of the average uncertainty of the next symbol when the preceding symbol is known, is given (Ref. 1) by

$$H = -\sum_{i,j} \rho(i,j) \log_2 \rho_i(j)$$
$$= -\sum_{i,j} \rho(i,j) \log_2 \rho(i,j) + \sum_i \rho(i) \log_2 \rho(i) \qquad (6\text{--}13)$$

which gives the information value of a symbol in bits when digram statistics are taken into account. The indices i and j range over all possible symbols.

The first term on the right-hand side of (6–13) can be calculated from digram frequencies for printed English (Ref. 34). The second term is similar in form and can be calculated from a table (Ref. 34) of the frequency of occurrence of letters in English text.

For printed English the complete digram calculation (Ref. 6) gives the result

$$H = - \sum_{i,j} \rho(i, j) \log_2 \rho(i, j) + \sum_{i} \rho(i) \log_2 \rho(i)$$
$$= 7.70 - 4.14 = 3.56 \text{ bits per letter.} \tag{6–14}$$

The digram entropy, 3.56, is less than 4.14, the entropy that reflects letter frequency only, and this in turn is less than 4.7, the maximum entropy per letter for a 26-letter alphabet. The digram structure has reduced the information value of the language to $3.56/4.7 = 0.758$, or 76 per cent of the maximum possible.

The trigram entropy is given (Ref. 6) by

$$H = - \sum_{i,j,k} \rho(i, j, k) \log_2 \rho(i, j, k) + \sum_{i,j} \rho(i, j) \log_2 \rho(i, j) \tag{6–15}$$

and for printed English

$$= 11.0 - 7.7 = 3.3, \text{ approximately.}$$

The N-gram entropy measures the amount of information or entropy due to statistics extending over N adjacent symbols of text and is given (Ref. 6) by

$$H = - \sum_{i,j} \rho(b_i, j) \log_2 \rho_{b_i}(j) \tag{6–16}$$

or

$$H = - \sum_{i,j} \rho(b_i, j) \log_2 \rho(b_i, j) + \sum_{i} \rho(b_i) \log_2 \rho(b_i) \tag{6–17}$$

where b_i is a block of $N - 1$ symbols $[(N - 1)\text{-gram}]$;
  j is an arbitrary symbol following b_i;
  $\rho(b_i, j)$ is the probability of the N-gram b_i, j;
  $\rho_{b_i}(j)$ is the conditional probability of symbol j after block b_i and
  is given by $\dfrac{\rho(b_i, j)}{\rho(b_i)}$.

Equation (6–17) is a measure of the average uncertainty (conditional entropy) of the next symbol when the preceding $N - 1$ symbols are known.

It would be natural to extend the numerical treatment to N-gram entropies. For example, the statistical structure in English text extends over much greater distances than three letters. However, tables for printed English are not available for $N > 3$. Moreover, the labor increases. In 7-letter sequences there are about 26^7, or roughly 10^{10}, separate sequences to examine.

Word frequencies have been tabulated (Ref. 35) and can be used (Ref. 6) to obtain a closer approximation to the entropy of printed English. Shannon shows a log-log plot of the 1,000 most frequent English words against frequency rank. The probability of the most common word "the" is 0.071 and is plotted against 1. "Of" is the next most common word and its probability of 0.034 is plotted against 2. When all points are plotted in this manner, the locus can be approximated by a straight line whose slope is minus one. If ρ_n is the probability of the nth most common word, roughly,

$$\rho_n = \frac{0.1}{n}. \tag{6-18}$$

Zipf (Ref. 36) has pointed out that $\rho_n = k/n$ is a rather good approximation to word probabilities in many different languages. Equation (6–18) cannot hold indefinitely, and at $n = 8{,}727$ the total accumulated probability is one. If we assume $\rho_n = 0$ for larger n, Shannon finds (Ref. 6) that the entropy is

$$-\sum_1^{8{,}727} \rho_n \log_2 \rho_n = 11.82 \text{ bits per word.} \tag{6-19}$$

This is 2.62 bits per letter, since the average word length is 4.5 letters. Shannon further notes that the space symbol is almost completely redundant when passages of several words are involved. Thus if spaces are introduced, the entropy of printed English using the 27-letter alphabet is $4.5/5.5 = 0.818$ that of the 26-letter alphabet. This reduces 2.62 to 2.14 bits per letter.

In Reference 6 Shannon is primarily concerned with a new method for estimating the entropy of printed English. The method exploits the fact that anyone speaking a language possesses an enormous knowledge of its statistics. For a 27-letter alphabet Shannon concludes that ". . . in ordinary literary English, the long-range statistical effects (up to 100 letters) reduce the entropy to something of the order of one bit per letter, with a corresponding redundancy of roughly 75 per cent."

To recapitulate, with reference to the entropy of an information source, the information measure of any particular message, H, specifies the number of binary digits necessary to distinguish the particular message from all others of the class considered. It gives the number of binary digits necessary to code that particular message, but uses a code that is most efficient for the class as a whole. A calculation of the entropy of the message source represents the first step in efficient communication because it evaluates the minimum information necessary for unambiguous specification. The next consideration is whether the entropy has been maximized.

Relative Entropy or Message Efficiency

The ratio of the entropy of a source to the maximum value it could have while still restricted to the same symbols will be called its *relative entropy*. The maximum value is a measure of the maximum compression possible when we encode into the same alphabet. Designated E, relative entropy is a measure of *message efficiency*, and

$$E = \lim_{n \to \infty} \frac{H(n)}{n \log q} \qquad (6\text{-}19)$$

where there are q symbols for each place, n places, and $H(n)$ is the entropy of a sequence of n symbols. An example would be an array of n code elements where each code element has q quantum steps.

Redundancy

One minus the relative entropy is the *redundancy*. Designated R, it is the complement of message efficiency, namely,

$$R = 1 - E. \qquad (6\text{-}20)$$

If statistical correlations exist between parts of a message, E will decrease and R will increase, but not without limit as we lengthen the messages on which we base our calculations. Redundancy is the fraction of the specification of the message that is unnecessary.

Optimum Code for Messages of Unequal Probability

When messages are encoded in a binary code, there must be a unique block of code elements for each possible message. If every possible message has equal probability of being generated by the source, and if the number of possible messages is 2^m, the relative entropy is unity and it is impossible to improve upon the simple code which uses a block of m binary elements to represent each message.* By translation, a binary code may be converted to an n'ary code so there is no loss in generality in confining the treatment to binary codes.

When the probabilities of different messages are *independent* but differ, it is possible to encode more efficiently by assigning, to the individual messages, code patterns having different numbers of binary elements.

Shannon (Ref. 1) has given a method of encoding as follows: If ρ_s is the probability of occurrence of any message s, assign to each message a sequence of m_s binary elements where

$$\log_2 \frac{1}{\rho_s} \le m_s < 1 + \log_2 \frac{1}{\rho_s}. \qquad (6\text{-}21)$$

* Later on, for example in Chapter 8, we shall be concerned with how to match this code to a noisy channel.

If the total number of possible messages is very great, this process will give a very close approximation to theoretically perfect encoding. If it is applied to a small group of messages, it will be found that it does not use up all of the possible blocks of code elements of a given length and hence requires some blocks to be longer than necessary. This is also true even for very large groups of messages. In either case, however, the relative increase is insignificant.

Shannon also refers to a method proposed by R. M. Fano (Ref. 37). His method is to arrange the message in order of decreasing probability. This series is divided into two groups such that the total probability of each group is nearly equal. If the message is in the first group, the first binary code element is 0; otherwise it is 1. Each group is divided into two subgroups to assign the second code element. The process is repeated until each subgroup contains only one message. This process is slightly inexact and may result in assignment of some codes in an incorrect order if carried out literally. This, however, would be apparent at a glance, and the operator could redivide the groups to eliminate the inconsistency. Best results will be obtained by shifting the group division so as to increase the probability of the group including the smaller number of messages.

A simpler method results from going more directly to the objective. One notes that the information measure associated with the specification of each possible message of the class is proportional to minus the logarithm of the probability of the message (Problem 4). Maximum efficiency of encoding would result if the number of bits, or binary code elements, required for the transmission of each message were equal to minus the logarithm to the base 2 of the probability of that message. The efficiency is best when the best approximation to this ideal is reached.

The procedure is to arrange the messages in order of decreasing probability. Tabulate minus $\log_2 \rho$ and minus $\rho \log_2 \rho$ for each message. Round out the former logarithm to the nearest integer on an arithmetic basis, thus dividing the messages into groups of approximately equal logarithmic probability. Assign to each of the first group a unique binary code of m_1 elements, where m_1 is the rounded logarithm of the probability of a member of the first group. Each remaining code pattern is expanded into two code patterns by adding one more code element. Some of these are assigned to the second group. This process is repeated.

If one runs out of code patterns before reaching the end of the sequence, the division point between groups must be moved upward at some place in the sequence. If one has unused code patterns at the end or finds that the code patterns may be of fewer binary elements than corresponds to the logarithm, this means some of the division points may be moved downward. The next example illustrates the procedure.

Efficient Encoding of English Text

To communicate efficiently, the entropy and relative entropy of a typical message should be known. Rarely is the message free from redundancy. This means an efficient encoder which will remove redundancy is needed. When a long message is in its most compact form, all sequences of patterns are equally probable and all sequences have maximum significance.

As an example we will consider English text and limit ourselves to an alphabet composed of 27 letters, counting the space between words as a letter. If messages subject to these restrictions are encoded by a synchronous telegraph system with its five-element binary code, we have more than enough letters and there is no unnecessary delay. But the cost of this undelayed message is 5 bits per letter, whereas the entropy of printed text is only about one bit per letter.

Since $\log_2 27 = 4.76$, we could save without too much trouble in the ratio of 5 to 4.76 at the expense of only a modest delay in getting the message through. This represents a zero order approximation (0-gram).

A first-order approximation (6–10) takes into account letter frequencies and, as we shall find, gives

$$H = -\sum_{i=1}^{27} \rho_i \log_2 \rho_i = 4.065 \text{ bits per letter.} \qquad (6\text{--}22)$$

This we will regard as our design ideal. The problem, therefore, is to encode by a reasonably simple method which takes letter frequencies into account and represents the message by about 4.065 bits per letter.

The first step will illustrate the application of (6–10) and indicate how the result given by (6–22) was obtained. Fletcher Pratt (Ref. 34) gives a table of the frequency of occurrence of letters in English text. Since the average word length is 4.5 letters, the frequency of the "space" (division between words) is one in 5.5 symbols. When the table of letter frequencies is modified to take account of the space, we get (Table 6–1) the probability of occurrence of the 27 symbols.

The rate at which information would be generated by a source that selected symbols according to the probability table but made each choice independently is given by (6–10). It is the sum of the products of each probability by the negative of the logarithm to the base 2 of the probability. This sum is 4.065. The significance of this sum is that it represents the minimum number of bits of information or binary code elements per symbol necessary for transmission of sequences of uncorrelated letters occurring with the same letter frequency as in English text.

Let us see what may be done with a reasonably simple encoding process to approach this theoretical minimum. A perfect encoding system would assign a number of code elements equal to the logarithm of the probability,

TABLE 6-1. PROBABILITY OF OCCURRENCE OF SYMBOLS IN ENGLISH TEXT

Symbol	Probability ρ	$-\log_2 \rho$	$-\rho \log \rho$	Binary Code Elements Used in Example Code
word space	0.1817	2.46	0.447	3
E	.1073	3.22	.345	3
T	.0856	3.54	.303	4
A	.0668	3.90	.260	4
O	.0654	3.94	.258	4
N	.0581	4.11	.239	4
R	.0559	4.16	.232	4
I	.0519	4.27	.222	4
S	.0499	4.33	.216	4
H	.04305	4.54	.195	4
D	.03100	5.02	.156	5
L	.02775	5.17	.144	5
F	.02395	5.38	.129	5
C	.02260	5.45	.123	5
M	.02075	5.60	.116	6
U	.02010	5.64	.1135	6
G	.01633	5.94	.0970	6
Y	.01623	5.95	.0966	6
P	.01623	5.95	.0966	6
W	.01260	6.32	.0796	6
B	.01179	6.42	.0756	6
V	.00752	7.06	.0531	7
K	.00344	8.20	.0282	8
X	.00136	9.54	.0130	10
J	.00108	9.85	.0106	10
Q	.00099	9.98	.0099	10
Z	.00063	10.63	.0067	10

because then the average number of code elements used by each symbol per unit interval of time would be identical with the fourth column of Table 6-1 and the actual sum would be equal to the assumed ideal. For simplicity we assume that we are constrained to use a whole number of code elements to represent each symbol. Accordingly, we will use the nearest whole number and translate into a simple binary code.

Assume that the transmitter and receiver are synchronized and that at a reference time the transmitter starts to send binary code elements which the receiver analyzes. In the first three periods, three code elements are sent. There are 2^3 or 8 possible sequences of three code elements. Let two of these patterns correspond to the word space and the letter E respectively, and let the remaining six patterns tell the receiver to wait for the next code element before taking any action.

After the fourth code element there will be available twice as many, or twelve possible decisions. Letters T to H inclusive, taken in order of descending probability, have (minus) logarithmic probability between 3.5 and 4.54. Assign eight of these twelve possible sequences to these eight letters, and let the other four tell the receiver to wait for the fifth element.

There are still available eight possible sequences of five code elements. Assign four to the letters O, L, F, and C, and let the other four order the receiver to wait for the sixth code element.

There remain available eight possible sequences of six code elements. Assign seven to the letters M to B inclusive, leaving one to form two sequences of seven code elements.

Assign one of these sequences of seven code elements to the letter V, leaving one sequence to be expanded to two sequences of eight code elements.

Assign one sequence of eight code elements to the letter K, and expand the other into four sequences of ten code elements for assignment to the remaining four infrequent symbols.

Whenever a character is identified and printed, the receiver drops into the state necessary for an analysis of the next code sequence regardless of whether the preceding symbol required 3, 4, 5, 6, 7, 8, or 10 binary code elements for its transmission.

No insurmountable technical problems would arise in designing such a system. Of course, an error in synchronization would result in printing utter gibberish. An error in the interpretation of one code element might result in the printing of a sequence of wrong symbols but eventually would print correctly, except perhaps for a bias in time.

Since the time required to transmit a letter varies from three to ten code-element periods, the letter speed varies with the message. Therefore, it would be necessary to have some storage, as on a punched tape, if binary elements were to be transmitted at a constant rate.

When the number of elements used by each symbol is multiplied by the probability of occurrence of that symbol and the results are added, we find that the average number of bits or binary code elements per symbol is 4.107. This is to be compared to the limiting value of 4.065.

If the symbols were grouped by pairs forming 27^2 such pairs, the negative of the logarithms of the probabilities of the pairs would be larger. Therefore, whole number approximations would be more accurate and would yield a closer approach to the limiting value. In this case digram probabilities (6–14) could be taken into account. This would result in decreasing the limiting value to 3.32 (Ref. 6). In this case the actual attainable value of the average number of code elements per symbol would approach 3.32, the digram entropy, even closer than 4.107 approached 4.065 in the first-order approximation.

Efficient Encoders for PCM

Suppose that quantized samples be taken 8,000 times a second of a continuously active telephone channel operating at constant volume. If the samples are quantized into 64 equal steps, the granularity noise due to quantization is little enough to satisfy the requirements for reasonable speech quality. In an ordinary PCM system, each quantized sample might be represented by six on-or-off pulses. It would be interesting to investigate the efficiency of such coding.

This we cannot do because little is known about the entropy of typical spoken messages. We can, however, at least explore the improvement in message efficiency that results merely from taking into account the frequency of occurrence of the quantized magnitudes of the signals that may be encountered in the output of a telephone transmitter.

Data are available on the distribution of voltages in speech (Ref. 38). Positive and negative signals of the same magnitude are considered equally likely, so it will be enough to consider positive values only and multiply by two. These data were plotted with a linear-voltage scale of ordinates instead of the decibel scale originally used. The voltage range was divided into 63 equal ranges to permit one additional quantum to cover all values in excess of the measured range. The probability of occurrence of each quantum level was read from the curve.

These probabilities together with their negative logarithms to the base 2 and their products are tabulated in Table 6–2. When the products are summed and the sum doubled, the result is 4.1 binary digits. This is the entropy per sample, to a 1-gram approximation, of an ordinary telephone message wave on a continuously active channel at controlled volume.

The computation shows the possibility of improvement in the ratio of 6 to 4.1. This saving could be realized by following the simple encoding procedure described in the two preceding examples.

Needless to say strong correlations in the statistical structure, extending back to include many earlier samples, play a dominant part in further reducing the entropy of a continuously active channel. Moreover, a typical telephone channel is only active a small fraction of the time. By taking these factors into account the encoding could be made more efficient, and far less information would need be transmitted.

Ordinarily, efficient encoding requires a long delay at the transmitting end to allow time for matching the statistics to corresponding lengths of sequences. With a multichannel system having a large number of channels, this delay can be shortened to negligible proportions if the ideal is not approached too closely in all respects. With 1,000 or 10,000 channels multiplexed in time division, we have 1,000 or 10,000 samples every 125 microseconds. In 6.25 milliseconds, 50,000 to 500,000 samples are pro-

TABLE 6-2. DISTRIBUTION OF VOLTAGES IN SPEECH

V	ρ	$-\log_2 \rho$	$-\rho \log_2 \rho$	V	ρ	$-\log_2 \rho$	$-\rho \log_2 \rho$
0–10	.250	2.00	.500	320–330	.00085	10.20	.009
10–20	.055	4.18	.230	330–340	.00085	10.20	.009
20–30	.035	4.84	.169	340–350	.00075	10.38	.008
30–40	.030	5.06	.152	350–360	.00075	10.38	.008
40–50	.015	6.06	.091	360–370	.00050	10.97	.005
50–60	.015	6.06	.091	370–380	.00050	10.97	.005
60–70	.011	6.51	.072	380–390	.00050	10.97	.005
70–80	.010	6.64	.066	390–400	.00050	10.97	.005
80–90	.009	6.80	.061	400–410	.00050	10.97	.005
90–100	.006	7.38	.044	410–420	.00050	10.97	.005
100–110	.0045	7.80	.035	420–430	.00040	11.29	.005
110–120	.0045	7.80	.035	430–440	.00040	11.29	.005
120–130	.0045	7.80	.035	440–450	.00040	11.29	.005
130–140	.0040	7.97	.032	450–460	.00040	11.29	.005
140–150	.0035	8.16	.029	460–470	.00040	11.29	.005
150–160	.0035	8.16	.029	470–480	.00035	11.48	.004
160–170	.0025	8.64	.022	480–490	.00030	11.70	.004
170–180	.0020	8.97	.018	490–500	.00030	11.70	.004
180–190	.0020	8.97	.018	500–510	.00025	11.97	.003
190–200	.0020	8.97	.018	510–520	.00020	12.29	.002
200–210	.0020	8.97	.018	520–530	.00020	12.29	.002
210–220	.0015	9.38	.014	530–540	.00020	12.29	.002
220–230	.0015	9.38	.014	540–550	.00015	12.70	.002
230–240	.0015	9.38	.014	550–560	.00015	12.70	.002
240–250	.0015	9.38	.014	560–570	.00015	12.70	.002
250–260	.00125	9.64	.012	570–580	.00015	12.70	.002
260–270	.00125	9.64	.012	580–590	.00015	12.70	.002
270–280	.00125	9.64	.012	590–600	.00010	13.29	.001
280–290	.00125	9.64	.012	600–610	.00010	13.29	.001
290–300	.00100	9.97	.010	610–620	.00010	13.29	.001
300–310	.00100	9.97	.010	620–630	.00010	13.29	.001
310–320	.00085	10.20	.009	>630	.00400	7.97	.032

Σ 2.054
and 2Σ 4.11

duced. These samples from many channels over a modest interval of time represent a long enough specimen of a typical message to display the statistical structure usually necessary for efficient encoding. In this case, we propose to take advantage of the diversity among channel signals, at recurrent instants of time.

For example, suppose we have a 1,000-channel, long-haul PCM system. Specifically, let us assume that the channels are multiplexed by time division and that each channel uses code characters composed of two code elements and that each code element may assume any one of four values. This corresponds to the four bits previously computed. In this case, if regenerative repeaters are used, the interference threshold is only 9.5 decibels as compared to the 83-decibel signal-to-noise ratio normally specified for a single repeater span of a long-distance, single-sideband system with 250 repeaters. Moreover, for the interference threshold assumed, the theoretical band width of the assumed PCM channel is 8 kilocycles per second.

Now, if we assume that the channels are active only one-eighth of the time, and if we are willing to hold up the delivery of all messages for one or two milliseconds, then, without detectable transmission impairments, our band-width occupancy per channel theoretically can be reduced from 8 kilocycles to but little more than one kilocycle. More complex encoding, of course, would be associated with this additional compression of the information content. In the case of this rather rudimentary use of the statistical structure of the message, if the number of channels were only five, our band-width saving would be rather small unless we were willing to introduce comparatively long delays or tolerate substantial transmission impairments.

Turning to another example, suppose that we are interested only in transmitting English speech (no music or other sounds), and, moreover, that the quality requirements on reproduction of speech at the receiver are merely that it be intelligible as to meaning. Individuality as represented by accents, inflections, et cetera, may be lost in the process of transmission. In such a case we could transmit, at least in principle, by the following scheme. Suppose we postulate at the transmitter a device which prints English text corresponding to the spoken words. This could be translated without delay into binary code elements in the ratio of about five binary elements per letter, or $5 \times 5.5 = 27.5$ per word. Taking 100 words per minute as a reasonable talking speed, we obtain 2,750 elements per minute or 45.8 bits per second as an estimate of the message output of the encoder.

As an alternative, by using thirteen binary code elements per code character we could take care of 8,000 of the most likely words and still have 192 code characters remaining. Separate thirteen-element code characters could be employed to denote the start and stop of intervals defining periods of time required to transmit according to the ordinary five-element code, letter by letter. Thus we could handle all words not included in the selected list of 8,000. With provision for storage, about 22 bits per second would be the average output of this encoder.

Since all 8,000 words are not equally likely to be used, the code is still inefficient. Merely by taking into account word frequency and encoding by the general method described in the two preceding examples, the bits per word (6–19) may be compressed to 11.8. In this case the output of the encoder would be about twelve bits per second. If we assume an interference threshold of 9.5 decibels, the band width required to accommodate the output of the assumed encoder would be 3 cycles per second.

Going further, assume that we encode systematically and utterly without regard to the complexity of the operation. Then we would require about 5.5 bits per word (Ref. 6) and the band width (6–1) for a ratio of average signal to average noise of 9.5 decibels would be reduced to 0.85 cycle per second.

Channel Capacity

Entropy may be expressed in bits per symbol, designated H; or bits per second, designated H'. If r is the average number of symbols per second, $H' = rH$ is the average entropy in bits per second. Since the message efficiency (6–19) is E,

$$M' = \frac{H'}{E} \tag{6-23}$$

where M' is the message rate expressed as bits of information per second that have to be transmitted. With an ideal encoder, E equals one.

If the transmitting channel has an average capacity of C bits per second, M' must not exceed C if we are to get the message through and yet not occupy the medium for a time longer than the time of the message. Thus,

$$C \geq M' \geq H'. \tag{6-24}$$

With efficient coding H' determines the channel capacity since it is not possible to transmit faster than

$$\frac{C}{H} \quad \text{symbols per second} \tag{6-25}$$

without introducing errors.

Curiously enough, the capacity of a noisy channel is sharply defined, and Shannon (Ref. 1) has produced some remarkable theorems which deal with equivocation and channel capacity. These theorems have engineering application. Prominent among them is the central theorem cited earlier in the summary.

Rate of Transmission of Information

Suppose the transmitter sends out a million binary digits per second, each equally likely to be 0 or 1 independent of previous digits. Suppose noise encountered along the way causes errors in identification at the receiver, for example, to the extent that in the output of the receiver, on the average, one digit in 1,000 is in error. *What is the rate of transmission of information?*

Certainly it is not 1,000,000 bits per second because, on the average, we encounter 1,000 wrong identifications per second. Also, certainly it is not $10^6 - 10^3$ bits per second because this fails to take into account the receiver's lack of knowledge of where the errors occur.

This last point may be made perfectly plain by assuming that there is so much noise on the transmitting medium that the digits in the output of the receiver are independent of the digits transmitted. Then half of the digits in the output of the receiver are right due to chance alone, and half are wrong. No information whatsoever is being transmitted. Obviously, therefore, we cannot give the system credit for sending half a million bits of correct information per second.

There are two ways to evaluate the rate of transmission of information. A first way is to subtract from the information originally transmitted the amount of missing information in signals that reach the input to the receiver. A second way is to evaluate the uncertainty after the receiver gets a message of what was actually sent.

Equivocation

Clearly, if no information is to be lost, the receiver must remove all uncertainty as to what was sent. When the transmitted signals encounter noise along the way, two statistical processes are at work: the source and the noise. Several entropies are involved.

First, of the entropies involved is $H'(x)$, the entropy of the transmitter output. This is the input to the communication channel between transmitter output and receiver input. Second, is $H'(y)$, the entropy of the receiver input. This is the output of the communication channel. We identify x as the signal output of the transmitter and y as the signal input to the receiver. In the absence of noise, $H'(y) = H'(x)$. $H'(x, y)$ is the joint entropy of the transmitter output and receiver input. The conditional entropy, $H_x'(y)$, is the entropy of the receiver input when the entropy of the transmitter output is known. The conditional entropy $H_y'(x)$ is the entropy of the transmitter output when the entropy of the receiver input is known. Among these entropies we have the relation

$$H'(x, y) = H'(x) + H_x'(y) = H'(y) + H_y'(x). \qquad (6\text{-}26)$$

$H_x'(y)$ is the uncertainty of the received message when the sent message is known. Plainly this irrelevant uncertainty, introduced by an extraneous source, can be identified with the noise on the communication channel. It is false information in the received message.

$H_y'(x)$ is the uncertainty of the sent message when the received message is known. $H_y'(x)$, Shannon terms *equivocation*. Equivocation measures the average ambiguity of the received signal. It is the residual remaining uncertainty when the received signal has been interpreted.

Consequently, the actual rate of transmission over the channel is given by three expressions:

$$\begin{aligned} M_s' &= H'(x) - H_y'(x), \\ &= H'(y) - H_x'(y), \\ &= H'(x) + H'(y) - H'(x, y). \end{aligned} \tag{6-27}$$

The first measures the information sent less the uncertainty of what was sent; that is, average rate of sending information minus average rate of losing information. The second measures the information received less the part of the information received that was due to noise.

By equating the right-hand members of the first two expressions in (6-27), we have

$$H_y'(x) = H'(x) + H_x'(y) - H'(y). \tag{6-28}$$

That is, equivocation equals the uncertainty of the transmitter output plus the uncertainty due to noise minus the uncertainty of the input to the receiver.

Numerical Example

We are now able to complete the unfinished numerical example involving the transmission of 10^6 binary digits per second. We recall that if a one is received, the *a posteriori* probability that a one was transmitted is 0.999, and the probability that a zero was transmitted is 0.001. If a zero is received, the figures are interchanged. From (6-10) and the definition of $H_y(x)$ we evaluate the equivocation, viz.,

$$\begin{aligned} H_y(x) &= - \,[0.999 \log_2 0.999 + 0.001 \log_2 0.001] \\ &= 0.001440 + 0.009956 = 0.011396 \text{ bits per digit.} \end{aligned} \tag{6-29}$$

Thus we have: 1,000,000 binary digits are transmitted each second; on the average there are 1,000 errors per second; and the system is transmitting information (6-27) on the average at the rate of $1,000,000 - 11,396 = 988,604$ bits per second. This we regard as the average rate of sending information minus the average rate of losing information.

In the extreme case where a zero is as likely to be received 1 as 0, and a 1 is as likely to be received 0 as 1; the *a posteriori* probabilities are 0.5 and 0.5. Consequently, $H_y(x)$ is one bit per digit; the equivocation is a million bits per second; and the rate of transmitting information over the system is zero as it should be because all of the sent information has been lost.

Evaluation of Channel Capacity

For the discrete case Shannon (Ref. 1) defines the capacity of a noisy channel as

$$C = \text{Max}\,[H'(x) - H_y'(x)] \tag{6-30}$$

where x is the input, y the output, and the maximization is over all x, that is, over all sources, that might be used as input to the channel. Shannon proves that, if information is sent at the rate C or slower, it is possible to encode so that the equivocation and frequency of error can be made as small as desired. When information is sent at a faster rate, say $(C + C_1)$, the equivocation is equal to or greater than C_1 so that no more information is getting through correctly than before.

The analysis when the signals are continuous functions of time is more complicated, but again there are companion and fundamental relationships. This is illustrated by Shannon's central theorem listed in the summary, namely,

$$C = B \log_2\left(1 + \frac{S}{N}\right) \tag{6-1}$$

where B is the band width, S the mean signal power, and N the mean thermal noise power. In this instance, C binary digits per second may be transmitted with arbitrarily small equivocation and more information cannot get through correctly.

In the more general case which deals with other types of noise, the transmitted signals should be complementary to the noise signals to the end that the received signals have their power uniformly distributed over the band B.

Ordinarily, as the rate C is approached, more and more delay is required at the receiving end to obtain a long enough sample of the perturbed signal for the receiver to make its final decision as to the original message. This implies an equal delay at the sending end. These delays are quite apart from companion delays associated with ideal encoding to remove redundancy (6–21).

Channel Capacity of Existing Systems

Of immediate interest are comparisons of existing types of systems with the nonsurpassable performance predicted by Shannon's central theorem. In Fig. 6–2 this function is plotted against S/N in decibels and represents the maximum channel capacity per unit of band width when the wanted signals are perturbed by resistance noise. Taken from Shannon's paper (Ref. 3), the circles and dots refer to PCM and PPM systems transmitting messages expressed in binary digits. In each instance the system is adjusted to permit about one error in 10^5 digits. In the PCM case the number adjacent to a point represents the number of quanta per code element, for example, three in a ternary PCM system. In all cases, positive and negative code elements are assumed. The PPM systems are quantized

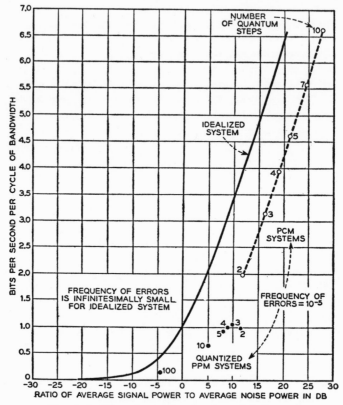

FIG. 6–2 Channel capacity of code-modulation systems

with a discrete set of possible positions for the pulse, the spacing is $1/2B$, and the number adjacent to a point is the number of possible positions for a pulse.

The series of points follows a curve of the same shape as the ideal but is displaced horizontally about 8 decibels. Part of the deficiency (Chap. 8) exists because these simple codes do not present a power spectrum complementary to the noise. At the expense of delay and more complicated coding, a saving approaching 8 decibels in transmitter power over the systems indicated is theoretically possible.

Additional theoretical studies have shown that at both extremes of signal-to-noise ratio (when we are well outside the practical range) the performance approaches more closely to the ideal. For very large signal-to-noise ratios, the PCM points are within 4.5 decibels of the ideal. With very small signal-to-noise ratios, the PPM points approach within 3 decibels of the ideal.

References

1. C. E. Shannon, "A Mathematical Theory of Communication," *The Bell System Technical Journal*, New York, Vol. 27, No. 3, July 1948, pp. 379–423, and Vol. 27, No. 4, October 1948, pp. 623–656.
2. Norbert Wiener, *Cybernetics*, John Wiley and Sons, Inc., New York, 1948.
3. C. E. Shannon, "Communication in the Presence of Noise," *Proceedings of the Institute of Radio Engineers*, New York, Vol. 37, No. 1, January 1949, pp. 10–21.
4. S. O. Rice, "Communication in the Presence of Noise — Probability of Error for Two Encoding Schemes," *The Bell System Technical Journal*, New York, Vol. 29, No. 1, January 1950, pp. 60–93.
5. C. E. Shannon, "Recent Developments in Communication Theory," *Electronics*, New York, April 1950, pp. 80–83.
6. C. E. Shannon, "Prediction and Entropy of Printed English," *The Bell System Technical Journal*, New York, Vol. 30, No. 1, January 1951, pp. 50–64.
7. C. E. Shannon and W. Weaver, *The Mathematical Theory of Communication*, The University of Illinois Press, Urbana, Illinois, 1949.
8. D. Gabor, "Theory of Communication," *Institution of Electrical Engineers Journal*, London, Vol. 93, Part 3, 1946, pp. 429–457.
9. D. Gabor, "New Possibilities in Speech Transmission," *Institution of Electrical Engineers Journal*, London, Vol. 94, Part 3, 1947, pp. 369–387.
10. D. G. Fink, "Band Width Versus Noise in Communication Systems," *Electronics*, New York, January 1948, pp. 72–75.
11. C. W. Earp, "Relationship Between Rate of Transmission of Information, Frequency Band Width, and Signal-to-Noise Ratio," *Electrical Communication*, New York, Vol. 25, No. 2, June 1948, pp. 178–195.
12. M. J. E. Golay, "Notes on the Relations Between Band Width, Available Energy, and Reception of Information in Communication Systems," Signal Corps Engineering Laboratories, Fort Monmouth, N. J., August 20, 1948.
13. S. Goldman, "Some Fundamental Considerations Concerning Noise Reduction and Range in Radar and Communications," *Proceedings of the Institute of Radio Engineers*, New York, Vol. 36, No. 5, May 1948, pp. 584–594.
14. A. G. Clavier, "Evaluation of Transmission Efficiency According to Hartley's Expression of Information Content," *Electrical Communications*, New York, Vol. 25, No. 4, December 1948, pp. 414–420.
15. W. G. Tuller, "Theoretical Limitations on the Rate of Transmission of Information," *Proceedings of the Institute of Radio Engineers*, New York, Vol. 37, No. 5, May 1949, pp. 468–478.
16. C. B. Feldman and W. R. Bennett, "Band Width and Transmission Performance," *The Bell System Technical Journal*, New York, Vol. 28, No. 3, July 1949, pp. 490–599.
17. M. J. E. Golay, "Note on the Theoretical Efficiency of Information Reception with PPM," *Proceedings of the Institute of Radio Engineers*, New York, Vol. 37, No. 9, September 1949, p. 1031.
18. C. E. Shannon, "Communication Theory of Secrecy Systems," *The Bell System Technical Journal*, New York, Vol. 28, No. 4, October 1949, pp. 656–715.
19. R. M. Fano, "The Transmission of Information — II," *Technical Report No. 149*, Research Laboratory of Electronics, Massachusetts Institute of Technology, Cambridge, Mass., February 6, 1950.

20. W. D. White, "Theoretical Aspects of Asynchronous Multiplexing," *Proceedings of the Institute of Radio Engineers*, New York, Vol. 38, No. 3, March 1950, pp. 270–275.

21. W. G. Tuller, "Information Theory Applied to System Design," *Transactions of the American Institute of Electrical Engineers*, New York, Vol. 69, Part 2, 1950, pp. 1612–1614.

22. Y. W. Lee, T. P. Cheatham, Jr., and J. B. Wiesner, "Application of Correlation Analysis to Detection of Periodic Signals in Noise," *Proceedings of the Institute of Radio Engineers*, New York, Vol. 38, No. 10, October 1950, pp. 1165–1171.

23. R. M. Fano, "Information Theory Point of View in Speech Communication," *The Journal of the Acoustical Society of America*, New York, Vol. 22, No. 6, November 1950, pp. 691–696.

24. N. Wiener, "Speech, Language, and Learning," *The Journal of the Acoustical Society of America*, New York, Vol. 22, No. 6, November 1950, pp. 696–697.

25. O. H. Straus, "Relation of Phonetics and Linguistics to Communication Theory," *The Journal of the Acoustical Society of America*, New York, Vol. 22, No. 6, November 1950, pp. 709–711.

26. R. W. Hamming, "Error-Detecting and Error-Correcting Codes," *The Bell System Technical Journal*, Vol. 29, No. 2, April 1950, pp. 147–160.

27. P. M. Woodward, "Information Theory and the Design of Radar Receivers," *Proceedings of the Institute of Radio Engineers*, New York, Vol. 39, No. 12, December 1951, pp. 1521–1524.

28. E. R. Kretzmer, "An Application of Auto-Correlation Analysis," *Journal of Mathematics and Physics*, New York, Vol. 29, October 1950, pp. 179–190.

29. G. A. Barnard, "The Theory of Information," *Journal of the Royal Statistical Society*, London, Vol. 13, No. 1, 1951, pp. 46–64.

30. B. M. Oliver, "Efficient Coding," *The Bell System Technical Journal*, New York, Vol. 31, No. 4, July 1952, pp. 724–750.

31. E. R. Kretzmer, "Statistics of Television Signals," *The Bell System Technical Journal*, New York, Vol. 31, No. 4, July 1952, pp. 751–763.

32. C. W. Harrison, "Experiments with Linear Prediction in Television," *The Bell System Technical Journal*, New York, Vol. 31, No. 4, July 1952, pp. 764–783.

33. Ladislav Dolansky and Marie Dolansky, "Table of $\log_2 \dfrac{1}{p}$, $p \log_2 \dfrac{1}{p}$, $p \log_2 \dfrac{1}{p} + (1 - p) \log_2 \dfrac{1}{1 - p}$," *Technical Report No. 227*, Research Laboratory of Electronics, Massachusetts Institute of Technology, Cambridge, Mass., January 2, 1952.

34. Fletcher Pratt, *Secret and Urgent*, Bobbs-Merrill, New York, 1942.

35. G. Dewy, *Relative Frequency of English Speech Sounds*, Harvard University Press, Cambridge, Mass., 1923.

36. G. K. Zipf, *Human Behavior and the Principle of Least Effort*, Addison-Wesley Press, Cambridge, Mass., 1949.

37. R. M. Fano, "The Transmission of Information," *Technical Report No. 65*, Research Laboratory of Electronics, Massachusetts Institute of Technology, Cambridge, Mass., March 17, 1949.

38. B. D. Holbrook and J. T. Dixon, "Load Rating Theory for Multichannel Amplifiers," *The Bell System Technical Journal*, New York, Vol. 18, No. 4, October 1939, pp. 624–644.

Problems

1. Within the limitations imposed by resistance noise and with the available choice of any physically realizable communication system, how much quantized information can be conveyed per second assuming:
   (a) An over-all band width of B cycles per second,
   (b) A transmitter whose average power output is limited to one watt,
   (c) A path loss over the medium of 100 decibels,
   (d) Negligible distortion from the medium,
   (e) Negligible expenditure of time in putting the information on the medium,
   (f) Negligible expenditure of time in identifying the received information,
   (g) All but 10^{-15} of the information delivered by the receiver is error-free.
2. State Shannon's theorem, a central result of information theory, which relates the maximum information carrying capacity of a system with frequency range, time available, and signal-to-noise ratio. State the units that may be used. Indicate roughly how far existing designs fall short of this theoretical ideal.
3. (a) Suppose a code language consists of 271 code words of which fifteen occur with a probability 1/16 and the remaining 256 have an individual probability of 1/4,096. If successive words are chosen independently at the rate of ten per minute, what is the entropy of the message source expressed in bits per minute? What is its relative entropy and what is its redundancy?
   (b) Suppose the words in (a) are transmitted by synchronous telegraph using groups of four binary code elements. Since a particular group of four binary code elements represents one of sixteen different possible patterns of combinations of four binary decisions, let each of fifteen of the sixteen possible arrangements of a group of four binary code elements uniquely correspond to one of the fifteen most probable words.

   Let the remaining combination operate a shift mechanism so that the receiving machine waits for the next eight binary code elements and then prints one of the less probable 256 words according to the particular eight-place binary number represented by the particular combination of eight binary code elements received. After the sequence of eight the machine reverts to normal to receive the next word.

   At what rate must binary code elements be transmitted to permit transmission of ten words per minute if we assume adequate storage, as on a punched tape, so that only the average rate is important? What is the efficiency of the machine in transmitting this type of message? How much redundancy is in the coded signals in the output of the machine?
4. Assume a source of messages such that each message is composed of a long sequence of N symbols, that successive symbols are independently chosen, that the number of distinct symbols is limited, say q, and that ρ_i is the probability of symbol i.
   (a) What is the approximate probability of any particular sequence of this length?
   (b) Show that the average information measure associated with the specification of a particular message expressed in bits is approximately equal to the logarithm to the base 2 of the reciprocal of the probability of sending this particular message of the ensemble.
   (c) Show that the average information measure associated with the specification of a symbol expressed in bits is approximately equal to the logarithm to the

base 2 of the reciprocal of the probability of any typical long sequence divided by the number of symbols in the sequence.

(d) Show that minus $\log_2 \rho_i$ is the number of bits that ought to be used to encode symbol i for most efficient encoding.

5. Consider a message source such that freedom of choice is restricted to one or the other of two possible messages, the likelihood of selecting one of the messages being p and the other q where $p \gg q$.   Next, assume a never-ending sequence of these selections with the restriction that each selection be independent of preceding selections.   The problem is to encode the sequence efficiently into an array of binary digits.   Describe a suitable code.

CHAPTER 7

SPEED OF SIGNALING AND CHANNEL CAPACITY

Systems of communication deal with bits of information. As brought out in Chapter 6, if H' expressed in bits per second is the entropy of the message source, H' is the minimum amount of information necessary for correct reception. When the specification of the message is compressed to this extent and the goal is error-free reception, no bit may be lost. Without sacrifice of generality we can assume the message representation is in this form. Our concern, therefore, will be with channel capacity.

Because a transmission channel is never noise-free, it has a sharply defined capacity for transmitting information. C bits per second may be transmitted with arbitrarily small error and no more. Hence, H'/C is the time in seconds per second of message representation that the channel must be available. If less time is available, errors in transmission are not arbitrarily small. In practical applications, however, it often is not easy to evaluate either H' or C exactly.

CHANNEL CAPACITY IN THE ABSENCE OF NOISE

All present-day applications of modern communication theory depend to some extent upon one of the theorems advanced by Nyquist in his paper on telegraph transmission (Ref. 1).* The theorem pertains to channel capacity and states that, if the speed of signaling does not exceed substantially $2B$ code elements per second over a system of band width B, intersymbol interference may be eliminated even in the presence of noise. Nyquist was dealing with quantized code elements; he pointed out that, with a given noise exposure, error-free operation would result, provided the signal power could be increased until the unwanted interference was less than half a quantum step. This constituted the basis for the interference-threshold concept developed in Chapter 6.

With an idealized low-pass filter and $\dfrac{\sin x}{x}$ type of code elements, intersymbol interference is zero at the instants the code elements are identified.

* The references cited are listed at the end of each chapter according to the number used in the text

Under these circumstances, the only theoretical ambiguity is due to noise. In the absence of noise, therefore, the quanta can be arbitrarily small and the available amplitudes finely graduated. Consequently, the amount of information per code element, even with finite signal power, is equal to the logarithm of q, where q may be arbitrarily large. However, because of the $\frac{\sin x}{x}$ response, the rate of signaling, even in the absence of noise, cannot exceed $2B$ code elements per second.

Today, it is common knowledge that, in the absence of noise and neglecting practical margins, a density approaching $2B$ code elements per second can be precisely identified. The only requirement is a sufficiently elaborate type of detection, for example, the Boothroyd-Creamer type (Ref. 2). Conventional systems theoretically do not signal faster except at the expense of transmitting less correct information. Years ago these matters were not very well understood, and many suggestions were advanced which purported to show how more than $2B$ signal elements per second could be transmitted successfully through a physical system. One of the most ingenious of these proposals was made by L. A. MacColl around 1926, shortly after Nyquist advanced his theorem to the contrary. Because of the fundamental importance of this subject, it seems worth while to re-examine the implications of these two proposals.

In the case of MacColl's proposal (which assumed zero noise), the amount of information per code element is $(\log q)$, but z code elements are transmitted in each Nyquist interval and z is assumed to be large. The proposal also postulates that the information is delivered virtually without delay other than the time of transmission over the medium. This means, other things being equal, that some information would be available at the output of the receiver slightly sooner than when we signal at the Nyquist rate. Also, when these signals are repeated, less time will be lost at each regenerative repeater.

Immediate delivery of the message, when we come to consider the effect of noise, might naturally be expected to reduce rather than increase the rate of transmitting correct information. This follows because, according to Shannon's theory, it is the function of an efficient receiver to allow as large a sample of noise as possible to affect the code elements before judgment is made as to the original message. The larger the sample, the sharper the possible statistical assertion.

Before presenting MacColl's proposal in its original form and then extending the treatment by discussing the effect of noise and interference, let us examine Nyquist's proposal in more detail. When we do this we shall be appraising pulse-code modulation in terms of modern theory. A good measure is how the signal power compares with the theoretical minimum on the basis of the same information rate and same band width.

SIGNALING AT THE NYQUIST RATE IN THE PRESENCE OF NOISE

It is assumed that all frequencies less than B cycles per second are transmitted with distortionless attenuation and phase characteristics. Noise is assumed to be resistance noise (Refs. 3 and 4) so that the magnitudes of samples of the noise alone taken at Nyquist intervals are distributed according to a Gaussian normal-error curve. It is assumed that all apparatus is functionally perfect and that the over-all transmission is perfectly stable at all times.

If message samples falling in the range plus and minus one (a convenient normalization that makes the signal and noise equations dimensionless) are quantized into q possible values and the $(q-1)$ quantum steps are all alike:

$$s_j = 1 - \frac{2j}{q-1}, \quad j = 0, 1, \ldots (q-1) \tag{7-1}$$

specifies the q possible values.

If all quantum values are independently chosen and equally likely, then using Theorem III on page 52 of Chapter 4,

$$S = \frac{1}{q} \sum_{j=0}^{q-1} s_j^2 \tag{7-2}$$

is the average signal power. This partial sum may be evaluated by recalling (Ref. 5, p. 137) that $\sum_0^n n = \frac{n(n+1)}{2}$ and $\sum_0^n n^2 = \frac{n(n+1)(2n+1)}{6}$, viz.,

$$S = \frac{1}{3}\left[\frac{q+1}{q-1}\right]. \tag{7-3}$$

Let N'' denote the square root of the average noise power, and write $aN'' = \frac{1}{q-1}$. This defines a. Since superposition holds, and again using Theorem III, the average noise power, N, is

$$N = \frac{1}{a^2(q-1)^2}. \tag{7-4}$$

Whence,

$$\frac{S}{N} = \frac{a^2}{3}(q^2 - 1). \tag{7-5}$$

From (6-1),

$$C = B \log_2\left[1 + \frac{a^2}{3}(q^2 - 1)\right] \tag{7-6}$$

is the ideal nonsurpassable capacity of the channel with ideal encoding.

Ideal encoding, it should be noted, is elaborate enough to permit correction of occasional errors by causing the final message produced by the receiver at any instant to depend upon signals transmitted considerably earlier. Common to all statistical behavior of this sort, Shannon's reception is reliable only on the average. It is true that the probability a code element chosen at random will be in error may be made arbitrarily small. Even so, a small fraction of the symbols or code patterns are allowed a much higher probability of error than the average, and in some applications this might not be desirable. However, simply by adding variable translators, one at each end, a nonuniform alphabet can be made uniformly reliable.

To continue, if $\frac{S}{N} = q^2 - 1$, (7–6) becomes

$$C = 2B \log_2 q. \tag{7-7}$$

The right-hand side of (7–7) is recognized to be the channel capacity (6–8) when we signal at the Nyquist rate with adequate power, and permit no avoidable delays in the coding and decoding of the message. It represents the theoretical channel capacity usually associated with the simple type of q'ary code familiar in conventional PCM and ordinary telegraphy. Any and all possible messages are equally acceptable and are delivered as received without delay.

If practical margins are neglected, we observe that $a^2/3$ represents the ratio of the average signal power for a conventional PCM system signaling at the Nyquist rate to the theoretical minimum signal power. This ratio neglects to take into account the loss of information due to noise. However, as will be seen in the example to follow, neglect of this factor is unimportant in most practical systems when making a comparison of this type.

Let ρ be the permissible average relative frequency of error in the identification of the quantized samples in the output of the receiver. Then $\left[1 - \frac{q}{q-1}\rho\right]$ is the required probability that the resistance noise (Refs. 3 and 4) lies within the range of plus or minus half a quantum. This requires (Chap. 9 of Ref. 6) that

$$\operatorname{erf}\left[\frac{a}{\sqrt{2}}\right] = 1 - \frac{q}{q-1}\rho. \tag{7-8}$$

Compared to an ideal system,

$$20 \log_{10} \operatorname{erf}^{-1}\left[1 - \frac{q}{q-1}\rho\right] + 10 \log_{10}\frac{2}{3} \tag{7-9}$$

is the extra signal power in decibels required by a conventional type of pulse-code modulation system signaling at the Nyquist rate. The result

(Table 7-1) depends on ρ, but in most applications of practical interest is little affected by q.

Example

Assume that the wanted code takes the form of a pattern of binary code elements. Assume further that each unperturbed code element may be represented by $+ \dfrac{\sin (2\pi Bt - m\pi)}{2\pi Bt - m\pi}$ or $- \dfrac{\sin (2\pi Bt - m\pi)}{2\pi Bt - m\pi}$ where m takes on the values $0, \pm 1, \pm 2, \ldots$. Also assume that each code element is so sampled at the receiver that, in the absence of noise, the sample will be either $+1$ or -1. Assume that $2B$ code elements are transmitted each second, that positive or negative code elements are equally likely, and that the probability of any element is independent of preceding elements. We then find that the energy (Chap. 4, p. 54) of each code element is $1^2/2B$ and the average signal power is 1^2.

Assume resistance noise. Let σ be the root-mean-square noise and write $a\sigma = 1$. Let ρ be the average frequency of errors in the output of the receiver. Then $1 - 2\rho$ is the required probability that the noise lies in the range -1 to $+1$. For example, consider $\rho = 10^{-5}$. This requires (Chap. 9 of Ref. 6) that $\operatorname{erf}\left[\dfrac{a}{\sqrt{2}}\right] = 1 - 2\rho = 0.99998$. Erf $(3.0157) = 0.99998$ (Ref. 7, pp. 116-120).

This means (7-9) that the average signal power is $20 \log_{10} 3.0157 + 10 \log_{10} 2 - 10 \log_{10} 3 = 7.83$ decibels more than the ideal.

The equivocation [Chap. 6, equation (6-28) p. 94] is

$$H_y(x) = - [0.00001 \log_2 0.00001 + 0.99999 \log_2 0.99999]$$
$$= 0.00018044 \text{ bit per bit.}$$

If $2B = 10^6$, $1,000,000$ bits per second are transmitted, on the average ten errors are made each second, and the excess of information sent over information received is

$$M_s' = 2B[\log_2 q + \rho \log_2 \rho + (1 - \rho) \log_2 (1 - \rho)]$$
$$= 1,000,000 - 166.1 - 14.3 \tag{7-10}$$
$$= 999,819.6 \text{ bits per second.}$$

It is correct to regard this as the amount of information actually being transmitted over the channel. Moreover, the equivocation, 180.4 bits per second, is the minimum additional channel capacity theoretically required for correcting all but an arbitrarily small fraction of the errors. When q is greater than 2, the formula for the equivocation is different, as illustrated by Problems 1 and 2.

In practical applications, by increasing the signal power only a slight amount (Table 7-1) the probability of errors from noise of this type may be drastically reduced as compared to the foregoing numerical example.

We further notice that, for $\rho = 10^{-5}$, all codes of this class require about 8 decibels more signal power than the theoretical ideal. For example, the decibel advantage of a q'ary code over a binary code is

$$20 \log_{10} \left[\text{erf}^{-1} \left(1 - \frac{q}{q-1} \rho \right) \right] - 20 \log_{10} \left[\text{erf}^{-1} (1 - 2\rho) \right]. \quad (7\text{-}11)$$

Table 7-1 indicates an upper limit for this difference for various values of ρ.

TABLE 7-1. SIGNALING AT THE NYQUIST RATE

Extra signal power in decibels compared with Shannon's theoretical ideal tabulated as a function of the average relative frequency of error in the identification of a code element

ρ	(1) $\text{erf}^{-1}(1-\rho)$	(2) $\text{erf}^{-1}(1-2\rho)$	(3) $20 \log (1)$	(4) $20 \log (2)$	(5) $(3)-(4)$	(6) $(3)+10 \log \frac{2}{3}$	(7) $(4)+\log 10\frac{2}{3}$
10^{-1}	1.1631	0.9062	1.3123	−0.8556	2.168	−0.449	−2.617
10^{-2}	1.8214	1.6450	5.2081	4.3233	0.885	3.447	2.562
10^{-3}	2.3268	2.1851	7.3352	6.7894	0.546	5.574	5.029
10^{-4}	2.7511	2.6297	8.7901	8.3981	0.392	7.029	6.637
10^{-5}	3.1234	3.0157	9.8926	9.5878	0.305	8.132	7.827
10^{-6}	3.4589	3.3612	10.7788	10.5299	0.249	9.018	8.769
10^{-7}	3.7666	3.6765	11.5190	11.3087	0.210	9.758	9.548
10^{-8}	4.0522	3.9683	12.1539	11.9721	0.182	10.393	10.211
10^{-9}	4.3200	4.2411	12.7097	12.5496	0.160	10.949	10.789
10^{-10}	4.5728	4.4982	13.2035	13.0607	0.143	11.443	11.300
10^{-12}	5.0420	4.9741	14.0521	13.9343	0.118	12.291	12.173
10^{-14}	5.4725	5.4098	14.7637	14.6636	0.100	13.003	12.903
10^{-16}	5.8724	5.8139	15.3763	15.2893	0.087	13.615	13.528
10^{-18}	6.2474	6.1923	15.9139	15.8371	0.077	14.153	14.076
10^{-20}	6.6016	6.5495	16.3930	16.3241	0.069	14.632	14.563
10^{-24}	7.2594	7.2119	17.2180	17.1610	0.057	15.457	15.400
10^{-28}	7.8632	7.8194	17.9120	17.8634	0.049	16.151	16.103

These figures (last two columns of Table 7-1) cannot be improved upon when each code element of the assumed code is transmitted with the least possible delay and is immediately delivered as received. Furthermore, they substantially exceed Shannon's ideal. To illustrate, if an average error incidence of 10^{-18} is sought, the required signal power will be about 14.1 decibels in excess of the theoretical nonsurpassable ideal.

It should be kept in mind that only when the noise has the characteristics of resistance noise, is the channel capacity given by

$$C = B \log_2 \left[1 + \frac{S}{N} \right]. \quad (6\text{-}1)$$

For instance, consider interference from another like system. Intersystem interference is independent of S. Errors will predominate unless the intersystem crosstalk is below the interference threshold, namely,

$20 \log_{10} (1 - q)$ decibels.   In this situation one also notices that, for like systems, the statistical structure of the message and interference are alike.

Assume, further, that as a practical matter it is uneconomical to reduce the intersystem crosstalk any more than necessary.   In this case, S will be somewhat increased over the value it otherwise would assume were resistance noise controlling, to the end that intersystem crosstalk becomes the dominating source of interference.   Under these conditions and assuming prompt transmission and delivery of the message, the channel capacity is given by

$$C = 2B \log_2 q. \tag{7-12}$$

MacCOLL'S PROPOSAL FOR RAPID SIGNALING IN THE ABSENCE OF NOISE

L. A. MacColl (Ref. 8) suggested that, in the absence of noise and interference, it is theoretically possible to transmit signals over any physical transmission system at any speed, and in such a manner that the reconstructed signals at the receiving end have the same duration and same wave form as the original signals.   The theoretical possibility of doing this is based on the assumed validity of ordinary circuit theory.

It is to be noticed particularly that the transmission characteristics of the transmission system (assuming only linear distortion) do not affect the speed of signaling, but merely exert a controlling influence on the complexity, accuracy, and necessary speed of operation of the equipment required for instrumenting the system.

Hence we have the following proposition: In the absence of interference and noise, it is possible, using only apparatus that in principle is easily constructed, to signal through any transmission system (producing linear distortion but negligibly small nonlinear distortion) at any speed and in such a manner that the time required to detect and interpret the message information in its original form is equal to the time required to put the message information on the line.

The proposition assumes that nonlinear distortion is negligible; hence, we will review what this implies.   In general, distortion in a transmission system is either linear or nonlinear.   If the distortion is linear, superposition applies.   If the distortion is nonlinear, the principle of superposition may not be used to evaluate the response of the system.   In the presence of nonlinear distortion there is, in addition, a multiplication of wave components which produces frequency components corresponding to the products.

Due to band-width limitations and because the phase and amplitude distortion as a function of frequency may be excessive, the wave forms of the arrival waves will differ from the impressed code elements.   For each code element, this difference will exist during the period allocated to the code element sent, and it will also persist beyond this time. The portion of the arrival wave that persists beyond the interval occupied by the applied code element causes intersymbol interference. Accurate identification of the original discrete code elements may be rendered difficult, especially with rapid signaling.

MacColl's Original Proposal

To reproduce MacColl's original proposal (Ref. 8) in detail, accurately timed code elements are applied, and each applied code element is of constant magnitude for a duration T'. Thus, the time allotted to successive code elements is $0 < t < T'$; $T' < t < 2T'$; $2T' < t < 3T'$; .... Furthermore, the constant value of the code element may be different in different intervals. The constant value is quantized and it may be of either polarity. Thus, the constant value assumed in any one interval is limited to one of a finite number of possible values, which may include the value zero. Although T', the duration of a code element at the sending end, is quite arbitrary, it is set once and for all in the case of any one particular system. Without loss in generality it is assumed the message information has the value zero for all negative values of t.

Now consider the code element of the sent message that occupies the interval $rT' < t < (r + 1)T'$ where r is zero or an arbitrary positive integer. This element, (a) of Fig. 7–1, will be denoted $f_0(t - rT')$. This element will give rise to a particular elementary signal at the receiving end, (b) of Fig. 7–1, which will be denoted by $f(t - rT')$. This implies that the delay introduced by the transmission system has been neglected and, therefore, amounts to using different zeros of time at the two ends of the system.

The significant properties of the function $f(t - rT')$ are that it vanishes for $t < rT'$; that it has appreciable values for some values of $t > (r + 1)T'$; and that its wave form may differ widely from that of $f_0(t - rT')$.

Consider the function $f_1(t - rT')$ which is obtained from $f(t - rT')$ by making the function equal to zero in the interval $rT' < t < (r + 1)T'$. In the case in which $f(t - rT')$ is as shown in (b) of Fig. 7–1, the function $f_1(t - rT')$ might be as shown in (c) of Fig. 7–1. It is easy to imagine a machine that would generate $f_1(t - rT')$. Such a machine will be called a corrector.

Assume that, at the receiving end, there are as many correctors, say R, as there are intervals of duration T' in which $f(t - rT')$ is appreciably different from zero: that is, not small compared to half a quantum step. Assume that the first corrector is set to produce in succession $C_{11}f_1(t)$, $C_{12}f_1(t - RT')$, $C_{13}f_1(t - 2RT')$, ... ; that the second corrector produces $C_{21}f_1(t - T')$, $C_{22}f_1(t - T' - RT')$, $C_{23}f_1(t - T' - 2RT')$, ... ; that the third corrector produces $C_{31}f_1(t - 2T')$, $C_{32}f_1(t - 2T' - RT')$,

$C_{33}f_1(t - 2T' - 2RT'), \ldots$; and so on, where the C's are, for the present, arbitrary constants.

Next, consider the reception of the message specification. There is no intersymbol interference during the interval $0 < t < T'$, because by hypothesis the received signal during that interval depends only upon the

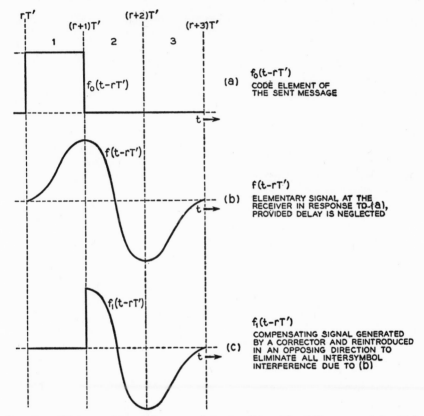

FIG. 7-1   Diagram of wave forms used in describing MacColl's proposal for high-speed signaling in the absence of noise

magnitude of the first code element in the message sent. Consequently, any particular measurement of the received signal during that interval, say of its integral over the interval, or of its magnitude at the center or a later end of the interval, gives complete knowledge of the first code element of the incoming information-bearing wave. Let this measurement set the first corrector to produce $C_{11}f_1(t)$, where C_{11} is given a value proportional to the magnitude of the first code element. This setting is maintained until $t = (R + 1)T'$, when the corrector is reset. The signal generated by the first correction may be subtracted from the received signal wave, with the result that all code elements following the first are freed from the intersymbol interference due to the first. We note that the intersymbol correction is both quantized and exact.

The second code element in the received signal is now free from intersymbol interference, and any particular measurement on it will determine the magnitude of the second code element in the sent signal. Let this measurement set the second corrector to produce $C_{21}f_1(t - T')$, where C_{21} is proportional to the magnitude of the second code element. This setting is maintained until $t = (R + 2)T'$. When the signal generated by the second corrector is subtracted from the received signal, the signal is free from intersymbol interference due to the second code element. This process is continued until all of the correctors are in operation.

After $t = RT'$, there is no need to continue the correction for the intersymbol interference due to the first code element. Hence the measure of the $(R + 1)$th code element of the incoming signal is caused to set the first corrector to generate the signal $C_{12}f_1(t - RT')$, where C_{12} is proportional to the magnitude of the $(R + 1)$th code element, and this signal is subtracted from the signal wave to eliminate the intersymbol interference due to that code element. Likewise, the determination of the $(R + 2)$nd code element is caused to set the second corrector to eliminate the intersymbol interference due to that code element. And so the process continues.

Conclusion

In the absence of noise, the amplitude of the received signal can be determined, in principle at least, in as short a time as may be desired after the arrival of the received code element. Hence, any desired number of code elements per second may be transmitted over any linear physical system, regardless of its band width. This seems to contradict Nyquist's theorem. However, closer scrutiny will show that MacColl's proposition for rapid signaling in the absence of noise is not a contradiction in a strictly technical sense. Nyquist's theorem is true under the assumptions on which it is based. MacColl recognized that certain restrictions implied by Nyquist were not necessary, and when they were removed, obtained a different result.

CHANNEL CAPACITY AND SIGNALING SPEED

Theory commonly postulates ideal filters and an over-all system response of the form $\dfrac{\sin x}{x}$. This implies signaling at the Nyquist rate, efficient band-width occupancy, no intersymbol interference, and no interchannel or other out-of-band interference. Under these conditions and in the presence of resistance noise, the capacity of the channel is given by the central theorem. With physically realizable networks the nonsurpassable capacity is evaluated by another expression.

Channel Capacity

In a practical system the over-all response may not even roughly approximate that of an ideal filter. Shannon accounts for this [Ref. 9, equation (32)] by letting $C = B \log_2 \left(1 + \dfrac{S}{N}\right)$ represent the differential capacity, ΔC_1, of a narrow band, ΔB, so that by integrating, we obtain

$$C_1 = \int_0^\infty \log_2 \left[1 + \frac{S(f)}{N(f)}\right] df. \tag{7-13}$$

In equation (7-13), $S(f)$ and $N(f)$ are now frequency dependent and represent average signal and average noise power (encountered at the output of the channel) per cycle per second of band width at frequency f. When the total signal power is fixed but its distribution as a function of frequency is arbitrary, to maximize C_1 requires that $N(f)$ plus $S(f)$ be invariant with frequency.

Band-Width Occupancy

Band-width occupancy is defined by physical filters and represents the frequency range that ought to be charged to a particular channel. Ordinarily, filters at each end restrict the frequency range. It is the function of the transmitting filter to suppress out-of-band frequencies so that adjacent channels are not interfered with. At the receiving end, the out-of-band loss of the receiving filter serves to keep adjacent channels from interfering with the wanted signal. Although these filters attenuate, they do not eliminate interchannel interference. Intersymbol interference is also introduced by these filters, so that it becomes the function of other parts of the system to eliminate or reduce this type of interference. Note particularly that: intersymbol and interchannel interferences are each independent of signal power, both decrease the amount of noise that can be tolerated at fixed signal power, and yet both are introduced by the physical filters that define band-width occupancy. In engineering applications it is useful to express signaling speed in terms of band-width occupancy.

Extension of MacColl's Proposal to Include the Effects of Noise

Assume MacColl's original proposition as stated on page 108 is modified and extended to include the effects of noise, and let us consider briefly the information rate and signaling speed of the modified system.

Information Rate. In essence, the modified proposal would represent a particular method of reducing intersymbol interference. There is, of course, no reason for expecting that the elimination of intersymbol interference would increase the theoretical information capacity of a physical system. In fact, one would suspect that, under favorable conditions, the extended proposal would only approach the limit given by existing theory, even if everything were optimized and the instrumentation executed with meticulous attention to detail.

Many factors enter into a careful analysis of the information rate. To illustrate one, once an error is made by the decoder, subsequent inter-symbol interference corrections are generally wrong. These wrong corrections cause the corrected signal to assume forbidden values. If left to its own devices, the decoder would be very likely to deliver utter gibberish ever thereafter. To control this, a relatively long sequence of M code elements is followed by a blank interval. The blank interval, during which no signals are transmitted, is slightly longer than RT'. For a specified equivocation there is an optimum value for M.

Signaling Speed. When signal elements are not quantized, we know their density on the time axis cannot exceed $2B$. This fundamental relationship assumes transmission through an ideal filter to insure freedom from out-of-band interference. If, on the other hand, the signals are quantized and the quanta are small, there would be practical difficulties in transmitting code elements faster than the Nyquist rate.

A more pertinent consideration is whether *binary* digits can be transmitted faster than the Nyquist rate. Here it is significant to note that MacColl's proposition deals with quantized signals. Therefore, the corrections are quantized. Nonlinear devices of this kind are not found in the usual conventional system employing linear equalizers. It is conjectured that, if the over-all band width is sharply limited so that at cutoff the attenuation rises rapidly to a very high out-of-band loss, code elements cannot be transmitted substantially in excess of the Nyquist rate. Incidentally, a corrector of this type might have considerable practical value either in other situations or where more moderate performance is acceptable.

This method of reception, if it permits faster signaling, might be advantageous when code elements are transmitted through a large number of regenerative repeaters in tandem. For example, assume each repeater output is band limited as effectively as practical. Then at each regenerative repeater, transmission is delayed at least as long as the interval between successive code elements.

Boothroyd-Creamer System

The Boothroyd-Creamer system (Ref. 2) apparently comes close to attaining the Nyquist rate. This system has been analyzed by W. R. Bennett whose results are yet to be published. Any notion that the Nyquist rate is exceeded will be quickly dispelled by a careful examination of the receiving apparatus. The actual selectivity is that of the receiving filter plus its associated intersymbol interference corrector. This corrector causes the net transmission to approach more nearly that of an ideal filter. When the frequency scale of the receiving filter was increased 15 per cent, a six-section corrector was reported to have reduced interchannel interference to 60 decibels below the wanted signal.

Channel capacity is another matter. When resistance noise is the controlling factor, noise at the corrector output proves to be peaked at the high frequencies, and this acts to reduce the capacity of the noisy channel as shown by equation (7–13).

Maximum Signaling Speeds of Existing Practical Systems

It is natural to ask whether any existing practical system ever signals at substantially the Nyquist rate. This is a difficult question to answer. Certain conventional systems (as currently used) commonly signal at rates ranging from one-half to one-quarter the Nyquist rate if band-width occupancy is the criterion. In fact, when existing types of systems are critically evaluated from the standpoint of band-width occupancy, it has to be concluded that the Nyquist rate is never approached except in the artificial sense of local transmission with no flanking channels.

References

1. H. Nyquist, "Certain Topics in Telegraph Transmission Theory," *Transactions of the American Institute of Electrical Engineers*, New York, Vol. 47, April 1928, pp. 617–644.
2. W. D. Boothroyd and E. M. Creamer, Jr., "A Time Division Multiplex System," *Transactions of the American Institute of Electrical Engineers*, New York, Vol. 68, Part I, 1949, pp. 92–97.
3. S. O. Rice, "Mathematical Analysis of Random Noise," *The Bell System Technical Journal*, New York, Vol. 23, No. 3, July 1944, pp. 282–332.
4. S. O. Rice, "Mathematical Analysis of Random Noise (Concluded)," *The Bell System Technical Journal*, New York, Vol. 24, No. 1, January 1945, pp. 45–156.
5. L. M. Milne-Thomson, "The Calculus of Finite Differences," Macmillan and Co., Limited, London, 1933.
6. H. W. Reddick and F. H. Miller, *Advanced Mathematics for Engineers*, John Wiley and Sons, Inc., New York, 1938.
7. B. O. Pierce, *A Short Table of Integrals*, Ginn and Company, Boston, 1929.
8. LeRoy A. MacColl, United States Patent 2,056,284, October 6, 1936.
9. C. E. Shannon, "Communication in the Presence of Noise," *Proceedings of the Institute of Radio Engineers*, New York, Vol. 37, No. 1, January 1949, pp. 10–21.

Problems

1. Substantially $2B$ binary code elements per second are transmitted over a channel of band width B. Information is delivered promptly. Assume distortionless transmission and negligible phase distortion. Positive or negative code elements are equally probable, and the probability of any element is independent

of preceding elements.   Assume resistance noise, and let the average frequency of errors in the output of the receiver be 0.1.   What is the equivocation in bits per second?   What is the ratio of average signal power to the theoretical minimum?   Assume 128'ary instead of binary code elements, positive and negative steps, all levels equally probable, et cetera, and again find the equivocation and the ratio of average signal power to the theoretical minimum.   (See Problem 2.)

2. Suppose q'ary code elements are transmitted at the rate of $2B$ code elements per second.   For example, envision the code elements as amplitude-modulated pulses which may be either positive or negative (or zero if q is odd) and whose $(q - 1)$ quantum steps are equal.   The q possible levels are equally likely, and the levels of the different code elements are all independent of one another.   Each code element is identified by the receiver during the period of time allocated to that particular code element.   Assume that, during transmission, resistance noise introduces errors so that, on the average, ρ is the *a posteriori* probability that a code element as received is not correctly identified.   If $2B = 10^6$, $q = 2^7$, and $\rho = 10^{-10}$, what is the rate of transmitting information in bits per second?

3. Subdivide time into equal intervals T' where T' is equal to $m + \alpha$ Nyquist intervals.   During each interval T', $M = mz$ code elements are preceded by an interval $\alpha/2B$ during which nothing is transmitted, that is, αz code elements are suppressed.   Thus, T' is regarded as a frame.   In each frame a blanking interval $\alpha/2B$ is followed by M q'ary code elements which are transmitted.   Assume that the decoder has the property that, in any particular frame, if one code element is falsely identified, the decoder delivers no message for the entire frame. Suppose ρ_1 is the average probability that a particular code element as received is not correctly identified.   Assume ρ_1 is very small.   What are the restrictions on ρ_1 and M in order that ρ, likewise assumed small, be the *a posteriori* probability that a block of M code elements is not delivered by the decoder?

4. In Problem 3,
   (a) What is the channel capacity C expressed in bits per second?
   (b) What is the equivocation expressed in bits per second?
   (c) What is the average rate of signaling correct information expressed in q'ary code elements per second?

5. In practical systems a guard space separates adjacent channels.   Assume that $1/8$ of $2B$ (that is, $1/8$ of the assigned frequency range) is guard space; that code elements are transmitted at equally spaced intervals at the rate of $7B/4$ code elements per second; that each code element is quantized into 256 possible levels; that all levels are equally probable, independently chosen and not correlated with earlier values; that the noise is resistance noise; and that the average noise power is $7Bn/8$ and is confined to a band of about $7B/8$. According to Shannon's central theorem, if the entire assigned frequency range could be occupied by the signals, by how many decibels might the signal power be reduced?

6. Resistance noise issues from the output of an idealized low-pass filter having a band width of B cycles per second.   After amplification by a quiet amplifier, the noise output is separated into two equal parts and transmitted with equal attenuation over two independent paths.   Over one of the paths the noise signals encounter a delay of $\tau/2B$ seconds.   The two paths are recombined in such a manner that the delayed noise is subtracted from the undelayed noise.   Plot the ratio, expressed in decibels, as a function of τ from $\tau = 0$ to $\tau = 1$, of the average noise power of the difference to the average noise power from one path.

7. Assume 10^9 binary code elements per second are transmitted over a distortion-less channel whose band width is 500 megacycles per second. What is the required order of magnitude of the *a posteriori* probability that a binary digit as received is not correctly identified if on the average one wrong digit every 27.4 hours can be tolerated? If each digit upon being received is promptly identified and resistance noise is the only cause for errors, by how many decibels will the average signal power need to exceed Shannon's nonsurpassable ideal, assuming a conventional system and a one-dimensional code? What additional decibel increase in signal power is required in order that the average relative rate of errors be (a) one per year and (b) one per 100 years?

8. Resistance noise emerges from the output of an ideal low-pass filter terminated by a resistance. What is the chance that the instantaneous noise power exceeds its average value by 17 decibels or more?

CHAPTER 8

REDUCTION OF SIGNAL POWER THROUGH THE USE OF REDUNDANT CODES

The entropy in bits per second of a continuous source of information is infinite and would require a channel of infinite capacity for exact recovery of the message at the receiver. A continuously varying quantity as a function of time can take on an infinite number of values and requires an infinite number of bits per second for its unambiguous identification. Any physical channel with its inevitable noise and finite signal power has only a finite capacity. Therefore, the output of a continuous source of information cannot be transmitted exactly over a physical channel.

Similarly, in the presence of resistance noise, a discrete system which transmits and receives without errors at a rate corresponding to its capacity is also impossible of realization with any finite encoding process, although in theory this rate can be approached as closely as desired. This means that in the presence of resistance noise it is not possible to transmit a non-redundant message without possibility of error.

Although the channel capacity can be realized with an arbitrarily small average relative frequency of errors, this can be done only at the cost of additional delay in the delivery of the message. The extent of this delay has not been estimated. Furthermore, no general directions are available for constructing a useful code capable of realizing substantially the full theoretical capacity of a noisy channel.

Our concern will be with how closely we can approach the ideal rate with a reasonably simple redundant code. Assume functionally perfect apparatus, perfect transmission between terminals, and ideal filters with negligible delay. Then, if it is also assumed there is to be no other avoidable delay in the delivery of each code element, one will find it impossible to improve upon synchronized signaling at the Nyquist rate with a simple q'ary code.

This means that according to present theory, the figures in Table 7–1 cannot be improved upon when each code element is immediately delivered as received. In most situations of practical interest, we find that these figures substantially exceed Shannon's ideal (which postulates delay). For an error incidence of 10^{-22}, for example, the required signal power when

116

each code element is delivered as received will be about 15 decibels in excess of Shannon's nonsurpassable ideal.

However, a little redundancy of the right kind will not seriously reduce the speed of signaling and will afford an opportunity for saving signal power at the expense of what could be regarded, in many instances, as a tolerable delay. Hence, such redundancy will permit a closer approach to the theoretical ideal. Apart from the advantage which may stem from intentional, appropriate redundancy, a small additional improvement can be realized by modifying the statistical structure of the signal. With less elaborate methods than might be expected, it is possible to envision a theoretical improvement of 4 to 6 decibels in the performance of certain types of systems. Some of these methods will be considered.

APPLICATION OF ERROR–CORRECTING CODES TO ONE–WAY SYSTEMS OF COMMUNICATION

Our consideration will be limited, in this section, to the synchronous transmission of binary digits. Different digits are presumed to be independently perturbed by resistance noise, and noise is assumed to be the only reason for errors. It is also assumed that transmitted digits specifying the selected message will occur at random, with plus and minus values equally probable and independent of one another. If a message source does not satisfy this description, it can readily be converted into one that almost does merely by preliminary encoding by various methods based on Shannon's Theorem 9. (Ref. 1.)*

Under these conditions transmission can be made more reliable by increasing the signal power (right-hand column of Table 7–1). Transmission can also be made more reliable, at the expense of a redundant signal utilizing an error-correcting code (Refs. 2 and 3). Which is better depends upon tolerance to errors, degree of correction, and rate of signaling. In any event, power will be conserved by using an appropriate error-correcting code, provided the average relative frequency of a wrong digit in the received signal is sufficiently small.

To illustrate the foregoing, assume a single-error-correcting code (Ref. 2) of the type described by Hamming. When the average chance of delivering a wrong digit is either 10^{-5}, 10^{-14}, or 10^{-24}; the saving in average power works out to be 1.5, 2.5, or 2.7 decibels respectively. Depending primarily upon the degree of correction (that is, the number of wrong digits corrected per sequence), there exists an optimum proportioning of the sequence and, hence, optimum redundancy for least signal power.

Associated with the 1.5 to 2.7 decibel reduction in signal power cited was

---

* The references cited are listed at the end of each chapter according to the number used in the text.

a minimum delay of 255 Nyquist intervals for the particular alphabet selected.

Error correction, because it adds redundancy, also reduces the net speed of signaling. In the instance under discussion, net speed of signaling was reduced in the ratio of 255 to 247. For purposes of comparison, it was assumed in the absence of error correction that we signal at this lower rate and, hence, conserve power.

Multidimensional optimal alphabets of the type discussed by Gilbert (Ref. 3) likewise afford an opportunity for modest savings in average signal power at the expense of a more complicated alphabet and a slight delay. It seems clear that these two types of savings can be compounded, that is, error-correcting alphabets for this type of encoding also can be constructed.

ERROR CORRECTION USING BOTH DIRECTIONS OF TRANSMISSION

If a two-way channel is available, it is theoretically possible to retransmit the lost information instead of correcting the mistakes locally by means of an error-correcting code. In some applications, even quite apart from the extra delay, retransmission of the lost digits would involve certain other complications. Nevertheless, error correction by retransmission is a handy procedure because it provides correction in varying degrees in a straightforward manner. On the other hand, in the case of a one-way system there is no general method for constructing an error-correcting alphabet which corrects for more than one wrong digit, even though such alphabets are known to exist.

In practice, the length of the sequence to be checked for errors should be so chosen as to require minimum signal power for a specified chance of error. To accomplish this, the signals to be transmitted are divided into optimal sequences ("frames") of M digits which include m message digits and n digits for error indication, as well as a means for synchronization, say a synchronizing pulse, s. To sense the general method of operation, assume that the n digits enable the decoder to decide whether a frame contains a wrong digit. Information known to be wrong need not be delivered. It would be discarded. With enough storage to hold several frames, virtually correct information can be delivered continuously. If an error is indicated, the entire frame is retransmitted. When the chance of error is small, very little extra channel capacity is required for this purpose. In such a system it is necessary to store as well as transmit each frame at the sending end. Moreover, each frame must be held long enough (considering round-trip time) to be sure that it will not have to be retransmitted.

The transmitter has to be informed whenever a frame needs to be retransmitted. This can be conveniently accomplished by synchronizing the two directions of transmission. Then, at the receiver, whenever a frame is indicated to be in error, the magnitude of the next synchronizing pulse to be transmitted in the opposite direction would be increased. At the transmitter, this larger pulse would be recognized as a command to retransmit a particular previous frame at a particular future time.

To conserve power, this larger pulse might be some one of the n digits in the case of a correct frame, and a different one of the n digits in the case of an incorrect frame. To insure reliability, its magnitude might correspond to ρ less than 10^{-30}.

The principle of error-detecting codes is best illustrated by what is usually termed a "single parity" check. Consider a sequence of M binary digits of which $(M - 1)$ digits are digits of information, and the remaining digit is made either $+1$ or -1 in order that the entire sequence of M digits will have an even number of $+1$'s. This is an error-detecting code, because one wrong digit or any odd number of wrong digits will leave an odd number of $+1$'s in the sequence of M digits. Any even number of wrong digits will escape detection. The relative redundancy of the code as a consequence only of its error-detecting feature is $1/M$. This does not imply an indefinitely large M. If ρ is the average relative chance that a digit will be wrong (remembering that the digits are equally probable and uncorrelated), the average chance, ρ_0, that a frame of M digits will contain wrong digits which escape detection is

$$\rho_0 = \frac{1 + (1 - 2\rho)^M - 2(1 - \rho)^M}{2}. \tag{8-1}$$

The average chance that a wrong digit will be delivered is still less.

By adding more digits for detecting errors, the chance of escape can be reduced. If to the single-parity check we add another digit to provide a "double-parity" check, the new digit will be $+1$ or -1 depending on whether the number of $+1$'s is an even or odd multiple of 2. Then $(M - 2)$ information digits remain. To a rough approximation, in addition to detecting all the odd numbers of wrong digits, half the errors due to even numbers of wrong digits are detected. But, extra digits and need for repeating parts of the message tend to reduce the net speed of signaling.

Let $m + n = 2^{n-1}$. Following Hamming's proposal (Ref. 3) for two-digit detection, the n digits may be so utilized as to detect the presence of all odd numbers of wrong digits and cases of two wrong digits. In addition they will detect about half the errors due to four and larger even numbers of wrong digits. The approximate over-all results to be expected with an error indicator of this type are shown in Table 8–1 and compared with single-error correction.

Associated with the 2.7 to 4.6 decibel reductions in signal power (Table 8–1, Case II) for the alphabet selected, the message is delayed by 64 Nyquist intervals. This is in addition to the round-trip time of transmission plus margins. Incidentally, with or without error correction, regenerative repeaters are not completely free of errors, residual probabilities being multiplied by the number of repeaters in tandem.

TABLE 8–1. ERROR CORRECTION TO SAVE SIGNAL POWER ASSUMING THAT RESISTANCE NOISE IS THE ONLY REASON FOR ERRORS

Case I: One-way system — corrects for one wrong digit

Average Chance of a Wrong Digit	Decibel Saving in Average Signal Power	Decibels the Reduced Signal Is above Shannon's Ideal	Net Information Rate in Bits per Second per Cycle per Second of Band Width
10^{-5}	1.5	6.3	1.94
10^{-8}	2.1	8.1	1.94
10^{-14}	2.5	10.4	1.94
10^{-16}	2.55	11.0	1.94
10^{-24}	2.7	.12.7	1.94

Case II: Two-way system — corrects for any odd number of wrong digits; corrects for two wrong digits; and corrects for approximately half the errors due to 4, 6, 8 . . . wrong digits

Average Chance of a Wrong Digit	Decibel Saving in Average Signal Power	Decibels the Reduced Signal Is above Shannon's Ideal	Net Information Rate in Bits per Second per Cycle per Second of Band Width
10^{-8}	2.7	6.8	1.68
10^{-16}	4.3	8.7	1.78
10^{-24}	4.6	10.4	1.78

Unlike the codes of the preceding section, the end result of the foregoing type of correction is not uniformly reliable. Particular symbols of the alphabet are allowed a larger chance of error and others a lesser chance of error to the end that the average relative frequency of a wrong digit or a frame that contains one or more wrong digits will not exceed a specified value. For some purposes this would not be satisfactory. However, any alphabet that is not uniformly reliable may always be converted to one that is. Conversion simply requires the addition of a variable translator at each end of the system.

MAXIMIZING THE ENTROPY OF THE SIGNAL PER UNIT OF AVERAGE SIGNAL POWER

Shannon's ideal can be approached only by adding redundancy and allowing a delay in the delivery of the message. An error-correcting code adds a small redundancy which, at the cost of a modest delay, affords an improvement amounting to several decibels.   Even so, the average signal power is substantially more than the theoretical ideal.

An essential postulate of the published proof of the central theorem is that the signals have Gaussian distributions. Since resistance noise requires more bits per unit band width per unit of average power for its unambiguous specification than any other type of signal, and since the statistics of PCM are far from Gaussian, it has often been suggested we could expect a simple PCM system to fall far short of the nonsurpassable ideal.

To explore this suggestion, let resistance noise emerge from an ideal low-pass filter.   Imagine this noise to be sampled $2B$ times a second (or slightly faster).   Quantize the samples, and determine H_N, the entropy of the quantized samples expressed in bits per sample.   Assume small and equal quantum steps, and let q_0 represent the density of quanta.   If

$$\rho(x_i) = \frac{1}{\sqrt{2\pi}\,\sigma}\,\epsilon^{-\frac{x_i^2}{2\sigma^2}}\,\Delta x_i,$$

since

$$H(x) = -\sum_{-\infty}^{\infty}\rho(x_i)\,\ln\rho(x_i),$$

as $\Delta x_i \to dx$,

$$H(x) \to \ln\sqrt{2\pi\epsilon}\,\sigma + \ln q_0,$$

or, in bits per sample,

$$H_N = \log_2 4.133 q_0 \sqrt{N}$$

where N is the average noise power.

Let $N = 1$ and encode the preceding noise samples (by the sort of decoder implied by Shannon's Theorem 9) into quantized samples having q possible levels, each level being equally probable and independent.   Then S, the average power of an ensemble of these new samples is $S = \frac{1}{3}\frac{q+1}{q-1}A^2$ where A is the maximum absolute value that a sample can assume.   We will also require that $H_q = H_N$ so that $q = 4.133 q_0$, whence $S = \frac{\pi\epsilon}{6} + \cdots \to 1.423$.   Thus, S is about 1.53 decibels greater than N.

Consequently, if we start with an array of conventional PCM digits of many places q and maximum entropy per digit, if we convert these digits to an equal number of quantized Gaussian digits having the same entropy, and if we then pass the Gaussian digits through a low-pass filter, the line signal that emerges will have the statistics of finely quantized resistance noise.   Moreover, with a proper procedure for decoding, the average signal power can be 1.53 decibels less than for the original conventional PCM code, assuming that we are seeking the same average frequency of errors in identifying the perturbed code elements.

Signal power can be conserved to this extent and in this manner only at the cost of delaying delivery of the message. The encoding and decoding operations essential to the reduction in power utilize the principles of Shannon's Theorem 9 and consequently have to provide the variable storage which this theorem implies. This means variable storage has to be provided in the coder in order to permit the continuous transmission of data and in the decoder to allow for a corresponding delay in the interpretation and continuous delivery of the message. Moreover, this variable storage has to be large enough so that the chance of its being inadequate will not seriously increase the net chance of error.

We may see the extent to which tails of the Gaussian distribution are responsible for the improvement by assuming the samples are limited to $\pm\sigma$ and $\pm 2\sigma$ respectively, viz.,

$$\left.\begin{array}{l} \rho(x_i) = \dfrac{1}{0.683} \times \dfrac{1}{\sqrt{2\pi}\,\sigma}\,\epsilon^{-\frac{x_i^2}{2\sigma^2}}\Delta x_i, \quad -\sigma \leq x_i \leq \sigma \\[2mm] \rho(x_i) = 0, \quad -\sigma > x_i \text{ or } x_i > \sigma \end{array}\right\} \quad (8\text{--}2)$$

and

$$\left.\begin{array}{l} \rho(x_i) = \dfrac{1}{0.954} \times \dfrac{1}{\sqrt{2\pi}\,\sigma}\,\epsilon^{-\frac{x_i^2}{2\sigma^2}}\Delta x_i, \quad -2\sigma \leq x_i \leq 2\sigma \\[2mm] \rho(x_i) = 0, \quad -2\sigma > x_i \text{ or } x_i > 2\sigma. \end{array}\right\} \quad (8\text{--}3)$$

and

Thus, an array of conventional PCM digits of many places q and maximum entropy per digit is to be converted into an equal number of digits having the same entropy; in Case I, according to (8–2), and in Case II, according to (8–3). For (8–2), assuming 21-place digits, the improvement works out to 0.14 decibel and for (8–3), when $q = 41$, it is 1.35 decibels. Thus (8–3) realizes most of the possible 1.53 decibel reduction in signal power.

When code elements are transmitted at the Nyquist rate, savings of this general type depend upon the fineness of the quantization. For example, with plus or minus binary digits, either $+1$ or -1 requires the same signal power and no savings result. On the other hand, when, for example, quaternary digits are transmitted at the Nyquist rate, if on the average each of the two center levels is occupied 39.5 per cent of the time and each of the extreme levels 10.5 per cent of the time, then with the type of coding previously described, the information rate works out to be $3.52B$ bits per second; and, for equal chance of errors, the power saving is about one decibel. In this instance, the effect of a wrong quaternary digit is more serious. However, by applying error correction to the quaternary code, this difficulty can be adequately minimized; and, in addition, we still gain most of the advantages previously credited to error correction.

The reason for this saving becomes evident when we note that the average signal power of the foregoing quaternary code happens to equal that of a tertiary whose three values are equally probable, provided the size of the quantum steps is the same in the two cases. Assume that the possible levels of the quaternary code are $+3$, $+1$, -1, and -3, that each center level is occupied 39.5 per cent of the time and that other levels are each occupied 10.5 per cent of the time, then the average power per symbol is proportional to 2.68 and the entropy is 1.74 bits per symbol. With a tertiary code the levels would be $+2$, 0, and -2; and, since each level is used one-third of the time, the average power is proportional to 2.67 and the entropy is 1.58 bits per symbol.

Thus, as might be surmised, it is theoretically impossible to realize the maximum capacity, $C = B \log_2 \left[1 + \dfrac{S}{N} \right]$, by signaling at the Nyquist rate with q'ary code elements when the values of different code elements are independent of one another and the q possible values are equally likely. Were this possible, it would also be possible to construct an infinite number of alphabets each capable of exceeding Shannon's nonsurpassable limit.

References

1. C. E. Shannon, "A Mathematical Theory of Communication," *The Bell System Technical Journal*, New York, Vol. 27, No. 3, July 1948, pp. 379–423; and Vol. 27, No. 4, October 1948, pp. 623–656.
2. R. W. Hamming, "Error Detecting and Error Correcting Codes," *The Bell System Technical Journal*, New York, Vol. 29, No. 2, April 1950, pp. 147–160.
3. E. N. Gilbert, "A Comparison of Signaling Alphabets," *The Bell System Technical Journal*, New York, Vol. 31, No. 3, May 1952, pp. 504–522.

Problems

1. A particular single-error-correcting code (Ref. 2, pp. 150 to 153) has the property that a code character consists of 7 binary code elements, 4 of the 7 binary digits depict the wanted message in the absence of noise; and, if no more than one of the 7 binary digits as received is in error, the receiver corrects the error. Suppose the digits are transmitted at the Nyquist rate over a distortionless channel whose band width is $7B$. Assume that delays are reduced to a minimum and the only reason for errors is resistance noise. The message source has the property that the 2^4 possible message values are equally probable, and are statistically independent. If 10^{-8} is the *a posteriori* probability that a binary digit as received is not correctly identified, by how many decibels must the average signal power exceed the nonsurpassable ideal given by Shannon's central theorem? What is the average relative frequency of code characters that are corrected? What is the average relative frequency of code characters that contain errors? Is the code uniformly reliable?
2. Suppose the average signal power in Problem 1 be utilized to transmit under the same conditions $8B$ binary digits per second over a distortionless channel whose band width is $4B$. What is the average relative chance that a four-digit code character as received is not correctly identified? What relative average signal

power would be required in order that the average relative frequency of unde-
tected errors be the same as was encountered with the error-correcting code used
in Problem 1? (Ref. 3 includes a generalized discussion of these topics.)

3. Show that it is theoretically impossible to realize the maximum capacity, $C = B \log_2 \left(1 + \dfrac{S}{N} \right)$, by signaling at the Nyquist rate with q'ary code elements when
the values of different code elements are independent of one another and the
q possible values are equally likely.

4. (a) Binary digits are transmitted at the Nyquist rate. In each frame of M
code elements some one digit is $+1$ and all the rest zero. The time of
appearance of the $+1$ digit indicates the selected message. All possible
messages are equally likely. What is the average signal power? Express
the entropy of the transmitted signal in terms of bits per symbol of M code
elements and bits per second. (Hint: the entropy is not given by $-\Sigma \rho_i$
log ρ_i.)

   (b) Suppose the code is changed so that digits produced at different times are
independent of one another and the average chance of $+1$ is $1/M$. What
is the entropy of the transmitter output in bits per second, and what is
the average signal power? What is the average signal power and what is
the entropy in bits per second if the digits assume the values ± 1 instead
of 1 or 0?

CHAPTER 9

AMPLITUDE MODULATION

Amplitude modulation is one of the oldest forms of modulation. When utilized to best advantage, its efficiency can either equal or exceed that of all other modulation processes, as has been successively pointed out by Carson, Hartley, and Wiener. Furthermore, amplitude modulation is commonly encountered as a preliminary step in many complex modulation schemes.

Messages transmitted by amplitude modulation will not, however, necessarily be in the form desired for delivery to their ultimate destinations. Also, if a communication system of maximum efficiency is the goal, the specification of the message must be reduced to its simplest form, not for a particular message but on the average taking into account the whole class of possible messages; and, this most efficient form, if it does not match the noisy channel, must be translated into an optimal signal representation that will maximize the rate of communication over the transmitting medium. As mentioned in Chapter 6, these are general stipulations and apply equally well to any other form of modulation.

DEFINITION OF AMPLITUDE MODULATION

An amplitude-modulated wave is a carrier wave the amplitude factor of which is varied in accordance with a modulating wave.

This is a generalized definition and includes a wide range of possible systems using sinusoidal carriers, pulse carriers, or any other form of carrier that has an amplitude factor capable of being varied. Furthermore, the variation of the amplitude factor may be related to the modulating wave in any unique manner.

In this and the two chapters to follow, the general definition will be restricted to a sinusoidal carrier having an amplitude factor that is a linear function of the modulating wave. Other carriers may be treated in a similar way by the application of Fourier analysis.

ANALYTICAL EXPRESSION FOR AN AMPLITUDE-MODULATED WAVE

With these restrictions, an amplitude-modulated sinusoidal carrier may be written as a function of time in the form

$$M(t) = A_c[1 + kV(t)] \cos(\omega_c t + \Phi_c) \tag{9-1}$$

where $A_c \cos (2\pi f_c t + \Phi_c)$ is the sinusoidal carrier, $V(t)$ is the modulating wave, $[1 + kV(t)]$ is the modulating function, and $|kV(t)|$ multiplied by 100 is the so-called percentage modulation. When the negative modulation factor, $|kV(t)|$, is equal to unity, the instantaneous amplitude of the carrier just falls to zero and the modulation is said to be complete. If the negative modulation factor exceeds unity, the carrier is said to be over-modulated, and serious distortion may be present in the output of some types of demodulators.

Positive and negative modulation factors, and the corresponding percentage modulations, may be defined separately if the largest positive instantaneous value of the modulating wave is different from the largest negative instantaneous value. In this case it is important to note that the envelope of the modulated wave will have the property that the maximum positive and maximum negative departures from its long time average will be different. For example, a modulating wave varying with time might always be positive.

Logic of the Analysis

Fundamentally, the crux of any analysis of an amplitude-modulated wave will be found to lie in the description of the modulating wave. To convey information, the modulating wave must occupy a nonzero band of frequencies. If, however, the frequency range of the modulating wave is limited, its magnitude endures, strictly speaking, for an unlimited period of time. Thus, in an exact sense it is inconsistent to specify that the modulating wave be limited both in its frequency range and in time of duration. For purposes of analysis, both are specified through the artifice of suppressing and neglecting nonessential frequencies, and by ignoring frequency components the magnitudes of which are regarded as sufficiently small. It is the theoretical information rate of a noisy channel that implies the minimum extent to which this fundamental uncertainty limits the useful capacity of the channel.

For example, the time-frequency duality implied by the Fourier integral is fundamental and the resulting uncertainty is unescapable. As expressed by Hartley (Ref. 1),*

$$g(t) = \int_{-\infty}^{\infty} \mathcal{C}(f) \text{ cas } 2\pi f t \, df \qquad (9\text{--}2)$$

$$\mathcal{C}(f) = \int_{-\infty}^{\infty} g(t) \text{ cas } 2\pi f t \, dt \qquad (9\text{--}3)$$

where† f is cyclic frequency, t is time, and cas denotes cosine added to sine.

---

* The references cited are listed at the end of each chapter according to the number used in the text.

† $\mathcal{C}(f) = A(2\pi f) + B(2\pi f)$ where $A(2\pi f)$ and $B(2\pi f)$ are given by (9–6) and (9–7).

These relations reflect the general property that the response $g(t)$ cannot be confined within a small region on the time scale when $\mathcal{C}(f)$, the steady-state transmission characteristic, is confined to a narrow range on the frequency scale. For example, it is well known that, if a telegraph dot is made narrower and narrower, its corresponding significant frequency spectrum becomes broader and broader until, in the limit when the dot becomes an impulse, its significant frequency spectrum is of infinite extent. Although there are more efficient shapes than a telegraph dot for producing a wave localized both in time and frequency, modern information theory indicates a theoretical limit to the best physically realizable result that can be obtained with an optimum signal.

Fourier-Integral Representation of the Modulating Wave

The basic concept underlying the analysis is the assumption that the modulating wave, or in general an arbitrary function satisfying well-known restrictions, may be represented by the Fourier method as a plurality of sinusoids. With the function known, the method permits finding the spectrum of the sinusoidal components. For a continuous spectrum the components will be infinite in number with infinitesimal amplitudes. Conversely, if the spectrum is known, the function is known. Formally, the existence of both is recognized at once, viz.,

$$g(t) = \frac{1}{2\pi} \int_{-\infty}^{\infty} C(\omega) \epsilon^{i\omega t} \, d\omega \qquad (9\text{-}4)$$

and

$$C(\omega) = \int_{-\infty}^{\infty} g(t) \epsilon^{-i\omega t} \, dt. \qquad (9\text{-}5)$$

From a mathematical point of view, either or both $g(t)$ and $C(\omega)$ might be complex. In a physical system, t and $g(t)$ are real, although $C(\omega)$ may be complex. The treatment to follow assumes t and $g(t)$ are real. Also, t is identified with time in seconds and ω with angular velocity in radians per second.

The factor $1/2\pi$ may raise questions. Alternatively, the factor could have been placed in front of (9-5). Obviously, $1/\sqrt{2\pi}$ could have appeared in front of both (9-4) and (9-5) with the object of improving the symmetry. All of these conventions are commonplace and useful. The convention adopted amounts to an arbitrary choice of scale and is governed by convenience. Naturally not all functions can be represented by a Fourier integral.

When the foregoing representations are expressed in trigonometric instead of exponential form, we have

$$A(\omega) = \int_{-\infty}^{\infty} g(t) \cos \omega t \, dt, \quad \text{(an even function of } \omega\text{)} \qquad (9\text{-}6)$$

and

$$B(\omega) = \int_{-\infty}^{\infty} g(t) \sin \omega t \, dt, \quad \text{(an odd function of } \omega) \tag{9-7}$$

with

$$S(\omega) = \sqrt{A^2(\omega) + B^2(\omega)}, \quad \text{(an even function of } \omega) \tag{9-8}$$

and

$$\tan \Phi(\omega) = \frac{-B(\omega)}{A(\omega)}, \quad \begin{array}{l} \text{[both } \tan \Phi(\omega) \text{ and } \Phi(\omega) \text{ are} \\ \text{odd functions of } \omega\text{]} \end{array} \tag{9-9}$$

so that from (9-5)

$$C(\omega) = A(\omega) - iB(\omega) \tag{9-10}$$

and

$$C(-\omega) = A(\omega) + iB(\omega) = C^*(\omega),\ddagger \tag{9-11}$$

whereas from (9-4)

$$g(t) = \frac{1}{2\pi} \int_{-\infty}^{\infty} S(\omega) \cos [\omega t + \Phi(\omega)] \, d\omega \tag{9-12}$$

$$= \frac{1}{\pi} \int_{0}^{\infty} S(\omega) \cos [\omega t + \Phi(\omega)] \, d\omega. \tag{9-12a}$$

A function of x is said to be even if $g(-x) = g(x)$ and is said to be odd if $g(-x) = -g(x)$. Accordingly, we may write

$$g_e(t) = \frac{1}{2} [g(t) + g(-t)]$$

$$= \frac{1}{2\pi} \int_{-\infty}^{\infty} A(\omega) \cos \omega t \, d\omega \tag{9-13}$$

and

$$g_0(t) = \frac{1}{2} [g(t) - g(-t)]$$

$$= \frac{1}{2\pi} \int_{-\infty}^{\infty} B(\omega) \sin \omega t \, d\omega. \tag{9-14}$$

It has come to be recognized (Ref. 1) that the performance of a physical system that is both stable and linear should be adequately described by a single function of positive frequencies. Consequently, as Hartley (Ref. 1) suggests, there must be something in the nature of such systems that makes it unnecessary to specify $C(\omega)$ for both positive and negative frequencies and, as a result, unnecessary to specify both its real and imaginary components.

This "something" is the fact that time only moves in one direction. Consequently, when a pulse is applied to a physical system, the resulting response is confined to the period following the pulse. Call this response

$\ddagger C(-\omega) = C^*(\omega)$ only because $g(t)$ was assumed to be real.

$g(t)$, $t > 0$. Then $g(-t)$ is always zero. This means from (9–13) and (9–14) that

$$g_e(t) = g_0(t) = \frac{1}{2} g(t), \quad t > 0. \tag{9-15}$$

From (9–13), $g_e(t)$ is described by $A(\omega)$. But $A(\omega)$ is an even function and so is completely described by its values for positive frequencies. From (9–14), $B(\omega)$ is adequate. Consequently, either of the spectra contains all of the essential information. Accordingly, when it is expedient to do so, we will express the modulating wave which must emerge from a physical system by functions of positive frequencies.

Single-Frequency Modulating Wave

Before passing to the general case, the over-all picture can be grasped by considering simple modulating waves. Let C and V_1 be defined by $C \equiv 2\pi f_c t + \Phi_c$ and $V_1 \equiv 2\pi f_{v_1} t + \Phi_{v_1}$. Let $A_1 \cos V_1$ be the modulating wave. From (9–1) we have in this case

$$M(t) = A_c \cos C + \frac{1}{2} k A_c A_1 [\cos (C + V_1) + \cos (C - V_1)]. \tag{9-16}$$

Two-Frequency Modulating Wave

In this case let $V(t) = A_1 \cos V_1 + A_2 \cos V_2$. Then,

$$M(t) = A_c \cos C + \frac{1}{2} k A_c A_1 [\cos (C + V_1) + \cos (C - V_1)]$$

$$+ \frac{1}{2} k A_c A_2 [\cos (C + V_2) + \cos (C - V_2)]. \tag{9-17}$$

Compare (9–16) and (9–17). Except for the carrier frequency term which is common to both, (9–17) is the sum of two expressions similar to the one expression in (9–16) but corresponding to frequencies f_{v_1} and f_{v_2}. This is consistent with the fact that superposition holds generally. Consequently the modulated wave may be evaluated by considering each frequency component of the modulating wave as separately modulating the carrier and then adding the results.

General Modulating Wave

By the Fourier method (Ref. 2) we may represent the modulating wave by an infinite number of components, each of the form $A_v \cos (\omega_v t + \Phi_v)$. Here A_v and Φ_v vary with $\omega_v/2\pi$, the cyclic frequency. Neglect unimportant frequency components and consider that the modulating wave is restricted to the range ω_{v_1} to ω_{v_2}. In this case we have from (9–1),

$$M(t) = A_c \cos (\omega_c t + \Phi_c) + k A_c \cos (\omega_c t + \Phi_c) \int_{\omega_{v_1}}^{\omega_{v_2}} A_v \cos (\omega_v t + \Phi_v) \, d\omega_v. \tag{9-18}$$

Spectrum of the Modulated Wave

The first term of (9–18) is the carrier itself, and the amplitude of this term is independent of the modulating wave. In fact, the net carrier amplitude is independent of all but the d-c component of the modulating wave. When the spectrum of the modulating wave is continuous, the second term of (9–18) represents an infinity of terms, each derived from only one component of the modulating wave. Each component of the modulating wave may be expanded into two terms as in (9–19). Thus, each component of the modulating wave is represented in the modulated wave, $M(t)$, by an expression of the form

$$\frac{1}{2} k A_c A_v \left(\cos \left[(\omega_c + \omega_v)t + \Phi_c + \Phi_v \right] + \cos \left[(\omega_c - \omega_v)t + \Phi_c - \Phi_v \right] \right). \quad (9\text{–}19)$$

The frequencies of the two components of (9–19) differ from the carrier frequency by the frequency of that particular component of the modulating wave which the notation implies. Every other frequency component of the modulating wave yields two components similarly disposed in relation to the carrier frequency.

Sidebands and Carrier

All components of the modulated wave of the form (9–19) when taken together form a pair of frequency bands extending from either side of the carrier frequency in mirror symmetry in the same way that the spectrum of the modulating wave extends from $\frac{\omega_{v_1}}{2\pi}$ to $\frac{\omega_{v_2}}{2\pi}$, that is, from f_{v_1} to f_{v_2}. For many years these bands of frequencies have been called "sidebands," and the component currents of these frequencies have been called "sideband currents" or more often simply sidebands. The sideband which extends above the carrier frequency is spoken of as the upper sideband and the other as the lower sideband.

The transmitted carrier carries no information except the frequency, phase, and amplitude of the unmodulated wave. Either sideband carries the complete specification of the modulating wave. To utilize a single sideband implies that it can be separated from the other and that means can be devised for determining the information it carries. When the exact wave form of the message is significant, knowledge of the phase and frequency of the carrier is required.

It is important to emphasize that, except for a scale factor which would uniformly attenuate or amplify the entire spectrum, the upper sideband is the spectrum of the modulating wave displaced without inversion by an amount equal to the carrier frequency. Similarly, except for a similar scale factor, the spectrum of the lower sideband is the spectrum of the modulating wave also displaced by an amount equal to the carrier frequency, but with inversion. This assumes, of course, that the carrier frequency exceeds the highest frequency component of the modulating wave.

Nonoverlapping Spectra

If pairs of sidebands are to be separated by frequency selection, it is essential that the two frequency intervals do not overlap. As another example, if the modulator is unbalanced and only one sideband is to be transmitted, we require $f_c > f_{v_2}$, where the symbols have their previous meaning. With a balanced modulator, $2f_c > f_{v_2}$ is sufficient.

Similarly, the information of the message can be obtained by applying the upper sideband to a balanced product demodulator followed by a low-pass filter cutting off at f_{v_2}, provided $2f_c > f_{v_2}$. Otherwise, the demodulated sidebands overlap, causing distortion and loss of information.

Carrier and Sideband Power for Complete Modulation

Effective utilization of signal power is an important characteristic of any system of communication. Hence, it is of considerable interest to investigate the ratio of the power in the information-bearing sidebands to that of the carrier. This ratio is given by the ratio of the mean-square-voltage of the components provided these voltages appear across a pure resistance. However, to obtain this ratio, we must first obtain an expression for the mean-square-voltage of a wave in terms of its spectrum.

A procedure which for some purposes is becoming a common practice is to equate mean-square-voltage or current to power. This convention assumes that the value of the resistance is unity so that one may disregard the difference in dimensions between power and mean-square-voltage or current. With this convention, the mathematical definition of average power is

$$\overline{g^2(t)} = \lim_{T \to \infty} \frac{1}{T} \int_0^T g^2(t) \, dt \tag{9-20}$$

which assumes that $g(t)$ is zero for all negative t. Physically, our period of observation is limited, although for the average to be meaningful, the period must be long enough to sample a typical structure of the signal.

M. A. Parseval's theorem for integrals (Ref. 3, pp. 428–429) which is the analogue for integrals of Parseval's theorem for series is obtained from (9-2) and (9-3) by writing

$$\int_{-\infty}^{\infty} g_1(t)g_2(t) \, dt = \int_{-\infty}^{\infty} g_1(t) \int_{-\infty}^{\infty} \mathcal{C}_2(f) \text{ cas } 2\pi ft \, df \, dt$$

which upon changing the order of integration becomes

$$= \int_{-\infty}^{\infty} \mathcal{C}_1(f)\mathcal{C}_2(f) \, df. \tag{9-21}$$

Set $g_1(t) = g_2(t)$ and write

$$\int_{-\infty}^{\infty} g^2(t)\, dt = \int_{-\infty}^{\infty} \mathbb{C}^2(f)\, df = \frac{1}{\pi} \int_0^{\infty} C(\omega)C^*(\omega)\, d\omega, \qquad (9\text{--}22)$$

which is the theorem.

Assume $g(t)$ is zero for $t < 0$ and issues from a stable linear system. Then,

$$\int_0^{\infty} g^2(t)\, dt = \frac{1}{\pi} \int_0^{\infty} S^2(\omega)\, d\omega = \frac{2}{\pi} \int_0^{\infty} A^2(\omega)\, d\omega$$

$$= \frac{2}{\pi} \int_0^{\infty} B^2(\omega)\, d\omega = \frac{T}{2\pi} \int_0^{\infty} P(\omega)\, d\omega \qquad (9\text{--}23)$$

where $P(\omega)$ is known as the power spectrum or power density.

With large enough T,

$$\mathcal{P}(f) = \frac{2|C(\omega)|^2}{T} = P(2\pi f) \qquad (9\text{--}24)$$

where f is the cyclic frequency. Thus, the total power, which is defined as the mean square of the total current assuming a large enough T, works out to be

$$\frac{1}{T} \int_0^T g^2(t)\, dt = \int_{f_1}^{f_2} \mathcal{P}(f)\, df = \frac{2}{T} \int_{f_1}^{f_2} S^2(\omega)\, df \qquad (9\text{--}25)$$

where the significant frequency range of $g(t)$ extends from f_1 to f_2.

Although (9–25) readily gives the total power when the signal spectrum is continuous, caution is required if $g(t)$ contains discrete spectral components because these imply infinite power densities at their frequencies. For example, consider a sinusoidal component $A_v \cos \omega_v t$ embedded in resistance noise of P_n watts per cycle per second. The usual modification of the definition of the power spectrum is to write in place of $\mathcal{P}(f)$ in (9–25)

$$W(f) = \mathcal{P}(f) + \sum_{i=1}^{l} W_i\, \delta(f - f_i) \qquad (9\text{--}26)$$

where $W(f)$ is the modified definition, $\delta(f - f_i)$ is a unit impulse of infinite amplitude and unit area centered at f_i, W_i is the mean power of the ith component, and l is the number of discrete components. For the example cited, $W(f) = P_n + \frac{1}{2} A_v^2\, \delta(f - f_v)$ and the average power is given by

$$\int_{f_1}^{f_2} W(f)\, df = P_n(f_2 - f_1) + \frac{1}{2} A_v^2.$$

In general, the first two members of (9–25) become

$$\overline{g^2(t)} = \int_{f_1}^{f_2} W(f)\, df. \qquad (9\text{--}27)$$

For a continuous spectrum with discrete spectral components superimposed, $S(\omega)$ in the third member of (9–25) would be appropriately modified.

It is also significant to note that the power spectrum ignores all information pertaining to phase and by the same token does not uniquely describe the wave form of $g(t)$. Moreover, since shifting the frequency of a sinusoid does not change its power, this means that the total average power of each sideband of an amplitude-modulated carrier is the same and is proportional to the average power of the modulating wave.

Let a bar denote the mean value of a quantity. Then from (9–1)

$$\overline{M^2(t)} = \frac{A_c{}^2}{2} + \overline{k^2 A_c{}^2 V^2(t) \cos^2 (\omega_c t + \Phi_c)}$$

and since, provided $\overline{V(t)} = 0$, the result is independent of Φ_c

$$= \frac{A_c{}^2}{2} + \overline{k^2 A_c{}^2 V^2(t) \left[\frac{1}{2} + \frac{1}{2} \cos 2\omega_c t \right]}$$

and since the trigonometric term on the right contributes negligibly to the long-time average,

$$= \frac{A_c{}^2}{2} [1 + k^2 \overline{V^2(t)}] = P_c + 2P_s \qquad (9\text{–}28)$$

where P_c is average carrier power and $2P_s$ is total average power in both sidebands. Thus,

$$\frac{2P_s}{P_c} = k^2 \overline{V^2(t)}. \qquad (9\text{–}29)$$

For complete modulation, k multiplied by the maximum negative value of $V(t)$ is just unity and in this case

$$\frac{2P_s}{P_c} = \frac{\overline{V^2}}{V_{-p}{}^2} \qquad (9\text{–}30a)$$

where $\overline{V^2}$ replaces $\overline{V^2(t)}$ and $V_{-p}{}^2$ is the peak instantaneous voltage squared for negative values of $V(t)$.

When the modulation is 100 per cent, the modulating factor is unity and either $|kV_{p+}|$ or $|kV_{p-}|$ or each factor is just one and

$$\frac{2P_s}{P_c} = \frac{\overline{V^2}}{V_p{}^2} \qquad (9\text{–}30)$$

where $kV_p = 1$ identifies V_p when the factors are unequal.

Examples

Expressed in decibels, for a completely modulated wave, the ratio of the average carrier power to the average power of both sidebands is $20 \log_{10}$ [negative peak factor of the modulating wave]. For a square wave, the ratio is one and the average carrier power is twice the average power in one of the two sidebands. If $V(t)$ is a sinusoidal wave, the peak factor is $\sqrt{2}$ and the average carrier power is four times the average power in a single sideband. If $V(t)$ is an ensemble of n sinusoids harmonically related in frequency and so phased that their like amplitudes periodically add in the negative direction, the square of the peak factor of the modulating wave is $2n$, the average carrier power is $4n$ times the average power of a single sideband, and the ratio of total average power to average carrier power is $\frac{2n + 1}{2n}$.

If $V(t)$ is a typical speech wave at controlled volume, its peak factor is known to be approximately 18 decibels and thus the average carrier power is about 126 times the average power of a single sideband. If the talker's volume is not controlled and varies as in ordinary telephony, the peak factor is about 31 decibels and the average power is 1,259 times the average power in both sidebands and 2,518 times the average power of a single sideband. This illustrates that in an ordinary amplitude-modulation system the available average power may not be used efficiently.

NOISE AND INTERFERENCE

Susceptibility to various interfering waves is one of the most important characteristics of any communication system. Interference may be introduced at the sending end, during transmission, at repeaters or other intermediate stations, and at the receiving end.

Small-Signal Interference

Effects of intersystem interference or interchannel crosstalk often differ from those of noise. For practical reasons the structure of the interfering signal is likely to have a fairly definite functional form whereas a noise wave can generally be specified only in statistical terms. In the main, the effects of interference and noise depend upon the type of detector and other receiver details as well as upon the source of interference and many other factors. References 4 to 11 should be consulted for a more comprehensive treatment of these topics.

For purposes of illustration, the interfering wave will be assumed to be another amplitude-modulated carrier. Let $M(t)$ designate the incoming wanted signal and $M_x(t)$ the incoming interfering signal. It will also be assumed in the treatment to follow that the two carriers differ in frequency enough so that the sidebands do not overlap. This means the interference can be reduced by selectivity. However, it is the approximate effect of the interference that indicates the approximate necessary selectivity. It will be assumed that the tolerable interference is small enough so that after filtering $M_x(t) \ll M(t)$.

Product Demodulator. As might be surmised, an ideal product demodulator multiplies the incoming wave by a sinusoidal carrier of adequate amplitude and exactly the desired frequency and phase. When the incoming wave is a delayed replica of the modulated wave, this amounts to a repetition of the original modulation process applied to the incoming modulated wave. Two components are created. One has a spectrum proportional to that of the original wave plus d-c components. The other has a spectrum proportional to that of the original modulated wave moved up in frequency by an amount equal to the carrier frequency. That is, it is composed of a discrete component whose frequency is twice the original carrier frequency, plus upper and lower sidebands around this discrete component.

Under the assumptions that the sidebands of the wanted and unwanted carriers do not overlap and that the product modulator does not produce distortion, et cetera, the interference causes no frequency components in the output of the product demodulator that fall within the frequency range of the desired signal.

Rectifier Detector. When calculated to a first approximation, the output of a rectifier type of demodulator after filtering gives the same result as for a product demodulator, provided the interfering signal is sufficiently small.

When the interfering signal is appreciable, exact calculation becomes complicated even though we only consider the case of an almost perfect rectifier in series with appropriate resistances and assume that the modulating wave is a simple sine wave. Despite these difficulties, J. G. Kreer, Jr., has produced a useful approximation, namely (9–33). The desired result is approximated along the lines of Bennett's treatment (Ref. 6, particularly Table I, p. 234). The approximate procedure is as follows. When Bennett's quantities are expressed in terms of our notation, we obtain

$$P = A_c[1 + kV(t)], \quad k = \frac{A_x[1 + k_x V_x(t)]}{A_c[1 + kV(t)]}, \quad \frac{1}{2} A_{00} = D(t) \quad (9\text{–}31)$$

where $D(t)$ is the output of the demodulator before filtering. When these expressions are placed into the appropriate entry in Bennett's Table I, one finds that to a reasonable approximation,

$$D(t) = \frac{2}{\pi^2}\left[2E\left(\frac{A_x[1 + k_x V_x(t)]}{A_c[1 + kV(t)]}\right) \right.$$
$$\left. - \left(1 - \frac{A_x[1 + k_x V_x(t)]}{A_c[1 + kV(t)]}\right) K\left(\frac{A_x[1 + k_x V_x(t)]}{A_c[1 + kV(t)]}\right)\right] \quad (9\text{–}32)$$

where $K(u)$ and $E(u)$ are the complete elliptic integrals of the first and second kinds, respectively. However, it should be noted that (9–32) is valid only if at all times $\dfrac{A_x[1 + k_x V_x(t)]}{A_c[1 + kV(t)]} < 1$. This means that for (9–32) to be applicable, A_c must not be completely modulated. Actually, many modulating waves reach their peak value only a very small fraction of the time; in these instances, if A_c is completely modulated, the result would be to introduce bursts of distortion contributed by terms that we have already ignored.

The functions $K(u)$ and $E(u)$ may be expanded in power series which converge quite rapidly even for values of u very close to one. Such expansion may be found, for example, in Jahnke and Emde (Ref. 13). The result of substituting these series for the functions in (9–32), grouping terms, and ignoring terms involving either or both modulating waves to powers higher than the first, gives

$$D(t) = A_c kV(t) + \frac{1}{\pi}\left[\frac{3}{2}\frac{A_x}{A_c} - \frac{52}{64}\frac{A_x^3}{A_c^3} - \frac{252}{512}\frac{A_x^5}{A_c^5} - \cdots\right] A_x k_x V_x(t). \quad (9\text{–}33)$$

From (9–33) it can be seen that the modulating wave of the interfering signals will appear in the output as intelligible crosstalk proportional to the square of the ratio of the interfering signal to the wanted signal. Equation (9–33) also illustrates that, at least to a certain extent, it is possible to cause an amplitude-modulation system to display the familiar "channel-grabbing" effect that characterizes a frequency-modulation system.

For large values of A_x/A_c, computations become unwieldy. An experimental curve in which $A_c kV(t)$ is zero is shown in a paper by Fubini and Johnson (Ref. 12). This curve shows in effect the change in the second term of (9–33) due to the presence of a strong carrier.

Square-Law Detector. In this case the output ideally is proportional to the square of the input. The principles involved relate primarily to the generation of new frequency components in the detector. For purposes of illustration, assume that the detector input is limited to $M(t) + M_x(t)$, and that the output is the square of the input. Then,

$$D(t) = [A_c(1 + kV(t)\cos(\omega_c t + \Phi_c) + A_x(1 + k_x V_x(t)\cos(\omega_x t + \Phi_x)]^2$$

which will be written as

$$= [A\cos C + kAV(t)\cos C + A_1\cos C_1 + k_1 A_1 V_1(t)\cos C_1]^2. \quad (9\text{–}34)$$

Upon carrying out the indicated multiplication, expanding products and powers of the trigonometric terms, rejecting components outside the frequency range of the desired signal, and letting y denote the sum of the rejected terms,

$$D(t) - y = \left[\frac{1}{2}(A^2 + A_1^2)\right] + \left[A^2 kV(t)\right] + \left[\frac{1}{2}A^2 k^2 V^2(t)\right]$$
$$+ \begin{bmatrix} AA_1 kk_1 V(t)V_1(t)\cos(C_1 - C) \\ +AA_1 kV(t)\cos(C_1 - C) \\ +A_1^2 k_1 V_1(t) \\ +\dfrac{1}{2}A_1^2 k_1^2 V_1^2(t) \end{bmatrix} \quad (9\text{–}35)$$

$$= [\text{d-c}] + \begin{bmatrix}\text{wanted} \\ \text{signal}\end{bmatrix} + \begin{bmatrix}\text{intrinsic} \\ \text{distortion}\end{bmatrix}$$
$$+ [\text{interference}]. \quad (9\text{–}35a)$$

The interference term $AA_1kV(t) \cos(C_1 - C)$ may be significant if the essential frequency ranges of $V(t)$ and $V_1(t)$ are not equal and if the frequency range of $V(t)$ exceeds $(C_1 - C)/2$. As in the previous case, the dominating interference is proportional to the square of the ratio of the incoming modulated waves.

Signal-to-Noise Advantage of SSM over AM

Single sideband modulation (SSM) is modulation (Chap. 3) whereby the spectrum of the modulating wave is translated in frequency by a specified amount either with or without inversion. One way to produce SSM is to suppress the carrier and one of the sidebands of an amplitude-modulated sinusoid. The signal-to-noise advantage of SSM is illustrated by a comparison based on the following assumptions:

(a) Each system is limited to the same maximum instantaneous peak power.
(b) Each system has the same over-all frequency response.
(c) The AM system is restricted to 100 per cent modulation.
(d) The transmission band, namely, $[f_c - B \text{ to } f_c + B]$ for AM and either $(f_c + B)$ or $(f_c - B)$ for SSM and B for direct transmission is limited by filters.
(e) $f_c > 2B$.
(f) Transmission is distortionless and each system is stable and linear and is equipped with ideal filters, apparatus that is functionally perfect, et cetera.
(g) Each demodulator is an ideal product demodulator followed by a perfect filter.
(h) The only source of noise is resistance noise, and the noise-power density is the same for all systems.

Consider a modulating wave $V(t)$ with significant frequency components limited to the interval $0 < f < B$ where B is expressed in cycles per second. Designate the mean power by $\overline{V^2}$ and the maximum instantaneous peak power by $V_p{}^2$.

Direct Transmission. Assume $V(t)$ is the wanted signal at the input to the receiver; then the ratio of average signal power to average noise power is $\overline{V^2}/N = \overline{V^2}/Bn$ where n is the noise-power density. By definition, $V_p{}^2$ is the maximum instantaneous peak power. V_p may be positive or negative or V_{p^+} may equal V_{p^-}.

Single-Sideband Modulation. At the receiver input, let $P_s = \overline{V^2}$ be the average sideband power and note that $[f_c - (f_c - B)]n = Bn = N$ is the average noise power. By Parseval's theorem, $\overline{V^2}/N$ is the average signal-to-noise ratio after demodulation. Associated with P_s is $S_p{}^2$, the maximum instantaneous peak sideband power. If peak power is controlling, the incoming sideband current must be multiplied by a factor V_p/S_p. Compared to direct transmission, the average noise power will be multiplied by $S_p{}^2/V_p{}^2$. The noise advantage of SSM as compared to direct transmission is $10 \log_{10} V_p{}^2/S_p{}^2$ decibels where $|S_p| > |V_p|$ represents a degradation.

Amplitude Modulation. Since $|kV_p| = 1$ because the modulation is to be 100 per cent, we already have from (9–30)

$$\frac{2P_s}{P_c} = \frac{\overline{V^2}}{V_p^{\,2}}. \tag{9–30}$$

With 100 per cent modulation we note, from (9–1) and (9–28), that either $P_p \rightarrow 8P_c$ or $P_p = 8P_c$ and that to good accuracy

$$\frac{2P_s}{P_p} = \frac{\frac{1}{8}\overline{V^2}}{V_p^{\,2}}. \tag{9–36}$$

We require $P_p = V_p^{\,2}$ because AM is to be limited to the same peak power as SSM and direct transmission. Moreover, since the noise-power density is uniform and uncorrelated, nothing is lost nor gained in the way of signal-to-noise ratio if the signal power is spread over a plurality of sidebands, in this case two. This fundamental and understandable result was discovered by John R. Carson over thirty years ago in connection with his researches into the properties of time division systems. Thus, $2P_s$ would have to equal $\overline{V^2}$ for the AM system to have the same signal-to-noise ratio as direct transmission. Hence, from the SSM result,

$$\left[\begin{array}{c}\text{On the Basis of Equal Peak Power the}\\ \text{Signal-to-Noise Advantage}\\ \text{of SSM over AM}\\ \text{Expressed in Decibels}\end{array}\right] = 10 \log_{10} 8\, \frac{V_p^{\,2}}{S_p^{\,2}}. \tag{9–37}$$

One of the assumptions leading to (9–37) was a complete lack of correlation between the noise currents in the two sidebands of the AM system. If the resistance noise in these sidebands had been highly correlated (if it had been produced, say, by modulating the transmitter carrier by a band B of resistance noise), the signal-to-noise advantage of SSM over AM would have been 3 decibels more than the figure given by (9–37).

References

1. R. V. L. Hartley, "A More Symmetrical Fourier Analysis," *Proceedings of the Institute of Radio Engineers*, New York, Vol. 30, March 1942, pp. 144–150.
2. R. V. L. Hartley, "Relations of Carrier and Sidebands in Radio Transmission," *The Bell System Technical Journal*, New York, Vol. 2, No. 2, April 1923, pp. 90–112.
3. Harold Jeffreys and Bertha Swirles Jeffreys, *Methods of Mathematical Physics*, Cambridge, at the University Press, Great Britain, 1946.
4. E. V. Appleton and D. Boohariwalla, "The Mutual Interference of Wireless Signals in Simultaneous Detection," *Wireless Engineer and Experimental Wireless*, London, Vol. 9, March 1932, pp. 136–139.
5. R. T. Beatty, "Apparent Demodulation of a Weak Station by a Stronger One," *Wireless Engineer and Experimental Wireless*, London, Vol. 5, June 1928, pp. 300–303.

6. W. R. Bennett, "New Results in the Calculation of Modulation Products," *The Bell System Technical Journal*, New York, Vol. 12, No. 2, April 1933, pp. 228–243.

7. S. Butterworth, "Note on the Apparent Demodulation of a Weak Station by a Stronger One," *Wireless Engineer and Experimental Wireless*, London, Vol. 6, November 1929, pp. 619–621.

8. Stanford Goldman, *Frequency Analysis, Modulation and Noise*, McGraw-Hill Book Co., New York, 1948.

9. John R. Ragazzini, "The Effect of Fluctuation Voltage on the Linear Detector," *Proceedings of the Institute of Radio Engineers*, New York, Vol. 30, June 1942, pp. 277–288.

10. E. W. Herold, "The Operation of Frequency Converters and Mixers for Superheterodyne Reception," *Proceedings of the Institute of Radio Engineers*, New York, Vol. 30, February 1942, pp. 84–103.

11. Hans Roder, "Superposition of Two Modulated Radio Frequencies," *Proceedings of the Institute of Radio Engineers*, New York, Vol. 20, December 1932, pp. 1962–1970.

12. Eugene G. Fubini and Donald C. Johnson, "Signal-to-Noise Ratio in AM Receivers," *Proceedings of the Institute of Radio Engineers*, New York, Vol. 36, December 1948, pp. 1461–1466.

13. Eugene Jahnke and Fritz Emde, *Tables of Functions*, Dover Publications, New York, 1945, p. 73.

Problems

1. If $2 \cos \omega_c t$ is amplitude-modulated by $\cos \omega_v t$ in a suppressed-carrier product modulator, what is $M_1(t)$, the modulated wave? If $2 \cos \left[\omega_c t - \dfrac{\pi}{2} \right]$ is similarly amplitude-modulated by $\cos \left[\omega_v t - \dfrac{\pi}{2} \right]$, what is $M_2(t)$, the modulated wave? What is $M_1(t) + M_2(t)$?

2. If $C(\omega)$ describes the steady-state transmission characteristic of a system that is both linear and stable, show that $f(t) = \dfrac{1}{2\pi} \displaystyle\int_{-\infty}^{\infty} C(\omega)\epsilon^{i\omega t}\, d\omega$ is the transient response that accompanies excitation by an ideal unit impulse whose center of symmetry is at the reference time zero.

3. The function $f(t)$ is a real and even function of a real variable t; it may be represented by a Fourier integral and $C(\omega)$ is its spectrum. Let $C_1(\omega)$ and $C_2(\omega)$ be the spectra of $\dfrac{1}{2}f(t + \tau)$ and $\dfrac{1}{2}f(t - \tau)$, respectively. Show that $C_1(\omega) + C_2(\omega) = C(\omega)\,[\cos \omega\tau]$. Is $C(\omega)$ complex or real, even or odd?

4. In Problem 3, if $C_3(\omega)$ and $C_2(\omega)$ are the spectra of $-\dfrac{1}{2}f(t + \tau)$ and $\dfrac{1}{2}f(t - \tau)$, respectively; express $C_2(\omega)$, $C_3(\omega)$, and their sum in terms of $C(\omega)$.

5. Consider $f(t) = \dfrac{1}{2\pi} \displaystyle\int_{-\infty}^{\infty} C(\omega)\epsilon^{i\omega t}\, d\omega$ and its spectrum $C(\omega) = \displaystyle\int_{-\infty}^{\infty} f(t)\epsilon^{-i\omega t}\, dt$. What are the three time functions corresponding to the spectra $\dfrac{1}{2} C(\omega + \omega_c)$, $\dfrac{1}{2} C(\omega - \omega_c)$, and their sum?

6. If $\cos \omega_c t = g(t) = \displaystyle\int_{-\infty}^{\infty} \mathcal{C}(f) \text{ cas } 2\pi f t \, df$, derive $C(\omega)$ from $\mathcal{C}(f) = \displaystyle\int_{-\infty}^{\infty} g(t)$ cas $2\pi f t \, dt$.

7. Assume that the upper and lower sidebands of an amplitude-modulated wave may be represented by $2 \cos C \cos V$ which is demodulated by multiplying by $2 \sin C$. Express the product as a sum of sinusoids. Repeat multiplying by $2 \cos C$ instead of $2 \sin C$.

8. If $I(t) = ke^3$ and $e = \displaystyle\sum_{n=1}^{10} c_n \cos (2\pi f_n t + \Phi_n)$, enumerate the different frequencies present in $I(t)$. Assume that all of the frequencies and also all of the amplitudes are incommensurable. Furthermore, assume that no amplitude, c_n, and no frequency, f_n, is zero.

9. An amplitude-modulated wave $[1 + kV(t)] \cos 2\pi f_c t$ confined to the frequency range $(f_c - B)$ to $(f_c + B)$ cycles per second is perturbed by resistance noise. Let n be the noise-power density per cycle per second expressed in appropriate units. The perturbed wave is briefly sampled at regular intervals f_c times a second and the instants of sampling correspond to $t = 0, \pm 1/f_c, \pm 2/f_c, \ldots$. For convenience assume $f_c = qB$ where q is a positive integer greater than 1. The samples are filtered by an ideal low-pass filter that has a cutoff frequency of B cycles per second. The output after amplification is $2kV(t)$ plus noise. What is the signal-to-noise ratio? The perturbed wave is also briefly sampled f_c times a second at times corresponding to $t = \dfrac{1}{4f_c}, \pm \dfrac{5}{4}\dfrac{1}{f_c}, \pm \dfrac{9}{4}\dfrac{1}{f_c} \cdots$. These samples are samples of the noise alone because at these instants the signal is zero. These samples are reversed in sign and applied to the input of the low-pass filter in addition to the previous ensemble of signal-plus-noise samples. What is the effect on signal-to-noise ratio?

10. What are the restrictions on $V(t)$ in order that the instants at which the modulated wave, $A_c[1 + kV(t)] \cos (\omega_c t + \Phi_c)$, goes through zero will be independent of the modulating wave, $V(t)$?

CHAPTER 10

AMPLITUDE MODULATORS AND DEMODULATORS

There are many ways of producing an amplitude-modulated sinusoidal carrier and many ways of recovering the modulating signal. Each has its advantages and disadvantages. A more complete discussion of these topics will be found in the references (Refs. 1 to 39*) listed at the end of this chapter.

MODULATORS

Since an amplitude-modulated sinusoid is the product of two factors (9-1), one of which includes the modulating wave and the other only the carrier, an obvious way of producing such a wave is to devise a mechanism having an output that is proportional to the product of two input waves.

Product Modulators

Modulators possessing this property are commonly referred to as product modulators. One example would be a loudspeaker coupled to a microphone. The acoustic wave generated by the loudspeaker is proportional to the product of the currents flowing in its voice coil and field winding respectively, whereas the output current from the microphone is proportional to the acoustic wave. Therefore, if the modulating wave, plus in general a d-c component, is applied to the voice coil, and if a sinusoidal carrier is applied to the field winding, the output current from the microphone is given by

$$M(t) = K_1 K_2 I_c [E_{\text{d-c}} + V(t)] \cos (\omega_c t + \Phi_c) \qquad (10\text{-}1)$$

where K_1 is the factor of proportionality between microphone output and pressure (acoustic wave), K_2 is the factor of proportionality between the pressure wave and the product of the currents in the field winding and voice coil, and I_c is the amplitude of the sinusoidal carrier in the field winding. Equation (10-1) is already in the form of (9-1) if we set $K_1 K_2 I_c E_{\text{d-c}} \equiv A_c$ and $\dfrac{1}{E_{\text{d-c}}} \equiv k$, viz.,

$$M(t) = A_c [1 + kV(t)] \cos (\omega_c t + \Phi_c). \qquad (9\text{-}1)$$

* The references cited are listed at the end of each chapter according to the number used in the text.

141

A similar result is obtained if the sinusoidal carrier is applied to the field winding and the modulating wave to the ribbons of a light valve (Ref. 40) and if, in addition, constant-intensity light is passed through the light valve into a photocell.

Since each of these examples involves mechanical motion, they are restricted to relatively low frequencies. A corresponding result without this restriction can be obtained by replacing the light valve by two Kerr cells (Ref. 41).

The desired result also can be obtained by sampling the modulating wave briefly at regular intervals at the carrier rate and applying the ensemble of samples to the input of a band filter having a center frequency coincident with the carrier frequency. The modulated wave appears in the output, provided a fixed component of zero frequency is added to the modulating wave. This operation can be regarded as multiplying the modulating wave by a d-c term plus a carrier and its harmonics instead of by a single sinusoid. The result is upper and lower sidebands around the carrier and harmonics of the carrier plus the spectrum of the modulating wave, viz.,

$$M(t) = V(t)U(t) = kV(t) \sum_{m=-\infty}^{\infty} \frac{\sin mk\pi}{mk\pi} \cos m\omega_c t \qquad (10\text{-}2)$$

where $U(t)$, it will be recalled, is zero except for the brief intervals when it takes on the value unity, k represents the fraction of time $U(t)$ is unity, and $U(t)$ is so related to time zero that it is an even function of time.

One fundamental property of a product modulator is that the carrier is normally suppressed. For many applications this is a highly desirable feature. However, if it is desired to transmit the carrier, then it becomes necessary to add a d-c component to the modulating wave in order to produce the equivalent of the first term of (9-1).

Square-Law Modulators

Modulators in this category are widely used and all employ devices in which the output is proportional to the square of the input. Vacuum tubes and numerous other devices when connected in series with suitable resistors have nonlinear current-voltage characteristics of nearly the desired shape. If a modulating wave and sinusoidal carrier are the input to such a device, we have, owing to the square-law term,

$$M(t) = K_1[E_c \cos (\omega_c t + \Phi_c) + V(t)]^2$$

which will be written

$$M(t) = A_c{}^2 \cos^2 C + 2A_c V(t) \cos C + V^2(t). \qquad (10\text{-}3)$$

The first term of (10-3) contributes a d-c term and another discrete frequency component that is the second harmonic of the carrier. If the spectrum of an amplitude-modulated sinusoid is recalled, the second term will be recognized as contributing lower and upper sidebands having frequency components confined to $f_c - f_{v_2}$ and $f_c + f_{v_2}$, respectively, where f_{v_2} is the highest cyclic frequency component of the modulating wave. The third term is represented by a spectrum with frequency components as high as $2f_{v_2}$. Accordingly, if $f_c > 3f_{v_2}$, the frequency components of $A_c^2 \cos^2 C$ and $V^2(t)$ lie outside the frequency range of interest defined by $2A_cV(t) \cos C$, and the desired sidebands can be obtained by filtering.

Practical applications are not usually quite as simple as the preceding description might imply. Because the square-law characteristic is only approximated over a limited region by physically realizable elements, a fixed component is sometimes added to the carrier and modulating waves to center the sum in the region where the approximation is optimum. This modification introduces new terms. Of these, only a carrier component falls within the frequency interval of interest. Balanced modulators can be used to suppress the carrier when this is desired, as will be discussed in a later section.

Rectifier-Type Modulators

Rectifier characteristics represent a form of nonlinearity which occurs very commonly and which has been widely used in modulators. Numerous characteristics are available, but for purposes of illustration it will be assumed that the rectifier characteristic is linear. In an ideal linear rectifier, the flow of current is proportional to the applied voltage, provided the voltage is positive, and no current flows when the applied voltage is negative.

If a modulating wave in series with a sinusoidal carrier is applied to such an element, the resulting current will be a series of pulses of approximately the shape of a half sine wave but varying both in width and amplitude with the modulating wave. If the amplitude of the carrier is much greater than the peak value of the modulating wave, then the instants at which the resultant wave goes through zero will depend very little upon the modulating wave. Since a reactive impedance complicates matters, assume the admittance is real and let $1/R$ represent the conductance of the circuit including the rectifier in the forward direction. Then to a first approximation the resultant current is obtained by multiplying the applied voltage by a sampling function which is $1/R$ during the intervals the carrier is positive and zero when the carrier is negative. Thus, we have

$$M(t) = [A_c \cos \omega_c t + V(t)] \frac{1}{2R} \sum_{m=-\infty}^{\infty} \frac{\sin m \frac{\pi}{2}}{m \frac{\pi}{2}} \cos m\omega_c t$$

where $M(t)$ represents the output of the modulator before filtering. By performing the indicated operations, we get

$$M(t) = \frac{A_c}{\pi R} + \frac{V(t)}{2R} + \frac{A_c}{2R} \cos \omega_c t + \frac{2V(t)}{\pi R} \sum_{1,3,5,\ldots}^{\infty} (-)^{\frac{m+3}{2}} \frac{1}{m} \cos m\omega_c t$$

$$+ \frac{2A_c}{\pi R} \sum_{2,4,6,\ldots}^{\infty} (-)^{\frac{m+2}{2}} \frac{1}{m^2 - 1} \cos m\omega_c t. \qquad (10\text{-}4)$$

Thus, before filtering, the modulated output contains a d-c component proportional to the applied carrier, a spectrum of the modulating wave itself, a term proportional to the carrier, upper and lower sidebands around the carrier and also around odd harmonics of the carrier, and a series of discrete components corresponding to even harmonics of the carrier.

General Nonlinear Element

In the preceding treatment of square-law and rectifier-type modulators it was found that nonlinear elements, provided they approximated certain special characteristics, could be utilized to produce amplitude modulation. We now assume that the nonlinear element has a more general characteristic and describe arrangements that are capable of closely approximating the performance of an ideal product modulator.

When such an element is connected in series with a resistance, a carrier, and the modulating wave, the resulting current may be expressed in terms of a power series, provided the characteristic curve is single-valued, continuous, et cetera. This gives

$$M(t) = a_0 + a_1[A_c \cos \omega_c t + V(t)] + a_2[A_c \cos \omega_c t + V(t)]^2 + \cdots$$

which can be written as

$$= \sum_{i=0}^{\infty} a_i[A \cos C + V(t)]^i$$

and, upon expanding by means of the binomial theorem, becomes

$$= \sum_{i=0}^{\infty} \sum_{k=0}^{i} \binom{i}{k} A^k[V(t)]^{i-k} \cos^k C \qquad (10\text{-}5)$$

in which the symbol $\binom{i}{k}$ designates the coefficient of x^k in the expansion of $(1 + x)^i$, that is, $\binom{i}{k} = \dfrac{\lfloor i}{\lfloor i - k \, \lfloor k}$. When the integral powers of $\cos C$ are expressed in terms of multiple angles, as in Problem 1, (10-5) becomes

$$M(t) = \sum_{i=0}^{\infty} \sum_{k=0}^{i} \sum_{l=0}^{k} a_i \binom{i}{k}\binom{k}{l} 2^{-k} A^k[V(t)]^{i-k} \cos (k - 2l)C. \qquad (10\text{-}6)$$

The value of (10-6) is mainly that it enables us to enumerate the terms constituting a particular product. For example, in addition to the wanted sidebands, consider the two additional pairs representing second-order and third-order products of distortion involving frequency components of the modulating wave: that is, the upper and lower sidebands of $V^2(t)$ and also of $V^3(t)$ around the carrier. Sorting out these terms and designating by a subscript the order of the voice products that modulate the carrier, we get

$$
\left.
\begin{aligned}
M_1(t) &= \sum_{i=1}^{\infty} a_{2i} \frac{2i}{2^{2i-1}} \left[\binom{2i-1}{i} + \binom{2i-1}{i-1} \right] A^{2i-1} V(t) \cos \omega_c t, \\
M_2(t) &= \sum_{i=1}^{\infty} a_{2i+1} \frac{(2i+1)2i}{2^{2i}} \left[\binom{2i-1}{i} \right. \\
&\qquad\qquad \left. + \binom{2i-1}{i-1} \right] A^{2i-1} V^2(t) \cos \omega_c t, \\
M_3(t) &= \sum_{i=1}^{\infty} a_{2i+2} \frac{(2i+2)(2i+1)2i}{3 \cdot 2^{2i}} \left[\binom{2i-1}{i} \right. \\
&\qquad\qquad \left. + \binom{2i-1}{i-1} \right] A^{2i-1} V^3(t) \cos \omega_c t.
\end{aligned}
\right\} \quad (10\text{-}7)
$$

When terms of these expressions are compared, we conclude that the ratio of the wanted sideband terms to these particular distortion terms may be made as large as desired by sufficiently reducing $V(t)$. In practice such a reduction might or might not be feasible.

Balanced Modulators. In practical applications it is usually preferable to use some form of a balanced modulator (Ref. 5) and, for purposes of illustration, (b) of Fig. 10–1 indicates a particular arrangement. Here two similar modulators are so connected that the modulating wave is reversed in sign on one of them and the output is connected to transmit the difference between the two modulated waves. In this case the net output is the difference between two expressions of the form of (10–6) with $V(t)$ reversed in sign in one of them, viz.,

$$
M(t) = \sum_{i=0}^{\infty} \sum_{k=0}^{i} \sum_{l=0}^{k} [1 - (-)^{i-k}] a_i \binom{i}{k} \binom{k}{l} 2^{-k} A^k [V(t)]^{i-k} \cos(k - 2l)\omega_c t. \quad (10\text{-}8)
$$

In (10–8) all of the terms for which $i - k$ is even vanish and all the odd terms are doubled. This means that the second, fourth, and higher even-order distortion products contributed by the modulating wave are eliminated. The largest remaining distortion product of this type is $V^3(t)$ which is rapidly reduced as $V(t)$ is reduced. In practice it is never possible to make the modulators exactly alike, and in many cases it is not practical to count on an improvement due to balance of more than 20 to 30 decibels.

When the carrier frequency is close to the highest modulating frequency, the spacing between the wanted sidebands around the carrier and the unwanted sidebands around the second harmonic of the carrier becomes small, thus imposing stringent requirements upon filters used for separating these components. Such a condition may be relieved by linearizing the modulator with respect to the carrier rather than the modulating wave, merely by interchanging the two. When this is done, the bracket under the summation (10–8) becomes $[1 - (-)^k]$ instead of $[1 - (-)^{i-k}]$ and, hence, the terms for which k is even will cancel out. As a result only sidebands around odd multiples of the carrier will appear.

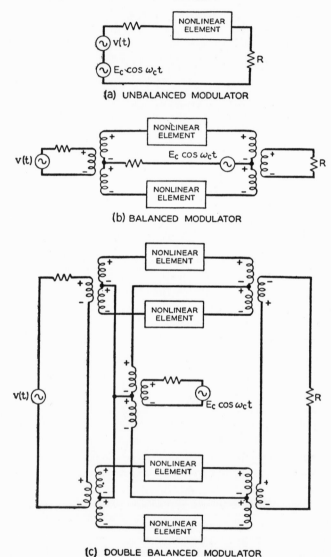

FIG. 10–1 Block diagrams of unbalanced, balanced, and double-balanced modulator circuits

Double-Balanced Modulators. When both linearity with respect to the signal and wide frequency spacing are required, it is possible to accomplish this with a double-balanced modulator as shown in (c) of Fig. 10–1. In this circuit only odd powers of $V(t)$ modulating odd multiples of the carrier appear in the output. In practical applications, a double-balanced modulator may take on various different forms and, in some cases, it may produce an improvement of as much as 20 to 30 decibels.

Theoretically, it is possible to extend the process by using phase shifts other than 180 degrees. For example, to extend the process with respect to carrier balance, suppose three double-balanced modulators are set up with their carriers 120 degrees apart in phase. Then all even multiples of the carrier and all multiples of a power of three balance out. Consequently, the first interfering components are those around 5, 7, and 11 times the carrier frequency.

Higher-Order Modulators for Special Purposes

Production of the desired modulated wave does not have to depend upon the generation of second-order modulation products. Certain nonlinear elements have characteristics in which some of the a_i factors of the power series expansion are inherently zero. One example is the silicon carbide varistor (Ref. 42). In this instance all values of a_i corresponding to even values of i are inherently essentially zero. Advantage may be taken of such properties in the design of modulators for special purposes. An example, suggested by Hartley about thirty years ago, is the design of a modulator in which the carrier is suppressed.

To produce such an effect with ordinary modulators would require a very high degree of balance, and in applications where the requirement for minimizing the carrier leak is very stringent, such balances are achieved only with difficulty and are not readily maintained. In this case, it is possible to use an element having odd symmetry such as a silicon carbide resistor, make the carrier supply generator have half the frequency of the desired carrier, and utilize third-order products of modulation of the form, $2C \pm V$.

If in (10–8), ω_c is replaced by $\omega_c/2$ and if $a_0 = a_2 = a_4 = \cdots = 0$, then

$$M(t) = \sum_{i=0}^{\infty} \sum_{k=0}^{2i+1} \sum_{l=0}^{k}$$

$$[1 - (-)^{1+2i-k}]a_{2i+1}\binom{2i+1}{k}\binom{k}{l} 2^{-k}A^k[V(t)]^{1+2i-k}\cos\frac{k-2l}{2}\omega_c t. \quad (10\text{–}9)$$

Since "carrier leak" corresponds to terms in which $V(t)$ appears to the zero power, and since k is odd for such terms, carrier leaks all appear at frequencies corresponding to odd multiples of $f_c/2$. On the other hand, the wanted sidebands are contributed by terms in which $V(t)$ appears to the first power, which means that k must be even; and therefore the sidebands appear around discrete components that are even multiples of $f_c/2$. Consequently, there exists a spacing of $f_c/2$ between f_c and the nearest carrier leak. This makes it possible to eliminate the carrier leaks to a high degree by filtering.

High-Power Amplifiers and Modulators

The most familiar and widespread use of amplitude modulation is for radio broadcasting. Naturally, the emphasis is on simplifying the many millions of home receivers. For this reason, the carrier and both sidebands

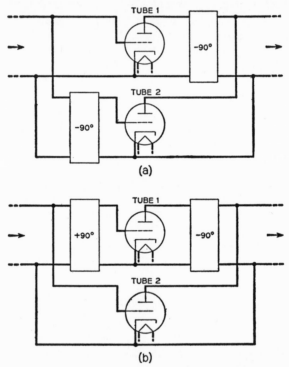

FIG. 10-2   Location of phase-shift networks in a Doherty amplifier

are transmitted. Moreover, to obtain good coverage and better reception, the modulated wave is radiated at the highest permitted power.

Transmitter outputs range from 500 watts to 500 kilowatts. Accordingly, the aim (Refs. 8, 14, 15, 17, 18, 37, and 38) is high efficiency in the parts of the transmitter where the amounts of power are large. Many high-frequency systems have been proposed in which the step of modulating the carrier is carried out in the high-power part of the transmitter. In recent years the most successful and outstanding methods in widespread use reduce to two. One utilizes a high-level Class B modulation system combined with a Class C radio-frequency amplifier.   The other is an ingenious quadrature-phase-coupling circuit invented by W. H. Doherty (Ref. 14) for paralleling two tubes (Fig. 10–2) and thereby achieving a new type of linear power amplifier.   Applicable to the linear amplification of

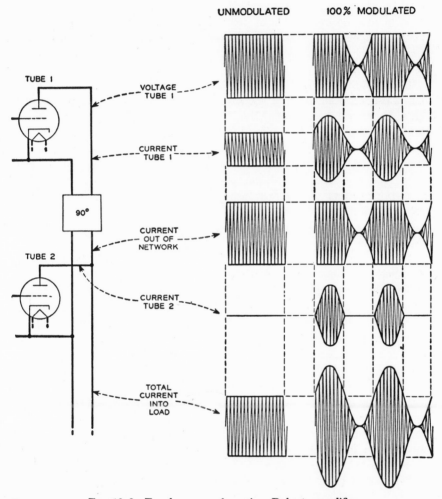

FIG. 10–3   Envelope wave forms in a Doherty amplifier

any wave, the attainment of 60 to 65 per cent plate efficiencies independent of output is the result of the combined action of a varying load distribution (Fig. 10–3) between two tubes and a varying circuit impedance changing with the varying load distribution.

Plate-Modulated Class C Amplifier.   In this system the transmitted carrier is amplified by a radio-frequency, high-power amplifier operated Class C with an efficiency of 80 per cent or more. The output stage of the Class C amplifier is plate-modulated by a high-power, audio-frequency amplifier system operated push-pull Class B, with tubes biased to cutoff for good efficiency and with substantial amounts of negative feedback for high-quality, stabilized, linear operation. The end result is a very high-quality type of modulator capable of delivering very large power outputs. The all-day efficiency for normal broadcast operation is somewhat better than that of a Doherty amplifier. At 100 per cent modulation the opposite tends to be true.

High-Efficiency, Grid-Modulated Amplifier. Some high-power modulators use a modification of the Doherty amplifier along lines proposed by H. A. Reise and A. A. Skene (Ref. 43) wherein the carrier-frequency excitation is fixed and the grid bias of both tubes is varied at audio frequency. In this modification the portions of the combined audio and carrier inputs that are effective in varying the output of each tube are of just the right wave form to produce the desired modulated wave in the combined output from both tubes. A description of this mode of operation has been published (Ref. 37) by Terman and Woodyard. The modified operation can be clarified by a brief review of the principles involved in the operation of the Doherty amplifier.

Doherty Amplifier. Maximum efficiency of a vacuum-tube amplifier is obtained only when it is delivering maximum voltage to its load. As indicated by the example in Chapter 9, in radio broadcasting maximum possible power is delivered by a modulated wave only on occasional momentary modulation peaks, and the unmodulated peak carrier voltage is half the maximum possible voltage. Thus, with a conventional type of amplifier, the average efficiency would be low, whereas the amounts of power involved are large. The Doherty amplifier resolves this difficulty by using one tube to deliver normal carrier power at high voltage and high efficiency. A second tube also operating efficiently supplies when needed the necessary additional voltage for the positive modulation peaks. An important feature of the operation is that, due to a special coupling network, as the modulation increases, the first tube works into a lower impedance and thereby delivers more power.

The action (Ref. 37) resembles that of an ordinary power system in which a generator G_1 is delivering power to a load at maximum voltage. To provide more voltage, a second generator G_2 would be put in series with G_1. This increases the load current, and since the currents are of the same frequency and phase, it reduces the impedance that G_1 faces. If both generator voltages are alike, G_1 operates into half its original impedance and delivers twice its original power although its voltage has not changed. G_2 delivers equal power and the total power is quadrupled.

In the case of a vacuum tube transmitter, parallel and not series operation is the desired embodiment. To achieve this, unaided by Tube 2, Tube 1 (Fig. 10–2) delivers unmodulated carrier to the load through a 90-degree, phase-shifting network. If R is the load resistance, the 90-degree network is terminated (Ref. 37) by $R\left(1 + \dfrac{P_2}{P_1}\right)$ where P_1 and P_2 are the instantaneous powers contributed by Tubes 1 and 2. Therefore, while Tube 2 is acting to supply power (Fig. 10–3) for the positive swings of modulation, the network termination increases from R to not more than $2R$. Since the inverting property of the 90-degree network acts like a $\lambda/4$ transmission line with an input impedance that is inversely proportional to its termination impedance, the impedance Tube 1 faces is lowered. Therefore, at the peak of a fully modulated wave, Tube 1 is enabled to increase its output power by a factor of two without increasing its voltage. Obviously the grid voltages should differ by 90 degrees as indicated in Fig. 10–2. It should be noted, as mentioned previously, that an amplifier of this type is not limited to the amplification of amplitude-modulated waves and, moreover, for multichannel services has all the important advantages that result from stabilized negative feedback around the high-power, radio-frequency stage. In addition it has the advantage of not requiring a modulation transformer. which in high-power installations is a large and expensive component.

TRANSMISSION DISTORTION

Since transmission distortion may affect different types of demodulators differently, it is desirable to look into the consequences of nonideal transmission media before considering the behavior of various kinds of demodulators. If we neglect nonlinear distortion, the residual distortion will take the familiar form, $Y(\omega) = |Y(\omega)|\epsilon^{i\psi(\omega)}$, of a magnitude-frequency characteristic and a phase-frequency characteristic. When the distortion is expressed as a complex function of frequency, it may be introduced analytically (Ref. 44, p. 452; Ref. 45, Ch. 10; and Ref. 46, p. 24) by multiplying it by the spectrum of the modulated wave. In practice, there are several ways of dealing with the spectrum of the modulating wave and evaluating the effects of transmission distortion.

Spectrum of the Modulating Wave

By the Fourier method, if $kV(t)$ is the modulating wave, its complex amplitude spectrum $C_v(\omega)$ is given by (9–5) as

$$C_v(\omega) = \int_{-\infty}^{\infty} kV(t)\epsilon^{-i\omega t}\, dt. \qquad (10\text{–}10)$$

Commonly referred to as the "direct" Fourier transform as well as the complex amplitude spectrum, this transform represents, strictly speaking, the complex amplitude-density spectrum, so-called because the term "density" recognizes that it is dimensionally "per cycle per second."

Spectrum of the Modulated Wave

Accordingly, the complex spectrum $C(\omega)$ of $\epsilon^{i\omega_c t}kV(t)$, which represents a nonphysical complex function of time, is given by

$$C_1(\omega) = \int_{-\infty}^{\infty} kV(t)\epsilon^{i\omega_c t}\epsilon^{-i\omega t}\, dt = C_v(\omega - \omega_c). \qquad (10\text{--}11)$$

Similarly, the complex spectrum $C_2(\omega)$ of another nonphysical complex function of time $\epsilon^{-i\omega_c t}kV(t)$ is $C_v(\omega + \omega_c)$.

Hence the complex spectrum $C_3(\omega)$ of $kV(t) \cos \omega_c t$, a physical function of time, is given by

$$C_3(\omega) = \tfrac{1}{2}[C_v(\omega - \omega_c) + C_v(\omega + \omega_c)]. \qquad (10\text{--}12)$$

Occasionally referred to as the "theorem of modulation," this is the usual Fourier representation, as a function of positive and negative values of ω, of the spectra of the products of modulation present in an amplitude-modulated wave. If $kV(t)$ is any even real function of time, its complex spectrum $C(\omega)$ is both a real and an even function of ω.

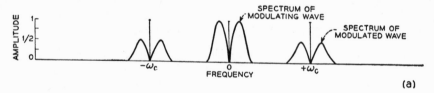

(a)

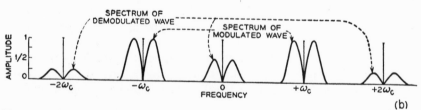

(b)

FIG. 10-4   Amplitude spectra of a modulating wave and the corresponding modulated and demodulated waves

Thus, if $M(t)$ is an amplitude-modulated wave and C_M its complex spectrum, we have

$$M(t) = A_c[1 + kV(t)] \cos (\omega_c t + \Phi_c) \qquad (9\text{--}1)$$

and

$$\begin{aligned}
C_M(\omega) = \tfrac{1}{2}A_c[&\epsilon^{i\Phi_c}\delta(\omega - \omega_c) + \epsilon^{-i\Phi_c}\delta(\omega + \omega_c) \\
&+ \epsilon^{i\Phi_c}C(\omega - \omega_c) + \epsilon^{-i\Phi_c}C(\omega + \omega_c)] \qquad (10\text{--}13)
\end{aligned}$$

In equation (10–13), $\delta(\omega - \omega_c)$ is an impulse of infinite amplitude and area 2π centered at ω_c, and $\delta(\omega + \omega_c)$ is a similar impulse centered at $-\omega_c$. Figure 10–4 indicates the real part of each spectrum. Situations will be encountered in which there are analytical advantages in considering both negative and positive frequencies, and similarly cases arise where it is simpler to consider only positive frequencies.

Other Representations

Several alternative representations are convenient and widely used. Common among them are two methods of representation. One is by the so-called "in phase" and "quadrature" components about the carrier or mid-band frequency. The other method is concerned essentially with a finite ensemble of sinusoids. With either of these procedures, it is often convenient to deal only with positive frequencies and introduce the conventional impedance concept.

In-Phase and Quadrature Components. If $Y_f = Y(\omega) = |Y_f|\epsilon^{i\Phi_f}$ represents the steady-state characteristic of a spectrum that is essentially limited to positive frequencies ranging from $f_c - B$ to $f_c + B$, the characteristic may be represented exactly by the sum of what have been termed its in-phase and quadrature components. Theoretically, there exist an infinite number of such representations. If restricted to distortion, a quadrature component represents a distortion component that is proportional to the unsymmetrical part of the received modulated wave about f_c. In order not to possess a quadrature component, the magnitude of the received wave must have even symmetry and its phase must have odd symmetry about the carrier frequency. This treatment is applicable to any spectrum. For example, the average powers of the in-phase and quadrature components of band-limited resistance noise are equal when considered as the sidebands of quadrature carriers the frequency of which is the mid-band frequency.

As another example, let us consider the in-phase and quadrature components that may be produced by transmitting an amplitude-modulated wave, $V(t) \cos \omega_c t$ over a line having a transmission function given by

$$G(\omega) = S_G(\omega)\epsilon^{i\Phi_G(\omega)}, \quad \omega > 0. \tag{10–14}$$

Here $S_G(\omega)$ represents the attenuation factor and $\Phi_G(\omega)$ the phase shift in radians.

Let $2C(\omega_v) = 2S(\omega_v)\epsilon^{i\Phi(\omega_v)}$ completely describe the spectrum of $V(t)$ where ω_v is restricted to positive values ranging from ω_1 to ω_2. The carrier frequency is regarded as positive and is assumed to be high enough so that the spectra of $V(t)$ and $M(t)$ do not overlap.

As a function of positive frequencies, the spectrum of the modulated wave may be represented by

$$C_M(\omega) = A_c \epsilon^{i\Phi_c} \delta(\omega - \omega_c) + A_c T_{x_1}(\omega_c + \omega_v) \epsilon^{i[\Phi_c + \Phi(\omega_v)]}$$
$$+ A_c T_{x_2}(\omega_c - \omega_v) \epsilon^{i[\Phi_c - \Phi(\omega_v)]}. \quad (10\text{–}15)$$

In this expression $T_{x_1}(\omega_c + \omega_v)$ is so defined as to assume the values $S(\omega_v)$ at angular frequencies $(\omega_c + \omega_v)$ and similarly $T_{x_2}(\omega_c - \omega_v)$ takes on the values $S(\omega_v)$ at frequencies $(\omega_c - \omega_v)$.

The effect of transmission is to change the spectrum to

$$C_R(\omega) = A_c S_G(\omega_c) \epsilon^{i[\Phi_c + \Phi_G(\omega_c)]} \delta(\omega - \omega_c)$$
$$+ A_c T_{x_1}(\omega_c + \omega_v) S_G(\omega_c + \omega_v) \epsilon^{i[\Phi_G(\omega_c + \omega_v) + \Phi_c + \Phi(\omega_v)]}$$
$$+ A_c T_{x_2}(\omega_c - \omega_v) S_G(\omega_c - \omega_v) \epsilon^{i[\Phi_G(\omega_c - \omega_v) + \Phi_c - \Phi(\omega_v)]}. \quad (10\text{–}16)$$

Naturally the argument of $S_G(\omega)$ and $\Phi_G(\omega)$ must be the angular frequency of each particular component that is being modified. Let

$$C_R(\omega) = C_c(\omega_c) + C_1(\omega_c + \omega_v) + C_2(\omega_c - \omega_v) \quad (10\text{–}16a)$$

where the terms on the right are given in detail by (10–16). C_1 and C_2 are the spectra of the upper and lower sidebands respectively.

Finally, consider the representation of these sidebands by their in-phase and quadrature components. Note first that, if a delayed but undistorted amplitude-modulated wave is demodulated by multiplying by twice the received carrier and the resulting product is filtered by an ideal filter, we obtain, except for a d-c component, a signal that is proportional to a delayed replica of $V(t)$.

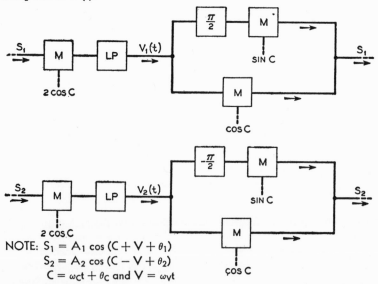

Fig. 10–5 A single sideband can be regarded as the sum of two pairs of in-phase and quadrature components

Note further that, in the absence of distortion, as the phase of the local carrier supplied to the product demodulator is altered, the output is merely attenuated without distortion. In fact, it is multiplied by cos Γ where Γ is the phase difference between the received carrier and the demodulator carrier supply. Of course, when $\Gamma = n\pi/2$, there is no output, and values of Γ other than zero impair the signal-to-noise ratio.

It is clear, therefore, that, if it is possible to produce $C_1 + C_2$ by the superposition of two amplitude-modulated sinusoidal carriers of the same frequency but in quadrature, then there will also exist an infinity of such representations. This follows because the essential requirement is the $\pi/2$ phase difference and not the values of the carrier phases.

For purposes of illustration, consider the in-phase and quadrature components of the sidebands of (10–16a) with respect to the received carrier. Let $E_c \cos(\omega_c t + \Phi_c)$ identify the amplitude, phase, and frequency of the received carrier. Let $V_1(t)$ be the result (after filtering) of demodulating the upper sideband alone by multiplying by $2 \cos(\omega_c t + \Phi_c)$. Similarly, as indicated in Fig. 10–5, let $V_2(t)$ be the result of demodulating the lower sideband alone in the same way. Analytically, $V_1(t)$ and $V_2(t)$ may be evaluated from the spectra $C_1(\omega)$ and $C_2(\omega)$.

Note further that causing $V_1(t)$ to amplitude-modulate $\cos(\omega_c t + \Phi_c)$ in a suppressed-carrier product-modulator and also letting $V_1(t)$, with all

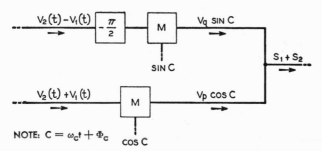

Fig. 10–6   Two sinusoids separate into in-phase and quadrature components of a carrier the frequency of which is the mean frequency of the sinusoids

of its components advanced in phase by $\pi/2$, similarly amplitude-modulate $\sin(\omega_c t + \Phi_c)$ results in the production of in-phase and quadrature components which, when added, give only the original upper sideband. This is indicated by the top diagram in Fig. 10–5. Similarly, as indicated by the bottom diagram in Fig. 10–5, if $V_2(t)$ amplitude-modulates $\cos(\omega_c t + \Phi_c)$, and $V_2(t)$, with all of its frequency components retarded in phase by $\pi/2$, amplitude-modulates $\sin(\omega_c t + \Phi_c)$; the sum of the four resulting sidebands, which also represents in-phase and quadrature components, gives only the original lower sideband.

Thus, if $[V_2(t) - V_1(t)] \left\lfloor -\frac{\pi}{2} \right.$ stands for $[V_2(t) - V_1(t)]$ after all its frequency components have been retarded in phase by $\pi/2$ radians,

$$[V_1(t) + V_2(t)] \cos (\omega_c t + \Phi_c) + \left([V_2(t) - V_1(t)] \left\lfloor -\frac{\pi}{2} \right.\right) \sin (\omega_c t + \Phi_c) \quad (10\text{--}17)$$

produces the desired in-phase and quadrature components with respect to $\cos (\omega_c t + \Phi_c)$. This result is illustrated by Fig. 10–6 and will be discussed further in the treatment of product demodulators.

The preceding treatment of in-phase and quadrature components was involved essentially because it elaborated upon the physical concepts. The analytical approach is short. Let $C \equiv \omega_c t$ and $V \equiv \omega_v t + \Phi_v$. Since superposition holds, consideration will be limited to an upper and lower sinusoidal sideband. Then,

$$\begin{aligned}
R(t) &= E_c \cos (C + \Phi_c) + A_1 \cos (C + V + \theta_1) + A_2 \cos (C - V + \theta_2) \\
&= [E_c + A_1 \cos (V - \Phi_c + \theta_1) + A_2 \cos (V + \Phi_c - \theta_2)] \cos (C + \Phi_c) \\
&\quad + [-A_1 \sin (V - \Phi_c + \theta_1) + A_2 \sin (V + \Phi_c - \theta_2)] \sin (C + \Phi_c) \\
&= [E_c + V_p(t)] \cos (C + \Phi_c) + V_q(t) \sin (C + \Phi_c) \quad (10\text{--}17a)
\end{aligned}$$

where $[E_c + V_p(t)]$ and $V_q(t)$ are the in-phase and quadrature components with respect to $\cos (C + \Phi_c)$.

Ensemble of Sinusoids. A usual procedure regards the modulating wave as an ensemble of sinusoids appropriate to a particular problem. The over-all result is then evaluated by modifying the components according to the various steady-state characteristics of the system. When modulation products coincide in frequency (as, for example, in the demodulation of the upper and lower sidebands of an amplitude-modulated wave or where overlapping spectra are involved), the additions obviously need to take into account the phases.

It is also significant to note that this general procedure may be justified by the sampling theorem. Suppose that B represents the significant frequency range of $g(t)$, and that T represents a period of time longer than a physical signal $g(t)$ endures. During this time, the signal can be represented by a series consisting of no more than $(BT + 1)$ sinusoids each of which has appropriate amplitude and phase, and, except for a d-c and fundamental component, each of which is a distinct harmonic of the fundamental frequency $1/T$. That the representation is periodic presents no formal difficulties. Let $C(\omega)$ be the spectrum of the signal. From the sampling theorem and the Fourier identity, sampling the direct transform $C(\omega)$ at regular intervals of $2\pi/T$ radians per second is sufficient to define $C(\omega)$ for all significant angular frequencies, and the discrete components defined by the particular ensemble of sinusoids are points on the spectrum of the signal. Moreover, this is the minimum number of samples of the spectrum and, hence, the minimum number of sinusoids if the signal is permitted to be arbitrary except as it is localized in time and frequency by the restrictions T and B.

DEMODULATORS

Demodulators, which could more appropriately be termed remodulators, provide means for recovering from the incoming modulated wave an approximation proportional to a delayed replica of the original modulating wave. Since amplitude modulation is essentially multiplication of the modulating wave by the carrier wave, it might be imagined that a natural method of recovery would be some process for dividing the modulated wave by the carrier. In applying such reasoning we must recognize certain difficulties. Because zero does not divide any number but itself, a determinate quotient would be sensitive to errors in the carrier phase, et cetera, to an utterly impractical degree. On the other hand, if we make the divisor nonzero, the process becomes essentially one of multiplication or remodulation.

Product Demodulators

$$V(t) \doteq C(\omega) \tag{10–18}$$

is a convenient convention for associating a time function with its amplitude-density function and vice versa. It implies that if either one is known the other can be determined. The right-hand side, for example, might represent the direct Fourier transform and in this case (10–18) would mean: $V(t)$ has $C(\omega)$ for its direct Fourier transform. For example,

$$V(t) \cos \omega_c t = M(t) \doteq \frac{1}{2} C(\omega \pm \omega_c). \tag{10–19}$$

Therefore, amplitude modulation may be regarded strictly as a frequency displacement effect (Fig. 10–4) in which the spectrum $C(\omega)$ of the modulating wave is replaced by two similar spectra. Each component of these spectra has half the magnitude of the corresponding element of the original spectrum and is shifted up or down in frequency by an amount equal to the carrier frequency.

If, before being modulated, the phase of the carrier is changed, the phases of all of the components of the modulated wave are changed by the same amount and in the same direction, viz.,

$$M(t) = V(t) \cos (\omega_c t + \Phi_c) \doteq \frac{1}{2} \epsilon^{-i\Phi_c} C(\omega + \omega_c) + \frac{1}{2} \epsilon^{i\Phi_c} C(\omega - \omega_c). \tag{10–19a}$$

Hence, there is no loss in essential generality in representing the original carrier by $\cos \omega_c t$.

If (10–19) is demodulated by multiplying by $\cos \omega_c t$, we have

$$M(t) \cos \omega_c t = D(t) \doteq \frac{1}{2} C(\omega) + \frac{1}{4} C(\omega \pm 2\omega_c). \tag{10–20}$$

Thus, in the absence of distortion, a repetition of the modulating process applied to the modulated wave produces (Fig. 10–4) two results. One is the recovery of a spectrum proportional to the original spectrum of the modulating wave. The other is a pair of spectra each of whose components is one-fourth the magnitude of the corresponding component of the original spectrum and moved up or down in frequency by twice the carrier frequency. If the carrier frequency is high enough, the spectra are sufficiently separated so that the modulating wave can be recovered by filtering.

Equation (10–20) ignored the received carrier. If this is represented by $\cos \omega_c t$, after demodulation $\cos \omega_c t$ becomes $\cos^2 \omega_c t$, which is equal to $\frac{1}{2} + \frac{1}{2} \cos 2\omega_c t$. Thus, the transmitted carrier adds a d-c term to the filtered output.

Transmission Distortion. Assume for purposes of illustration that the various spectra of interest do not overlap or fold back. Let $C_v = S_v \epsilon^{i\Phi_v}$ signify the value of the direct Fourier transform $C(\omega)$, expressed as a function of f_v, the positive cyclic frequency. That is, $C_v = C(2\pi f_v) = S(2\pi f_v)\epsilon^{i\Phi(2\pi f_v)}$ where f_v is restricted to positive values. Accordingly, $2C_v$ contributes a component, a differential component if the spectrum is continuous, of the form $2S_v \cos (\omega_v t + \Phi_v)$ to the time function (9–12a) which becomes

$$g(t) = 2 \int_{f_{v_1}}^{f_{v_2}} S_v \cos (\omega_v t + \Phi_v)\, df. \tag{10–21}$$

Here it is implied that the significant frequency components of $g(t)$ are limited to positive frequencies ranging from f_{v_1} to f_{v_2}. That is to say, the spectra of like positive and negative frequencies contribute equally to each sinusoidal component in (10–21) and hence it is enough to double the contributions arising from the positive spectra.

In order to treat the sidebands separately, we symbolically define $C(\omega_c + \omega_v) = [S_v \epsilon^{i\Phi_v}]_{c+v}$ where $\omega \equiv \omega_c + \omega_v$ restricts ω, and where the subscript, to be added when required for clarity, indicates the argument. Similarly, the spectrum of the lower sideband is represented symbolically by $C(\omega_c - \omega_v) = [S_v \epsilon^{-i\Phi_v}]_{c-v}$ where ω is defined by $\omega \equiv \omega_c - \omega_v$.

In terms of this symbolic notation we may write

$$C_v = \int_{-\infty}^{\infty} g(t)\epsilon^{-i\omega t}\, dt, \tag{10–22}$$

$$kV(t) \doteq 2C_v, \quad f > 0, \tag{10–23}$$

$$U(t) = \cos \omega_c t, \tag{10–24}$$

so that
$$M(t) = U(t)[1 + kV(t)], \tag{10-25}$$
where
$$C_{LS} = [C_v^*]_{c-v} \tag{10-26}$$
and
$$C_{US} = [C_v]_{c+v}. \tag{10-27}$$
Thus,
$$M(t) \doteq [1]_c + C_{LS} + C_{US}. \tag{10-28}$$

$M(t)$ is modified by distortion which is represented by
$$Y_f = |Y_f|\epsilon^{i\psi_f} \tag{10-29}$$
so that
$$R(t) \doteq Y_c + C_{c+v} + C_{c-v} \tag{10-30}$$
where
$$C_{c+v} \equiv C_v Y_{c+v} \tag{10-31}$$
and
$$C_{c-v} \equiv C_v^* Y_{c-v}. \tag{10-32}$$

In-Phase and Quadrature Spectra. The in-phase and quadrature components with respect to the received carrier constitute sideband components of quadrature carriers which, when superimposed, equal the received sidebands, viz.,

$$R(t) = [|Y_c| \cos(\omega_c t + \psi_c) + V_p(t) \cos(\omega_c t + \psi_c) + V_q(t) \sin(\omega_c t + \psi_c)]. \tag{10-33}$$

In this case,
$$V_p(t) \doteq C_v |Y_c| \left[\frac{Y_{c+v}}{Y_c} + \frac{Y_{c-v}^*}{Y_c^*} \right] \tag{10-34}$$
and
$$V_q(t) \doteq C_v |Y_c| \left[\frac{Y_{c+v}}{Y_c} - \frac{Y_{c-v}^*}{Y_c^*} \right] \epsilon^{i\frac{\pi}{2}} \tag{10-35}$$

so that the corresponding in-phase and quadrature components of the spectra of the upper and lower sidebands are

$$C_{c\pm v} = [C_{c\pm v}]_p + [C_{c\pm v}]_q \tag{10-36}$$
where
$$[C_{c\pm v}]_p = \frac{1}{2} C_v \left[Y_{c+v} + Y_{c-v}^* \frac{Y_c}{Y_c^*} \right]_{c+v} + \frac{1}{2} C_v^* \left[Y_{c+v}^* \frac{Y_c}{Y_c^*} + Y_{c-v} \right]_{c-v} \tag{10-37}$$
and
$$[C_{c\pm v}]_q = \frac{1}{2} C_v \left[Y_{c+v} - Y_{c-v}^* \frac{Y_c}{Y_c^*} \right]_{c+v} + \frac{1}{2} C_v^* \left[-Y_{c+v}^* \frac{Y_c}{Y_c^*} + Y_{c-v} \right]_{c-v}. \tag{10-38}$$

By adding the right-hand members of (10-37) and (10-38), we verify that the eight sidebands combine to give the two received sidebands.

Over-all Response. If a locally generated carrier $2 \cos(\omega_c t + \psi_c)$ is applied to an ideal product demodulator along with the received wave as given by (10-30), the output after filtering, as implied by (10-33) and

(10–34) or by (10–17a), will be $V_p(t) = V_1(t) + V_2(t)$ plus a d-c term. $V_1(t)$ is identified as the transmission and reception of the wanted signal over the upper sideband channel, and $V_2(t)$ as the transmission and reception of the same signal over the lower sideband channel. The spectra of $V_1(t)$ and $V_2(t)$ are given by (10–34). The d-c term is due to the product of the two carriers and, in this instance, is numerically equal to $|Y_c|$.

Suppose now the locally supplied carrier is shifted in phase θ radians. Then, as previously explained, the d-c component and the in-phase component $[V_1(t) + V_2(t)]$ are both multiplied by $\cos \theta$, and the quadrature component (previously missing when the received signal was demodulated by multiplying by the in-phase carrier) is multiplied by minus $\sin \theta$.

For purposes of illustration, assume the original modulating wave is represented as an ensemble of sinusoids, namely,

$$V = \sum 2a_v \cos (\omega_v t + \Phi_v)$$

where a_v, ω_v, and Φ_v are functions of frequency. Ideally, the received signal V_R would equal V. Actually, $V_R = H_v V + L_v V$. In this equation $H_v V$ represents demodulation of the received ensemble of sinusoidal waves transmitted over the upper sideband channel; $L_v V$, the result of demodulating the ensemble of sinusoidal waves received over the lower channel, assuming the locally supplied carrier is of the same frequency and phase as the received carrier. For example, H_v and L_v might be complex numbers that vary with frequency and represent complex operators of the familiar type. As the phase of the locally supplied carrier is varied,

$$V_R = [\text{d-c}] \cos \theta + \cos \theta (H_v + L_v) \sum a_v \cos (\omega_v t + \Phi_v)$$
$$- \sin \theta (L_v - H_v) \sum a_v \sin (\omega_v t + \Phi_v). \quad (10\text{–}39)$$

This illustrates the source of the name for the in-phase and quadrature representation suggested by Nyquist (Ref. 47, Appendix 5, pp. 636–639). Note also that the component frequencies of the modulated wave are inviolate as regards Y_f.

Basically the frequencies were inviolate because the transmitter and receiver were assumed not to be in relative motion. Were they moving toward or away from one another at an appreciable rate, the conditions would be different. In radio communication the Doppler effect could increase or decrease the frequency components of the received waves, and the duration of the received messages would be correspondingly shortened or lengthened.

Square-Law Demodulators

Essentially, a square-law demodulator is obtained by using a square-law modulator for demodulation. The square-law term is of the form $i(t) = Ke^2(t)$ and it will be convenient to ignore K. When nonlinearity is involved and new frequency components are generated, it becomes necessary to use appropriate time-function representations; whereas when a wave is modified by transmission, it is handy to use spectra.

The modulated wave is assumed to have been distorted by transmission and for purposes of analysis will be expressed in terms of its in-phase and quadrature components, viz.,

$$R(t) = [E_c \cos C + V_p(t) \cos C + V_q(t) \sin C] \qquad (10\text{–}40)$$

where C is identified with $(\omega_c t + \Phi_c)$, and V_p and V_q have their previous meaning. Thus,

$$D(t) = [E_c \cos C + V_p(t) \cos C + V_q(t) \sin C]^2$$

$$= \frac{E_c^2}{2} + \frac{E_c^2}{2} \cos 2C + \frac{1}{2} V_p^2(t) + \frac{1}{2} V_p^2(t) \cos 2C + \frac{1}{2} V_q^2(t)$$

$$- \frac{1}{2} V_q^2 \cos 2C + E_c V_p(t) + E_c V_p(t) \cos 2C + E_c V_q(t) \sin 2C$$

$$+ V_p(t) V_q(t) \sin 2C \qquad (10\text{–}41)$$

which, after filtering, leaves

$$E_c V_p(t) + \frac{1}{2} V_p^2(t) + \frac{1}{2} V_q^2(t), \qquad (10\text{–}41a)$$

assuming a sufficiently high carrier frequency and ignoring the zero frequency component.

The first term of (10–41a) is the desired signal, and the other two terms represent unwanted distortion. The two distortion terms yield a plurality of like frequency components, but ordinarily the contributions due to the quadrature products can be ignored. In this case, $2E_c/V_p(t)$ is the ratio of wanted signal to distortion. To make this ratio large we limit the percentage modulation. It is significant to note that the distortion is a continuous function of the percentage modulation.

With 100 per cent modulation, the peak distortion equals half the peak signal. A figure of one-fourth is sometimes quoted. This arises if the modulating wave is a single sinusoid and the d-c component of the distortion is disregarded. This, of course, is not generally valid when the modulating wave is complex.

By adding a synchronized local carrier of the proper phase, its amplitude can be made as large as the nonlinear element will tolerate, regardless of the value of the received carrier. By this means distortion introduced by this type of demodulator can be substantially reduced at the expense of complicating the receiver. Such an arrangement is known as an "enhanced carrier" receiver.

Rectifier Demodulator

This is a case of using a rectifier-type of modulator as a detector. As before, we will assume an ideal linear rectifier in series with a resistance R.

A generalized load impedance would lead to different results. To treat the simpler circuit, rewrite (10–40) in the form

$$R(t) = \sqrt{E_c^2 + 2E_c V_p(t) + V_p^2(t) + V_q^2(t)} \cos (C - \psi) \quad (10\text{–}42)$$

where

$$\psi = \tan^{-1} \frac{V_q(t)}{E_c + V_p(t)}.$$

The function under the radical is always positive. Angle modulation will not be contributed by the in-phase component if the quadrature component is zero. Therefore, if $Y(\omega)$ has the necessary symmetry around ω_c or if the quadrature component is unimportant for other reasons,

$$R(t) \rightarrow [E_c + V_p(t)] \cos C.$$

Under these circumstances, the desired result can be obtained by multiplying $R(t)/R \equiv gR(t)$ by a unit sampling function that is positive when the carrier is positive. Since the quadrature component is being ignored, represent $R(t)$ by $E_c[1 + kV_p(t)] \cos \omega_c t$. Then,

$$D(t) = E_c \cos \omega_c t [1 + kV_p(t)] \frac{g}{2} \sum_{-\infty}^{\infty} \frac{\sin \frac{m\pi}{2}}{\frac{m\pi}{2}} \cos m\omega_c t \quad (10\text{–}43)$$

which after filtering becomes $E_c \dfrac{g}{2} [1 + kV_p(t)]$. If the modulation is greater than one hundred per cent, additional reversals are introduced by the rectifier, and the filtered output is much the same as though the desired output $kV_p(t)$ were passed through a balanced rectifier.

Complete modulation is significant inasmuch as, with the assumptions made, no distortion is introduced until this point is reached. Enhanced carrier operation is particularly useful with this type of demodulator since, by its use, distortion due to overmodulation can be substantially eliminated with appropriate circuits.

Envelope Detector

So-called envelope detection is another way of using a rectifier as a demodulator. Envelope detection is only possible when the frequency of the carrier is a great deal higher than the highest significant frequency of the modulating wave. In an envelope detector, the load resistance is shunted by a capacitor the reactance of which at the carrier frequency is negligible compared to the resistance of the load. The capacitor acts to increase greatly the peaks of current, to store the resulting charge, and to allow it to leak off slowly during that portion of the carrier cycle that the rectifier is nonconducting. As a result, the voltage across the capacitor builds up to the peak of each carrier cycle and thus represents a good approximation to the envelope of the modulated wave.

Detailed analysis of the current wave that flows, or of the spectrum of the voltage across the load resistance, tends to get tedious and not to produce results in an interesting form. Results sufficient for most purposes materialize by merely noting that, as long as the applied wave is such that some current flows in each carrier cycle, then the voltage across the load resistance must pass through one point of the envelope for each carrier cycle. Accordingly we deduce from the sampling principle that any components of the output wave that differ significantly from corresponding components of the envelope must fall within or exceed the frequency range of the lower sideband of the carrier. Since the load is essentially short-circuited at the carrier frequency, and since the impedance of the capacitor is inversely proportional to frequency, it will be very low for any such distortion components and they will be negligible.

The problem becomes one of specifying the conditions that insure some current flow in the rectifier during each carrier cycle. Because of the inherent characteristics of a rectifier, the total instantaneous current entering the RC combination must be positive. In terms of our previous notation, if the voltage across the RC combination is assumed to equal the envelope of the modulated wave, the current is given by

$$\frac{E_c}{R} + \frac{V_p(t)}{R} + C\frac{d}{dt}V_p(t) > 0$$

or
$$E_c > V_p(t) + RC\frac{d}{dt}V_p(t), \tag{10-44}$$

provided the quadrature component can be ignored.

For example, if $V_p(t) = V\cos\omega_v t$, we must have

$$E_c > V\cos\omega_c t - RCV\omega_v\sin\omega_v t$$

for all values of t which, in turn, requires that

$$E_c > V\sqrt{1 + R^2C^2\omega_v^2}$$

and leads to the familiar result that the peak modulation factor must be less than the right member of

$$\frac{V}{E_c} = |kV(t)|_p < \frac{1}{\sqrt{1 + R^2C^2\omega_v^2}}. \tag{10-45}$$

References

1. Charles B. Aiken, "Theory of the Detection of Two Modulated Waves by a Linear Rectifier," *Proceedings of the Institute of Radio Engineers*, New York, Vol. 21, April 1933, pp. 601–629.
2. Stuart Ballantine, "Detection at High Signal Voltages: Plate Rectification with the High-Vacuum Triode," *Proceedings of the Institute of Radio Engineers*, New York, Vol. 17, July 1929, pp. 1153–1177.

3. Stuart Ballantine, "Detection by Grid Rectification with the High-Vacuum Triode," *Proceedings of the Institute of Radio Engineers*, New York, Vol. 16, May 1928, pp. 593–613.

4. J. R. Carson, "The Equivalent Circuit of the Vacuum Tube Modulator," *Proceedings of the Institute of Radio Engineers*, New York, Vol. 9, June 1921, pp. 243–249.

5. R. S. Caruthers, "Copper Oxide Modulators in Carrier Telephone Systems," *The Bell System Technical Journal*, New York, Vol. 18, April 1939, pp. 315–337.

6. E. L. Chaffee and G. H. Browning, "A Theoretical and Experimental Investigation of Detection for Small Signals," *Proceedings of the Institute of Radio Engineers*, New York, Vol. 15, February 1927, pp. 113–153.

7. B. Chance, V. Hughes, E. F. MacNichol, D. Sayre, and F. C. Williams, *Waveforms*, Radiation Laboratories Series, McGraw-Hill Book Co., Inc., New York, Vol. 19, 1949, Chs. 3, 9, 11, and 14.

8. H. Cheirex, "High-Power Outphasing Modulation," *Proceedings of the Institute of Radio Engineers*, New York, Vol. 23, 1935, pp. 1370–1392.

9. F. M. Colebrook, "The Frequency Analysis of the Heterodyne Envelope," *Wireless Engineer and Experimental Wireless*, London, Vol. 9, April 1932, pp. 195–201.

10. F. M. Colebrook, "The Rectification of Small Radio-Frequency Potential Differences by Means of Triode Valves," *Wireless Engineer and Experimental Wireless*, London, Vol. 2, December 1925, pp. 946–957.

11. F. M. Colebrook, "The Theory of the Straight-Line Rectifier," *Wireless Engineer and Experimental Wireless*, London, Vol. 7, 1930, pp. 595–603.

12. E. H. Colpitts and O. B. Blackwell, "Carrier Current Telephony and Telegraphy," *Transactions of the American Institute of Electrical Engineers*, New York, Vol. 40, 1921, pp. 205–300.

13. E. B. Craft and E. H. Colpitts, "Radio Telephony," *Transactions of the American Institute of Electrical Engineers*, New York, Vol. 38, 1919, pp. 305–343.

14. W. H. Doherty, "A New High-Efficiency Power Amplifier for Modulated Waves," *Proceedings of the Institute of Radio Engineers*, New York, Vol. 24, 1936, pp. 1163–1182.

15. R. B. Dome, "High Efficiency Modulating System," *Proceedings of the Institute of Radio Engineers*, New York, Vol. 26, 1938, pp. 963–982.

16. W. L. Everitt, *Communication Engineering*, Second Edition, McGraw-Hill Book Co., Inc., New York, 1937, pp. 530–545.

17. L. F. Gandernack, "A Phase-Opposition System of Amplitude Modulation," *Proceedings of the Institute of Radio Engineers*, New York, Vol. 26, August 1938, pp. 983–1008.

18. R. A. Heising, "Modulation in Radio Telephony," *Proceedings of the Institute of Radio Engineers*, New York, Vol. 9, August 1921, pp. 305–353.

19. E. W. Herold, "Superheterodyne Converter System Considerations in Television Receivers," *RCA Review*, New York, Vol. 4, January 1940, pp. 324–337.

20. E. W. Herold, "The Operation of Frequency Converters and Mixers for Superheterodyne Reception," *Proceedings of the Institute of Radio Engineers*, New York, Vol. 30, February 1942, pp. 84–103.

21. C. E. Kilgour and J. M. Glessner, "Diode Detector Analysis," *Proceedings of the Institute of Radio Engineers*, New York, Vol. 21, 1933, pp. 930–943.

22. A. W. Kishpaugh and R. E. Coram, "Low Power Radio Transmitters for Broadcasting," *Proceedings of the Institute of Radio Engineers*, New York, Vol. 21, 1933, pp. 212–227.

23. W. B. Lewis, "The Detector," *Wireless Engineer*, London, Vol. 9, 1932, pp. 487–499.
24. F. B. Llewellyn, "Operation of Thermionic Vacuum Tube Circuits," *The Bell System Technical Journal*, New York, Vol. 5, No. 3, July 1926, pp. 433–462.
25. Massachusetts Institute of Technology, Members of the Staff of the Department of Electrical Engineering, *Applied Electronics*, John Wiley and Sons, Inc., New York, 1943, Ch. 12, pp. 624–715.
26. W. N. Parker, "A Unique Method of Modulation for High-Fidelity Television Transmitters," *Proceedings of the Institute of Radio Engineers*, New York, Vol. 26, 1938, pp. 946–962.
27. Eugene Peterson and Clyde R. Keith, "Grid-Current Modulation," *The Bell System Technical Journal*, New York, Vol. 7, No. 1, January 1928, pp. 106–139.
28. E. Peterson and L. W. Hussey, "Equivalent Modulation Circuits," *The Bell System Technical Journal*, New York, Vol. 18, No. 1, January 1939, pp. 32–48.
29. E. Roberts, "Straight-Line Detection with Diodes," *Journal of the Institution of Electrical Engineers, Wireless Section*, London, Vol. 75, 1934, pp. 379–388.
30. H. A. Robinson, "An Experimental Study of the Tetrode as a Modulated Radio-Frequency Amplifier," *Proceedings of the Institute of Radio Engineers*, New York, Vol. 20, 1932, pp. 131–160.
31. M. J. O. Strutt, "On Conversion Detectors," *Proceedings of the Institute of Radio Engineers*, New York, Vol. 22, 1934, pp. 981–1008 (contains a bibliography of 89 references).
32. F. E. Terman, *Radio Engineers Handbook*, McGraw-Hill Book Co., Inc., New York, 1943, Sec. 7, pp. 531–588.
33. F. E. Terman, "Some Principles of Grid-Leak Grid-Condenser Detection," *Proceedings of the Institute of Radio Engineers*, New York, Vol. 16, October 1928, pp. 1384–1397.
34. F. E. Terman and R. R. Buss, "Some Notes on Linear and Grid-Modulated Radio-Frequency Amplifiers," *Proceedings of the Institute of Radio Engineers*, New York, Vol. 29, March 1941, pp. 104–107.
35. F. E. Terman and T. M. Googin, "Detection Characteristics of Three-Element Vacuum Tubes," *Proceedings of the Institute of Radio Engineers*, New York, Vol. 17, January 1929, pp. 149–160.
36. F. E. Terman and N. R. Morgan, "Some Properties of Grid-Leak Power Detections," *Proceedings of the Institute of Radio Engineers*, New York, Vol. 18, 1930, pp. 2160–2175.
37. F. E. Terman and J. R. Woodyard, "A High-Efficiency Grid-Modulated Amplifier," *Proceedings of the Institute of Radio Engineers*, New York, Vol. 26, August 1938, pp. 929–945.
38. A. W. Vance, "A High Efficiency Modulating System," *Proceedings of the Institute of Radio Engineers*, New York, Vol. 27, 1939, pp. 506–511.
39. Balth. van der Pol, "The Effect of Regeneration on the Received Signal Strength," *Proceedings of the Institute of Radio Engineers*, New York, Vol. 17, February 1929, pp. 339–346.
40. T. E. Shea, W. Herriott and W. R. Goehner, "The Principles of the Light Valve," *Journal of the Society of Motion Picture Engineers*, Vol. 18, June 1932, pp. 697–730.
41. F. G. Dunnington, "The Electro-optical Shutter — Its Theory and Technique," *Physical Review*, Vol. 38, October 15, 1931, pp. 1506–1534.
42. R. O. Grisdale, "Silicon Carbide Varistors," *Bell Laboratories Record*, New York, Vol. 19, No. 2, October 1940, pp. 46–51.

43. H. A. Reise and A. A. Skene, United States Patent 2,226,258, December 24, 1940.
44. Wilbur R. LePage and Samuel Seely, *General Network Analysis*, McGraw-Hill Book Co., Inc., New York, 1952, Ch. 13.
45. Hugh Hildreth Skilling, *Transient Electric Currents*, McGraw-Hill Book Co., Inc., New York, 1952, Ch. 10.
46. George A. Campbell and Ronald M. Foster, "Fourier Integrals for Practical Applications," American Telephone and Telegraph Company, New York, 1942, pp. 1–30. This printing includes 763 pairs, that is, direct and indirect transforms, and replaces an earlier publication in *The Bell System Technical Journal*, New York, Vol. 7, No. 4, October 1928, pp. 639–707.
47. H. Nyquist, "Certain Topics in Telegraph Transmission Theory," *Transactions of the American Institute of Electrical Engineers*, New York, Vol. 47, April 1928, pp. 617–644.

Problems

1. Show that $\cos^k x = 2^{-k} \sum_{l=0}^{k} \binom{k}{l} \cos (k - 2l)x$ where k is any positive integer.

2. Evaluate $\int_{-\infty}^{\infty} [A(\omega) \sin \omega t + B(\omega) \cos \omega t]\, d\omega$ where $A(\omega)$ and $-B(\omega)$ are the real and imaginary parts of the direct Fourier transform of a real function of a real variable.

3. Show that a pair of equal positive and negative values of ω in cas ωt corresponds to a pair of components that vary as the sine and cosine respectively of the same angle.

4. If $g(t) = \dfrac{1}{L} \epsilon^{-\frac{Rt}{L}}$ for $t > 0$ and equals zero for all negative values of t, show that $C(\omega)$, the direct Fourier transform of $g(t)$, is given by $C(\omega) = \dfrac{1}{R + iL\omega}$.

5. Given $C(\omega) = \dfrac{1}{R + iL\omega}$, obtain the inverse Fourier transform, $g(t)$, by evaluating by contour integration the infinite integral $\dfrac{1}{2\pi} \int_{-\infty}^{\infty} C(\omega) \epsilon^{i\omega t}\, d\omega$.

6. If $C_v(\omega) = \int_{-\infty}^{\infty} kV(t) \epsilon^{-i\omega t}\, dt$ is the complex amplitude-density spectrum of $kV(t)$, express the complex amplitude-density spectrum of $kV(t) \sin \omega_c t$ in terms of $C_v(\omega \pm \omega_c)$.

7. A receiving system is arranged as follows:

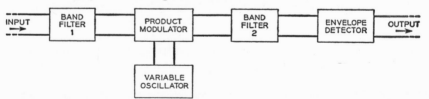

Band filter 1 transmits unchanged, except for delay, all frequency components between 500 and 1,500 kilocycles per second. Band filter 2 similarly transmits freely and without distortion all frequency components in a band 10 kilocycles per second wide and effectively suppresses all others. The input wave is a series of amplitude-modulated carriers spaced 10 kilocycles per second apart between 500 and 1,500 kilocycles per second. Each channel transmits the carrier and both sidebands.   The variable oscillator covers a continuous band of frequencies.

(a) What is the range of permissible values of the mid-band frequency of band filter 2 in order that any desired channel may be selected by varying the frequency of the variable frequency oscillator?   Assume ideal filters, a perfect product modulator, and a perfect envelope detector.

(b) For any chosen position setting of mid-band frequency of band filter 2 within the permissible range defined by (a): What is the required range of frequencies of the variable oscillator in order that each channel may be selected individually?

8. What is the complex amplitude-density spectrum of a pulse the magnitude of which is unity from $t = -t_0/2$ to $t = t_0/2$ and zero for all other times?   Express the transform as a function of f/f_0 where $f_0 = 1/t_0$.

9. The two Fourier integrals are usually written in the form

$$g(t) = \int_{-\infty}^{\infty} C(\omega)\epsilon^{i\omega t}\, df \quad \text{and} \quad C(\omega) = \int_{-\infty}^{\infty} g(t)\epsilon^{-i\omega t}\, dt$$

so that upon combining the two integrals, we have

$$g(t) = \int_{-\infty}^{\infty}\int_{-\infty}^{\infty} \epsilon^{i\omega(t-\lambda)}g(\lambda)\, d\lambda\, df.$$

Prove Fourier's fundamental discovery that the two functions in the Fourier integral representation may be transposed, provided the sign of one of the parameters is reversed, that is,

$$g(-t) = \int_{-\infty}^{\infty} C(\omega)\epsilon^{-i\omega t}\, df \quad \text{and} \quad C(-\omega) = \int_{-\infty}^{\infty} g(t)\epsilon^{i\omega t}\, dt.$$

10. What are the in-phase and quadrature components of

$$E_1 \cos\left[(\omega_c + \omega_v)t + \theta_1\right] \text{ and } E_2 \cos\left[(\omega_c - \omega_v)t + \theta_2\right]$$

with respect to $E_c \cos \omega_c t$?

11. If $R(t) = E_c \cos(\omega_c t + \Phi_c) + \sum_{j=1}^{M} a_{v_j} \cos\left[(\omega_c + \omega_{v_j})t + \Phi_{v_j}\right]$

$$+ \sum_{j=1}^{M} b_{u_j} \cos\left[(\omega_c - \omega_{u_j})t + \Phi_{u_j}\right],$$

what are the in-phase and quadrature time functions of $R(t)$ with respect to $\sin \omega_c t$?

12. On pages 13 and 14 of Reference 46 are listed twenty-one elementary properties of Fourier transforms.   As typical illustrations show that: If $g(t)$ is real and its direct Fourier transform $C(\omega)$ is pure imaginary or vice versa, then both are odd.   If both are real, both are even.   If one is even and real, both are even and real.   If one is odd and real, the other is odd and pure imaginary and vice versa.   If one is real, the other has conjugate values for opposite values of its parameter and conversely.

13. If $g(t) = \dfrac{1}{L}\epsilon^{-\frac{Rt}{L}}$, $t>0$, and $g(t) = 0$ for $t<0$, then $C(\omega) = \dfrac{R}{R^2+L^2\omega^2} - i\dfrac{L\omega}{R^2+L^2\omega^2}$.   Specify by inspection and verify by integration, two formulas for two time functions the complex amplitude-density functions of which are $\dfrac{R}{R^2 + L^2\omega^2}$ and $-i\dfrac{L\omega}{R^2 + L^2\omega^2}$, respectively.

CHAPTER 11

AMPLITUDE–MODULATION SYSTEMS

The transmission properties of different systems of amplitude modulation are usually different. In considering these differences, it will be assumed that the terminals are not in relative motion and that there is no change in frequency introduced by variations in the transmission path.

CARRIER AND BOTH SIDEBANDS

The oldest and best-known type of system transmits the carrier and both sidebands. This often makes for maximum simplicity and economy, particularly at low power outputs.

With a system of this type, the ratio of average carrier power to average power in both sidebands equals the ratio of peak to average power in the modulating wave. Examples were cited (Chap. 9) to show that this ratio may and does reach extremely high values for familiar kinds of modulating waves. When, under these conditions, it is necessary to transmit the carrier and both sidebands at high power, there is no recourse but to place the emphasis on high-efficiency, high-power systems. Systems in this category were discussed in Chapter 10.

However, in many fields and for many types of communication networks these factors do not dominate. For such applications various systems have been devised with the object of reducing the carrier or saving band width, or both.

REDUCED CARRIER

Reduced carrier has the obvious disadvantage that most types of demodulators produce serious distortion if the modulation is allowed to exceed one hundred per cent. Some types do so even for much lower percentages.

As mentioned in Chapter 10, this effect can be minimized or even eliminated by the process of enhancing the carrier at the receiving end. Consequently, it is only necessary to transmit enough carrier so that, at the receiver, the carrier can be selected and utilized to control the frequency and phase of a strong, locally generated carrier. Accordingly, the problem of transmitting the carrier essentially reduces to one of economics.

In point-to-point communications, where there is one transmitter for each receiver, substantial complication in the receiving equipment can be justified, provided it leads to large enough savings in expensive, high-power transmitting equipment. On the other hand, for a broadcast system with its many receivers for each transmitter, the economic argument is reversed.

SINGLE SIDEBAND

The essential function of a single-sideband system is to translate the spectrum of the modulating wave, with or without inversion, to a new location in the frequency domain. By the transmission of only a single sideband, band-width occupancy is halved. This accounts (Refs. 1 to 7)* for the popularity of such systems. Its principal field of application is where band width is at a premium.

Compared with double-sideband systems, a single-sideband system has the additional advantage that changes in carrier phase at the demodulator affect the phases but not the amplitudes of the spectral components of the recovered signal. For some applications this would be a disadvantage because changes in the phase of the demodulator carrier would alter the wave form of the recovered signal. In monaural telephone systems and systems for the high-quality reproduction of music, certain types of phase distortion may be ignored. Such distortion is only noticeable when it tends to spread in time the components of sharp sounds. Then the plosives in speech are dulled, and the percussion sounds of music lack crispness.

In multichannel, single-sideband, carrier-suppression systems, a common practice in both open-wire and cable carrier applications has been to generate the modulator and demodulator carriers locally with independent oscillators. Although these oscillators are very stable, they are not synchronized. Lack of synchronization produces a slight shift in the frequency of each spectral component but has little effect on the envelope of the derived modulating wave. These effects can be tolerated because, in ordinary telephony, phase and exact frequency relationships are relatively unimportant. On the other hand, the relation between the amplitudes of the various frequency components of the modulating wave constitutes much of the signal information. This relationship, therefore, is extremely important and must be substantially unchanged by the processes of modulation, transmission, and demodulation.

Methods of Generating Single Sideband

The better-known methods of generating a single sideband fall into two general classes which will be termed "frequency discrimination" and "phase discrimination."

---

* The references cited are listed at the end of each chapter according to the number used in the text.

Frequency Discrimination. Frequency-discrimination methods may be applied when the band of significant frequencies in the modulating wave is restricted and when the frequency of the carrier is appropriately related to that band. Under these conditions the desired sideband will appear in a nonoverlapping interval in the spectrum so that it may be selected by an appropriately chosen filter. Thus, a single-sideband modulator consists basically of a suitable amplitude modulator followed by a filter capable of passing the desired sideband and attenuating all other components sufficiently to meet the requirements of the system.

The most severe requirement usually stems from the unwanted sideband the nearest component of which is separated from the wanted sideband by twice the lowest frequency of the modulating wave. This means a separation of only 400 cycles per second in ordinary telephony, and only 40 cycles per second if the modulating wave comes from a high-quality program channel.

The latter in particular constitutes a very stringent requirement. It is often necessary in practical systems to resort to a multiple-modulation process in which the first carrier frequency is so chosen as to place a practical type of highly discriminating filter in its optimum frequency range. The output of this filter goes to a second modulator supplied with a carrier frequency that is so chosen as to place the selected sideband in the desired interval for transmission over the medium. By this process, the separation between the wanted and unwanted sidebands at the final filter can be increased from tens or hundreds of cycles to thousands of cycles per second.

A good example of such a system is a typical twelve-channel terminal of the type described in Reference 1. The frequency allocation, both for the original modulation and the spectrum applied to the line, is shown in Fig. 11–1. The original carrier frequencies range from 64 to 108 kilocycles per second because within this range crystal filters of the necessary discrimination can be built economically. The final carrier frequencies were fixed by the crosstalk and attenuation characteristics of the high-frequency medium. Figure 11–2 is a block diagram of a twelve-channel, cable-carrier terminal of this type.

The ability of a single-sideband modulator to shift a signal from one frequency band to another is of fundamental importance. For example, with appropriate changes in the group modulator, the above-mentioned, twelve-channel, cable-carrier terminal has also been used for open-wire carrier systems. Moreover, it is currently used (Ref. 2) as a basic building block to form more complex terminals, each capable of applying large numbers of channels to a single coaxial cable.

Phase Discrimination. This method of producing a single sideband was suggested by Hartley (Ref. 8) many years ago. Hartley's suggestion in effect envisions the application of equal parts of $2V(t)$, the modulating wave, to product-modulators. In the first, $V(t)$ is caused to modulate $\cos \omega_c t$. In the second, the phase of each component of $V(t)$ is retarded 90 degrees and caused to modulate $\sin \omega_c t$. The outputs of the two modulators are superimposed, with the result that their sum is the lower sideband only. If the sign of the second carrier is reversed, only the upper sideband is produced.

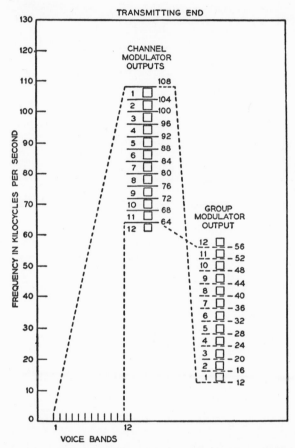

FIG. 11–1 Frequency allocation used in a twelve-channel, carrier telephone terminal

To explain the method of operation, consider the product $[V(t) \cos \omega_c t]$ which is equal to the sum of equal upper and lower sidebands around the carrier, $\cos \omega_c t$. We recall that, if the phase of the carrier is advanced by an amount Φ, the phase of all components of both sidebands advances by Φ. Similarly, if the phase of each component of $V(t)$ is advanced θ, the phase of each component of the upper sideband is advanced θ and the phase of each component of the lower sideband is retarded by θ.

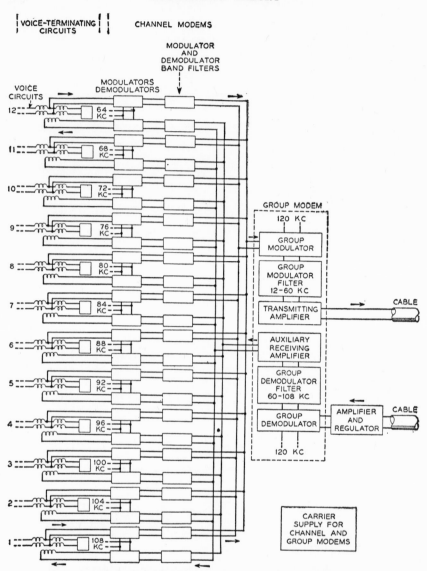

FIG. 11-2　Block diagram of a twelve-channel, carrier telephone terminal

Therefore, with reference to the phases in the output of the first modulator, if the components of the modulating wave and carrier associated with the second modulator are each retarded or each advanced 90 degrees, the phases of all components of the upper sideband are changed 180 degrees, whereas the phases of all components of the lower sideband are unaltered.　Similarly, if the components of the modulating wave are advanced and the carrier retarded by 90 degrees or vice versa, the phases of all lower sideband components are reversed and those of the upper sideband are unchanged.

In terms of our previous terminology, the in-phase spectrum of the sidebands is even and symmetrical about the carrier frequency. Similarly, the quadrature spectrum is odd and antisymmetrical. Thus, their superposition in equal amounts eliminates one of the sidebands.

In practice, to produce a single sideband in this manner, part of the modulating wave (Fig. 11–3) goes directly to a modulator. An equal part

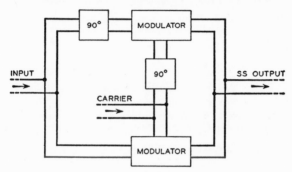

Fig. 11–3   Block diagram of a phase-discrimination, single-sideband modulator

is applied to a second modulator through an all-pass network having a constant phase-shift of 90 degrees over the band of frequencies in which the modulating wave has significant components. Carrier waves are applied to the two modulators in quadrature. The outputs of the two modulators are added or subtracted, depending on whether a lower or upper sideband is wanted. For a carrier suppression system, the modulators would be balanced.

Such a system does not require high degrees of discrimination over narrow-frequency intervals at high frequencies. It does, as originally proposed, require a network having a constant phase shift of 90 degrees and constant loss over the frequency range of the modulating wave. To approximate the desired result physically (Refs. 9 and 10), the modulating wave is passed through two networks having phase shifts that differ by 90 degrees over the frequency range of interest while the attenuation difference is substantially constant. Obviously, single-sideband demodulators (Refs. 11 and 12) can be obtained by the application of these same principles.

A high-quality 15-kilocycle-per-second program channel recently developed (Ref. 13) affords an example of such a system. In this case uniform transmission was desired for audio frequencies as low as 20 cycles per second. Thus, whereas the separation of the unwanted and wanted sidebands is only 40 cycles per second, a high degree of suppression of the unwanted sideband was required in order to prevent interference with other channels on the same system and vice versa. In this instance it proved more economical to produce the necessary phase-shifting networks than to build conventional filters.

With ordinary filters the discrimination can be increased by increasing the number of sections. With phase-shifting networks, the suppression of the unwanted sideband is limited by unavoidable variations in the networks, et cetera. Reference 14 illustrates a scheme for cascading 90-degree, phase-shift networks whereby in two steps, for example, the decibel discrimination is doubled, other factors being equal.

Limitations of Single-Sideband Systems

Low-Frequency Limit. As the lowest significant frequency of the modulating wave is reduced, it becomes increasingly difficult by either method to suppress the adjacent portion of the unwanted sideband. Obviously it is not possible to generate a single sideband when the spectrum of the modulating wave includes significant components to and including zero frequency. There must always be some lower limit to the frequency of the modulating wave if the system is to operate properly. The exact location of this limit will depend upon practical considerations, but for either generating method it must always exist and must always be greater than zero.

Delay Limit. Not so obvious is the delay inherent to the production of a single sideband. In a practical system this delay may be important. This is especially true when the signal is demodulated and remodulated in each link of a multilink system.

In a frequency-discrimination system it is possible to make a plausible estimate of the order of magnitude of this delay. The phase shift through any filter section changes at least 90 degrees in crossing the band from the lower cutoff frequency to the upper cutoff. Therefore, the average delay per section is at least

$$\tau_s = \frac{\pi}{2(\omega_2 - \omega_1)} \text{ seconds per section.} \tag{11-1}$$

Furthermore, the discrimination between a frequency within the band and one a given distance outside the band is approximately inversely proportional to the ratio of the band width of the filter to the distance from the outside frequency to cutoff. Thus, for a specified discrimination between the wanted and unwanted sidebands, the number of sections n must be proportional to this ratio. Multiplying this number of sections by the average delay per section gives

$$\tau = n\tau_s = K \frac{\omega_2 - \omega_1}{2\omega_1} \frac{\pi}{2(\omega_2 - \omega_1)} = \frac{K}{8f_1} \tag{11-2}$$

where $\frac{\omega_2}{2\pi}$ and $\frac{\omega_1}{2\pi}$ are the highest and lowest modulating frequencies and K is a constant determined by the required suppression of the unwanted sideband. When $2\omega_1 \gg \omega_2 - \omega_1$, K takes on its lowest value, which is unity. As ω_1 decreases or $\omega_2 - \omega_1$ increases, K increases so that certainly the delay will be at least $1/8f_1$.

Correspondingly, in a phase-discrimination system where 90-degree phase difference in the modulating waves applied to the two modulators is realized by the methods described in Reference 10, as f_1 becomes low enough and successively takes on lower and lower values; more and more sections have to be added and therefore more and more delay is added by the phase-shifting networks. By following this particular instrumentation, the delay will be no less than the $1/8f_1$ discussed above.

VESTIGIAL SIDEBAND

As a means of reducing delay and easing network requirements, Nyquist (Refs. 15 and 16) made the suggestion that, when the modulating wave contains significant components at extremely low frequencies, it is not necessary to suppress the unwanted sideband completely, but merely to attenuate it. If the shape of the characteristic $Y(\omega)$, which modifies the two sidebands represented by $[kV(t) \cos \omega_c t]$, satisfies certain requirements and if the demodulator is of the product type, the modulating wave will be recovered without distortion. The result is a vestigial-sideband system. Such systems are similar to single-sideband systems, except in a restricted region around the carrier frequency. Here a residual portion of both the wanted and unwanted sidebands is transmitted in such proportions that the required filters can be physically realized and the desired output obtained from the system. Clearly, the delay limitation inherent to this type of system is not likely to be serious.

If Y_f is the over-all admittance transfer factor, from equations (10–33) and (10–34), it follows that the foregoing requirement for a vestigial-sideband system is

$$C_v |Y_c| \left[\frac{Y_{c+v}}{Y_c} + \frac{Y_{c-v}^*}{Y_c^*} \right] = K \lfloor f_v \theta \qquad (11\text{-}3)$$

where K, and θ are independent of f_v, where $Y_{c\pm v}$ is the complex admittance transfer factor at the cyclic frequencies $f_c + f_v$ and $f_c - f_v$, respectively, and where C_v is defined on page 158 of Chapter 10. Reference 17 should be consulted for a detailed analysis of the transmission features of asymmetric-sideband networks.

In television systems where vestigial sidebands are most frequently encountered, product demodulators are not employed, principally for economic reasons. Instead, envelope detectors are used. It is, therefore, of interest to consider the distortion introduced by an envelope detector.

The action of an envelope detector produces an output proportional to the envelope of the applied wave, provided the restrictions mentioned in Chapter 10 are met. The input wave (Chap. 10) may be written as proportional to

$$R(t) = [E_c + V_p(t)] \cos (\omega_c t + \psi_c) + V_q(t) \sin (\omega_c t + \psi_c)$$

$$= \sqrt{[E_c + V_p(t)]^2 + V_q{}^2(t)} \cos \left[\omega_c t + \psi_c - \tan^{-1} \frac{V_q(t)}{E_c + V_p(t)} \right]. \quad (11\text{-}4)$$

Since angle modulation does not affect the envelope, the output of the envelope detector is closely proportional to

$$i(t) = [E_c + V_p(t)] \sqrt{1 + \frac{V_q{}^2(t)}{[E_c + V_p(t)]^2}}. \quad (11\text{-}5)$$

Distortion is contributed by the quadrature component and can be reduced by reducing the percentage modulation. The magnitude of $V_q(t)$ can also be controlled by changing the width of the vestigial sideband. If the vestigial sideband is increased to the width of a full sideband, the received wave becomes a symmetrical double-sideband wave with the result that $V_p(t) = kV(t)$, and $V_q(t)$ vanishes. Hence, the wider the vestigial sideband, the smaller $V_q(t)$. Both methods of reducing the distortion are used.

In standard television broadcasting, power is at a premium and frequency space is scarce. The vestigial sideband has a width of about 0.75 megacycle per second, or about one-sixth of a full sideband. This has been determined empirically as the width of vestigial sideband required to keep the distortion within tolerable limits when the carrier is nearly one hundred per cent modulated.

DAY'S SYSTEM

The purpose of using single sideband is to conserve frequency space. This may be accomplished equally well if in some manner we can superpose two modulating waves in the same portion of the spectrum and still recover the individual modulating waves.

A method of accomplishing this saving in frequency space was proposed by A. V. T. Day (Ref. 18) and R. V. L. Hartley independently and at about the same time. Use is made of quadrature carriers. Each carrier is amplitude-modulated by a separate and different modulating wave. The two modulated waves are added and applied to the transmitting medium. At the receiver, the transmitted wave is applied to a pair of product demodulators. Each demodulator is supplied with a carrier in phase with the corresponding component of the received carrier.

If we assume an ideal transmitting medium, the received wave can be represented by

$$R(t) = \sqrt{2} \cos\left(\omega_c t - \frac{\pi}{4}\right) + V_1(t) \cos \omega_c t + V_2(t) \sin \omega_c t \qquad (11\text{–}6)$$

where $V_1(t)$ and $V_2(t)$ are the two modulating waves.

When this wave is applied to two product demodulators supplied with carrier waves $E_c \cos \omega_c t$ and $E_c \sin \omega_c t$, respectively, the corresponding outputs after filtering will be

$$i_1(t) = \frac{1}{2} E_c[1 + V_1(t)]$$

and
$$i_2(t) = \frac{1}{2} E_c[1 + V_2(t)]. \qquad (11\text{–}7)$$

Thus, the two different modulating waves are recovered without crosstalk and distortion, thereby permitting full use of the information-carrying capacity of the occupied portion of the medium.

In principle this would permit full utilization of the available frequency space. In practice the situation is not so favorable. For example, it was assumed that the local carriers were of the right phase. Suppose they had been in error by an amount Φ. For either channel, the desired signal represents an in-phase component and the unwanted signal appears as a quadrature component. Therefore (Chap. 10, p. 160), the desired signal is multiplied by $\cos \Phi$ and the unwanted signal by $\sin \Phi$. The ratio of crosstalk to signal is $\tan \Phi$. This is expressed in decibels as a function of Φ in Fig. 11–4. If a crosstalk-to-signal ratio of 60 decibels is required,

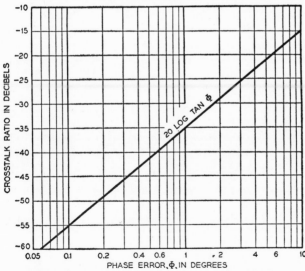

FIG. 11–4 Crosstalk as a function of the error in carrier phase for a quadrature-modulation system

which is not unusual, the phase of each local carrier must be maintained to within 1/20 degree of its desired value.

Although this represents a very stringent requirement, it presumably could be satisfied, given a suitable transmitting medium and the absence of instrumentation cost as a controlling factor. However, this is not the only factor. The two sidebands of each modulated wave will be slightly distorted as a result of transmission imperfections, and the resultant quadrature components (Chap. 10) will appear as interchannel crosstalk. To suppress these unwanted components to the extent implied by a 60-decibel crosstalk requirement would be difficult, except with an unusually favorable medium.

Conditions are more favorable for the transmission of binary digits. In this case the total of all interference can be just short of the magnitude of the wanted signal. Consequently the requirements are relaxed and the problems of instrumentation are reasonably straight forward. Such a system has the advantage of passing very low modulating frequencies, even including zero if appropriately organized.

The Day system is an example of what is commonly known as phase-discrimination multiplexing. The method, as pointed out in Chapter 5, is not limited to two channels but may include any number. Moreover, it is interesting to note that the two channels are not separated in either frequency or time. Each modulating wave may utilize all of its assigned frequency range all of the time. Furthermore, each modulating wave may or may not be quantized.

References

1. R. W. Chesnut, L. M. Ilgenfritz, and A. Kenner, "Cable Carrier Telephone Terminals," *The Bell System Technical Journal*, New York, Vol. 17, January 1938, pp. 106–124.
2. R. E. Crane, J. T. Dixon, and G. H. Huber, "Frequency Division Techniques for a Coaxial Cable Network," *Transactions of the American Institute of Electrical Engineers*, New York, Vol. 66, 1947, pp. 1451–1458.
3. R. A. Heising, "Production of Single Sideband for Trans-Atlantic Radio Telephony," *Proceedings of the Institute of Radio Engineers*, New York, Vol. 13, June 1925, pp. 291–312.
4. A. A. Oswald, "Short-Wave Single-Sideband Radio-Telephone System," *Proceedings of the Institute of Radio Engineers*, New York, Vol. 26, December 1938, pp. 1431–1454.
5. F. A. Polkinghorn and N. F. Schlaack, "A Single Sideband Short Wave System for Trans-Atlantic Radio Telephony," *Proceedings of the Institute of Radio Engineers*, New York, Vol. 19, April 1940, pp. 306–335.
6. N. F. Schlaack and A. C. Dickieson, "Cape Charles-Norfolk Ultra-Short Wave Multiplex System," *Proceedings of the Institute of Radio Engineers*, New York, Vol. 33, February 1945, pp. 78–83.
7. B. Lenehan, "A New Single-Sideband Carrier System for Power Lines," *Transactions of the American Institute of Electrical Engineers*, New York, Vol. 66, June 1947, pp. 826–830.

8. R. V. L. Hartley, United States Patent No. 1,666,206, April 17, 1928.
9. R. B. Dome, "Wide-Band Phase-Shift Networks," *Electronics*, New York, N. Y., Vol. 19, December 1946, pp. 112–115.
10. S. Darlington, "Realization of a Constant Phase Difference," *The Bell System Technical Journal*, New York, Vol. 29, No. 1, January 1950, pp. 94–104.
11. O. G. Villard, Jr., "Simplified Single Sideband Reception," *Electronics*, New York, Vol. 21, May 1948, pp. 82–85.
12. E. I. Green, United States Patent No. 2,020,409, November 12, 1935.
13. G. H. Huber, "A 15–KC Carrier Program Channel," *Bell Laboratories Record*, New York, Vol. 27, July 1949, pp. 251–254.
14. Oswald G. Villard, Jr., "Cascade Connection of 90 Degree Phase Shift Networks," *Proceedings of the Institute of Radio Engineers*, New York, Vol. 40, No. 3, March 1952, pp. 334–337.
15. H. Nyquist, "Certain Topics in Telegraph Transmission Theory," *Transactions of the American Institute of Electrical Engineers*, New York, Vol. 47, April 1928, pp. 617–644.
16. H. Nyquist and K. W. Pfleger, "Effect of the Quadrature Component in Single-Sideband Transmission," *The Bell System Technical Journal*, New York, Vol. 19, January 1940, pp. 63–73.
17. E. Colin Cherry, "The Transmission Characteristics of Asymmetric-Sideband Communication Networks," *The Journal of the Institution of Electrical Engineers*, London, Vol. 89, Part 3, 1942, pp. 19–42; Vol. 90, Part 3, 1943, pp. 75–88.
18. A. V. T. Day, United States Patent No. 1,885,010, October 25, 1932.

Problems

1. If $R(t) = S_1 \cos [(\omega_c + \omega_v)t + \theta_1] + S_2 \cos [(\omega_c - \omega_v)t + \theta_2]$, express $R(t)$ as the sum of two pairs of sidebands, one pair symmetrical, the other antisymmetrical.

2. Let $g(t)$ be the response of a network to a unit impulse centered at $t = 0$, and let $C(\omega)$ be its complex amplitude-density spectrum. Show that, if $g(t)$ is even, the network introduces no phase shift. Show that, if the response is $g(t - \tau)$ where $g(t)$ is even, the phase shift is proportional to frequency and equals $-\omega\tau$.

3. If $g(t)$, the response of a network to an impulse, is odd, show that the network introduces a phase shift equal to $\pm \dfrac{\pi}{2} \pm n\pi$ at all frequencies. Show that, if the response is $g(t - \tau)$ where $g(t)$ is odd, the phase shift introduced by the network is given by $-\omega\tau \pm \dfrac{\pi}{2} \pm n\pi$.

4. Assume that a filter transmits freely all frequencies $0 < f < B$, fails to transmit higher frequencies, and introduces a constant phase shift of $\pi/2$. By integration derive an expression, $g(t)$, for the response to a unit impulse. For what values of t is $g(t)$ zero?

5. Random binary digits having a wave form given by $\pm \dfrac{\sin 2\pi Bt}{2\pi Bt}$ are generated at the rate of B per second, are perturbed by resistance noise, and are then applied to a pair of idealized low-pass filters. Each filter transmits $0 \leqslant f \leqslant B$ without loss and fails to pass higher frequencies. The phase shift introduced by the first filter is $-\omega\tau_1$ and by the second, $-\omega\tau_2 - \pi/2$. The delays designated τ_1 and τ_2 are arbitrary and can be varied.

The output of the first filter is sampled briefly B times a second at regular intervals; and, by sampling at the right times, intersymbol interference is zero. The samples are the wanted digits perturbed by noise. By similarly sampling the output of the second filter at the right times, the samples are essentially samples of noise only. Can this result be used to improve signal-to-noise ratio?

6. If two channels are multiplexed by phase discrimination as in the Day system, is it possible and, if so, what are the necessary and sufficient conditions for each channel to be able to transmit and recover without interchannel interference its own arbitrarily chosen zero frequency component? Assume an ideal transmitter and a distortionless medium.

7. $V_1(t)$ and $V_2(t)$ represent arbitrary and independent band-limited modulating waves. The significant cyclic frequencies of each are restricted to $0 < f < f_2$. Assume $S_1(t)$ and $S_2(t)$ exist and represent the upper sideband of $V_1(t)$ and the lower sideband of $V_2(t)$ respectively about $\cos \omega_c t$. For convenience assume $\frac{\omega_c}{2} \gg f_2$. Assume that $A_c \cos \omega_c t$ is generated and available.

Given $S_1(t)$ and $S_2(t)$: by the use of phase discrimination and without the use of any electrical filter, show how to divide the frequency band at the carrier frequency, delete one of the channels, and separately recover $V_1(t)$ and $V_2(t)$.

8. In problem 7 assume $S_1(t)$ and $S_2(t)$ are embedded in resistance noise. Assume that phase shifting networks are utilized which, instead of introducing $\pi/2$, introduce a constant phase shift across the band of ψ_v radians. Assume $\psi_v \ll \pi/2$. Express the derived signal-to-noise ratio at the output of each channel as a function of ψ_v.

9. Diagram a bilateral modulator consisting of a low-pass filter followed by a modulator followed by a band filter, and having the following properties: When voice frequencies are applied to the low-pass filter, upper and lower sidebands appear in the band-filter output and vice versa. The voice-frequency impedance depends on the impedance termination of the band filter at sideband frequencies and vice versa. Transmission losses are minimized. All impedances are matched. Carrier is transmitted as well as supplied to the modulator. This terminal will be referred to as the "master" terminal.

At the other end of a short distortionless line is a "slave" terminal that requires no power supply. At the unattended slave terminal, equipment is the same as at the master terminal except for the absence of carrier supply. When the carrier and both sidebands are received from the master terminal, voice frequencies are delivered at the output of the low-pass filter. The system is a two-way system. In the bilateral modulator at the slave terminal, voice frequencies modulate the received carrier to produce the two sidebands which are transmitted back to the master terminal with a finite velocity.

Question: What special precaution has to be taken in order to realize maximum demodulated signal at the master terminal?

10. The essential frequency components of a modulating wave, $V(t)$, are restricted to $0 < f < B$. What is the lowest carrier frequency in order that each component of $V(t) \cos \omega_c t$ will be uniquely determined by $V(t)$?

11. As a function of time, write two equations for the two envelopes of $A_c[1 + kV(t)] \cos (\omega_c t + \Phi_c)$.

Show that at successive intervals of time each envelope just touches the modulated wave; that is, for each envelope enumerate these common points and verify that at each point of contact, the envelope and modulating wave have the same slope.

CHAPTER 12

FREQUENCY MODULATION

Frequency modulation, a particular form of angle modulation, is another well-known way of modulating a sinusoidal carrier. Its chief point of superiority over amplitude modulation lies in its ability to exchange band-width occupancy in the transmission medium for improved noise performance. John R. Carson (Ref. 1)* was the first to analyze the frequency-modulation process and to disclose the wide band involved. E. H. Armstrong (Ref. 2) was the first to have a real appreciation of the noise-reducing properties of frequency modulation.

Historically, frequency modulation is old. Sometimes it has seemed hard to avoid. In the 1870's a system of two-tone telegraphy was devised wherein one frequency was employed for mark and a different frequency for space. Years later, difficulties in modulating the amplitude of a Poulsen arc generator made frequency modulation a welcome substitute. J. C. Chaffee was led to his initial contributions in the general field of frequency modulation (Ref. 3) by difficulties in maintaining a constant frequency which he encountered in his efforts to amplitude-modulate high-frequency oscillators.

It will be shown later that, under certain conditions, the signal-to-noise ratio improves 6 decibels for each two-to-one increase in band-width occupancy. Frequency modulation also exhibits a so-called "channel grabbing" characteristic. If two signals in the same frequency band are available at the receiver, the one appearing at the higher level is accepted to the near exclusion of the other. Due to this characteristic, the area between radio transmitters where crosstalk is excessive, is much less than in the amplitude-modulation case. Frequency modulation also allows transmitting tubes to be operated at maximum power without the penalties associated with ordinary nonlinearities. Since the power output is usually independent of the modulating wave, this results in a high-efficiency transmitter.

Against these advantages there are, as might be expected, certain disadvantages. A wide frequency band in the transmitting medium is re-

* The references cited are listed at the end of each chapter according to the number used in the text.

181

quired in order to obtain the advantages of reduced noise and increased area of coverage. A frequency-modulation system is more complicated than a double-sideband, amplitude-modulation system. Although frequency-modulation systems are tolerant to certain types of nonlinearity, it is necessary to give special attention to the phase characteristics.

ANGLE MODULATION

In angle modulation, the angle of a sinusoidal carrier is the parameter subject to variation by the modulating wave. Thus, in the expression

$$M(t) = A_c \cos \theta(t) \tag{12-1}$$

$\theta(t)$ is the argument that is caused to vary. In keeping with this generalized definition of angle modulation, the variation of the argument $\theta(t)$ may be related to the modulating wave in any predetermined unique manner. Only a relatively few simple forms of the many possible general forms of angle modulation are of practical importance. Two practical forms are phase modulation and frequency modulation. As pointed out in Chapter 3, phase modulation and frequency modulation are not essentially different.

GENERAL CONCEPTS AND DEFINITIONS

Before entering upon an introductory treatment of frequency modulation, a few words of caution and some additional definitions are in order. For example, the well-known methods of elementary alternating-current theory in which $\cos \omega t$ is replaced by $\epsilon^{i\omega t}$ are no longer applicable when frequency is a function of time. Certain vector ideas resulting from the usual representation of complex numbers have their place, and where these ideas are helpful, they will be used. This usage of the term "vector," although in accordance with common engineering practice, should not be confused with the customary mathematical meaning of the term. Also, as will be indicated later, superposition is not applicable except under restricted conditions, and then only approximately. Other cautions will be mentioned as the treatment proceeds. For a more exact analysis of many of the problems, References 4 to 19 should be consulted.

Before defining particular forms of angle modulation, consider the familiar situation where, in (12-1), $\theta(t) = \omega_c t + \Phi_c$ and ω_c and Φ_c are constants. Now apply Carson's definition of instantaneous radian frequency (given in Chapter 3), that is, the time rate of change of the phase angle $\theta(t)$. The expected result follows, namely, that the instantaneous radian frequency is the constant ω_c. The constant Φ_c is merely an initial phase angle. This simple wave, $A_c \cos (\omega_c t + \Phi_c)$ will be referred to as the unmodulated sinusoidal carrier. Our concern will be with modifications of this carrier that yield phase and frequency modulation.

Phase modulation is that form of angle modulation in which the linearly increasing phase of the unmodulated carrier, $\omega_c t + \Phi_c$, has added to it a time-varying phase angle that is proportional to the applied modulating wave.

Frequency modulation is that form of angle modulation in which the instantaneous radian frequency $\dfrac{d}{dt}\,\theta(t)$ is equal to the constant radian frequency of the carrier, ω_c, plus a time-varying component that is proportional to the applied modulating wave.

It is important to note that with either phase or frequency modulation, the time-varying component proportional to the applied wave may be a function of the frequency of the modulating wave. For convenient reference we repeat the following definitions given in Chapter 3: *phase deviation* is the peak difference between the instantaneous angle of the modulated wave and the angle of the unmodulated carrier. *Frequency deviation* is the peak difference between the instantaneous frequency of the modulated wave and the frequency of the unmodulated carrier. *Modulation index* is the ratio of the frequency deviation to the frequency of a sinusoidal modulating signal.

PHASE MODULATION

To write an expression for a phase-modulated wave, we are first concerned with the time-varying component of the phase angle that is proportional to the applied modulating wave.

Expression for a Phase-Modulated Wave

Let $V(t)$ represent the modulating wave and K, the factor of proportionality. At times it will be convenient to refer to $KV(t)$ as the modulating wave. K is measured in radians per volt if the modulating wave is expressed in volts and, in any event, is a property of the design of the modulating system such that $KV(t)$ represents the desired radian phase departure. Accordingly, the function $\theta(t)$ is given by

$$\theta(t) = \omega_c t + \Phi_c + KV(t). \tag{12-2}$$

When (12-2) is put in (12-1),

$$M(t) = A_c \cos\left[\omega_c t + \Phi_c + KV(t)\right]. \tag{12-3}$$

For simplicity and to begin with, it will be assumed that the modulating wave is a sinusoid. Without loss of generality we may set $\Phi_c = 0$. Then

$$M(t) = A_c \cos\left[\omega_c t + \Phi_v \cos \omega_v t\right] \tag{12-4}$$

where Φ_v is the phase deviation of the resulting wave.

Since the instantaneous radian frequency, ω_i, is the time rate of change of the phase angle,

$$\omega_i = \omega_c - \omega_v \Phi_v \sin \omega_v t. \tag{12-5}$$

Thus, from the definition of frequency modulation, the phase-modulated wave given by (12-4) can be thought of, according to (12-5), as representing a frequency-modulated wave wherein the modulating wave is $-\omega_v \Phi_v \sin \omega_v t$. Hence, with a sinusoidal modulating wave, the frequency deviation of the phase-modulated wave is $\omega_v \Phi_v$ radians per second; and, if Φ_v is constant, the frequency deviation is proportional to the frequency of the modulating wave.

Small Phase Deviation

The right member of (12-4) will be evaluated for small phase deviations. The resulting spectrum and vector diagram will then be compared with the familiar spectrum and vector diagram of the corresponding amplitude-modulated wave. From (12-4) we have

$$M(t) = A_c[\cos \omega_c t \cos (\Phi_v \cos \omega_v t) - \sin \omega_c t \sin (\Phi_v \cos \omega_v t)]$$

$$= A_c \left[\cos \omega_c t \left(1 - \frac{\Phi_v{}^2 \cos^2 \omega_v t}{\lfloor 2} + \frac{\Phi_v{}^4 \cos^4 \omega_v t}{\lfloor 4} - \cdots \right) \right.$$

$$\left. - \sin \omega_c t \left(\Phi_v \cos \omega_v t - \frac{\Phi_v{}^3 \cos^3 \omega_v t}{\lfloor 3} + \cdots \right) \right]. \tag{12-6}$$

When Φ_v becomes small enough so that we may neglect higher order terms, we have from (12-6),

$$M(t) \rightarrow A_c \cos \omega_c t - A_c \Phi_v \sin \omega_c t \cos \omega_v t$$

$$= A_c \left[\cos \omega_c t - \frac{\Phi_v}{2} \sin (\omega_c + \omega_v) t - \frac{\Phi_v}{2} \sin (\omega_c - \omega_v) t \right]. \tag{12-7}$$

Thus, for the case in which Φ_v is sufficiently small, the phase-modulated wave of (12-4) can be resolved into a carrier plus two side frequencies. One of these is above the carrier by the frequency of the modulating wave, and the other below it by the same amount. It will be recalled that (12-4) is restricted to a sinusoidal modulating wave.

Since it is informative to view phase modulation from a vector point of view, (12-7) will be rewritten using a complex notation from which the vector diagrams follow naturally, viz.,

$$M(t) = A_c \left[\cos \omega_c t + \frac{\Phi_v}{2} \cos \left[(\omega_c + \omega_v) t + \frac{\pi}{2} \right] + \frac{\Phi_v}{2} \cos \left[(\omega_c - \omega_v) t + \frac{\pi}{2} \right] \right]$$

$$= \begin{bmatrix} \text{Real} \\ \text{part} \\ \text{of} \end{bmatrix} A_c \epsilon^{i\omega_c t} \left[1 + \frac{\Phi_v}{2} \epsilon^{i \left(\omega_v t + \frac{\pi}{2} \right)} + \frac{\Phi_v}{2} \epsilon^{i \left(-\omega_v t + \frac{\pi}{2} \right)} \right]. \tag{12-8}$$

A vector interpretation may be given to (12–8) in the usual way; that is, the instantaneous value of the modulated wave may be represented by the projection, in this case on the real axis, of a vector rotating in the complex plane. In (12–8), the component representing the carrier rotation has been factored out, and the factor in brackets indicates how the carrier is modified as a function of the modulating wave.

The way in which the vectors in the factor multiplying the carrier component add is indicated in Fig. 12–1 for time $t = 0$. Vector unity is shown in (a) of Fig. 12–1. The vector $+ \frac{\Phi_v}{2} \epsilon^{i(\omega_v t + \pi/2)}$ appears in (b) of Fig. 12–1. At $t = 0$ it is at an angle $\pi/2$ with the axis of reals and is rotating counterclockwise at a velocity of ω_v radians per second. The vector $\frac{\Phi_v}{2} \epsilon^{i(-\omega_v t + \pi/2)}$ at $t = 0$ is also at an angle $\pi/2$ with the axis of reals. It is therefore in phase with the vector $\frac{\Phi_v}{2} \epsilon^{i(\omega_v t) + \pi/2)}$, but rotates in a clockwise direction as shown in (c) of Fig. 12–1. Summation of the vectors modifying the carrier vector is shown in (d) of Fig. 12–1 where the phase angle Φ_v is clearly indicated. The way in which the vectors add for a large deviation will be treated later.

For purposes of comparison consider the corresponding amplitude-modulated wave when the modulating wave is a sinusoid, viz.,

$$M(t) = A_c(1 + k \cos \omega_v t) \cos \omega_c t$$

$$= A_c \cos \omega_c t + \frac{1}{2} kA_c \cos (\omega_c + \omega_v)t + \frac{1}{2} kA_c \cos (\omega_c - \omega_v)t$$

$$= A_c \left[\cos \omega_c t + \frac{1}{2} k \cos (\omega_c \pm \omega_v)t \right]. \qquad (12\text{–}9)$$

When (12–9) is compared with (12–7) it is apparent that, in both cases, there results a carrier and two side frequencies symmetrically placed above and below the carrier. However, the phases of the side frequencies are different. To show this difference in a convenient way, (12–9) will be written in complex form as was done in the case of phase modulation, viz.,

$$M(t) = \begin{bmatrix} \text{Real} \\ \text{part} \\ \text{of} \end{bmatrix} A_c \left[\epsilon^{i\omega_c t} + \frac{k}{2} \epsilon^{i(\omega_c + \omega_v)t} + \frac{k}{2} \epsilon^{i(\omega_c - \omega_v)t} \right]$$

$$= \begin{bmatrix} \text{Real} \\ \text{part} \\ \text{of} \end{bmatrix} A_c \epsilon^{i\omega_c t} \left[1 + \frac{k}{2} \epsilon^{i\omega_v t} + \frac{k}{2} \epsilon^{-i\omega_v t} \right]. \qquad (12\text{–}10)$$

The similarity between (12–10) and (12–8) is shown in a like manner in Fig. 12–1 for time $t = 0$. In this case, at time $t = 0$, the multiplier of the carrier, (d') of Fig. 12–1, does not include a phase angle but it is a real number.

PHASE MODULATION

ASSUMING A SINUSOIDAL MODULATING WAVE AND A SMALL PHASE DEVIATION, THE RESULTING MODULATED WAVE IS:

$$M(t) = A_c \cos \left[\omega_c t + \Phi_v \cos \omega_v t \right]$$

$$\approx \left[\begin{array}{c} \text{REAL} \\ \text{PART} \\ \text{OF} \end{array} \right] A_c \epsilon^{i\omega_c t} \left[\underbrace{1}_{a} + \underbrace{\frac{\Phi_v}{2}\epsilon^{i(\omega_v t + \frac{\pi}{2})}}_{b} + \underbrace{\frac{\Phi_v}{2}\epsilon^{i(-\omega_v t + \frac{\pi}{2})}}_{c} \right]$$

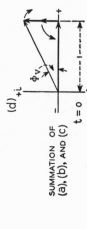

AMPLITUDE MODULATION

ASSUMING A SINUSOIDAL MODULATING WAVE, THE RESULTING MODULATED WAVE IS:

$$M(t) = A_c \left[1 + k \cos \omega_v t \right] \cos \omega_c t$$

$$= \left[\begin{array}{c} \text{REAL} \\ \text{PART} \\ \text{OF} \end{array} \right] A_c \epsilon^{i\omega_c t} \left[\underbrace{1}_{a'} + \underbrace{\frac{k}{2}\epsilon^{i\omega_v t}}_{b'} + \underbrace{\frac{k}{2}\epsilon^{-i\omega_v t}}_{c'} \right]$$

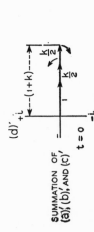

Fig. 12-1　Vector diagrams representing for time $t = 0$ a particular example of amplitude modulation and phase modulation

Figure 12–2 displays two arrays of vector diagrams similar to the diagrams in (d) and (d') of Fig. 12–1, except that in Fig. 12–2 the diagrams are drawn for a plurality of selected points in the cycle of the modulating wave. It is evident (Fig. 12–2) how the side-frequency vectors add in the case of amplitude modulation to produce a factor of varying magnitude and con-

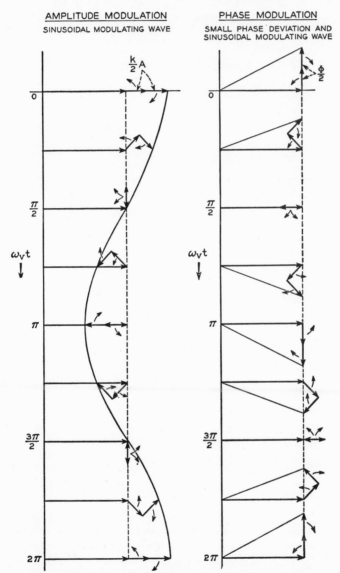

FIG. 12–2 Vector diagrams similar to Fig. 12–1(d) and Fig. 12–1(d') for a plurality of selected points in the cycle of the sinusoidal modulating wave

stant phase.   It is also clear that, in the case of phase modulation, they add to produce a factor of nearly constant magnitude but variable phase.

For purposes of illustration, the angle Φ_v shown in Fig. 12–2 was drawn fairly large.   It will be apparent (Fig. 12–2) that the length of the vector (magnitude of the factor) changes throughout the cycle of the modulating wave.   This shows that (12–6) is not a valid representation for large phase deviations.

Large Phase Deviation

When the modulating wave is a sinusoid, the modulated wave, given by (12–4), may be written

$$M(t) = A_c[\cos \omega_c t \cos (\Phi_v \cos \omega_v t) - \sin \omega_c t \sin (\Phi_v \cos \omega_v t)]. \quad (12\text{–}11)$$

This is conveniently expanded by recalling Jacobi's result that $\cos (x \cos y)$ and $\sin (x \cos y)$ each may be expanded in a Fourier series in which the coefficients are Bessel functions of the first kind with integer suffix and argument x, viz.,

$$\cos (x \cos y) = J_0(x) + 2 \sum_{m=1}^{\infty} (-)^m J_{2m}(x) \cos 2my$$

and

$$\sin (x \cos y) = 2 \sum_{1}^{\infty} (-)^{m+1} J_{2m-1}(x) \cos (2m - 1)y. \quad (12\text{–}12)$$

Similarly, for convenience of reference, Anger's later result,

$$\cos (x \sin y) = J_0(x) + 2 \sum_{1}^{\infty} J_{2m}(x) \cos 2my$$

and

$$\sin (x \sin y) = 2 \sum_{1}^{\infty} J_{2m-1}(x) \sin (2m - 1)y. \quad (12\text{–}13)$$

(See Ref. 20, p. 281 or Ref. 21, p. 190 or any work on Bessel functions for these relationships.)   The result of introducing (12–12) in (12–11), carrying out the indicated multiplications, and expanding the resulting trigonometric product terms into their equivalent sum and difference terms, is

$$M(t) = A_c \sum_{n=-\infty}^{\infty} J_n(\Phi_v) \cos \left[(\omega_c + n\omega_v)t + \frac{n\pi}{2} \right]. \quad (12\text{–}14)$$

From (12–14) it is evident that the spectrum of a phase-modulated wave includes side frequencies around the carrier which theoretically extend indefinitely.   Practically, the magnitude of the higher-order Bessel functions eventually diminishes, and the penalty for not transmitting beyond this is only a relatively small amount of distortion.   In fact, as indicated in the preceding section, only one upper and lower side frequency need be transmitted provided Φ_v is sufficiently small.

To obtain a more concrete picture of phase modulation when the modulating wave is a single sinusoid, the particular case of where the phase deviation, Φ_v, is one radian will be considered in further detail. The values of the Bessel functions as obtained from tables (Ref. 22, p. 156) are:

$$J_0(1) = 0.7652 \qquad J_2(1) = 0.1149 \qquad J_4(1) = 0.0025$$
$$J_1(1) = 0.4401 \qquad J_3(1) = 0.0196 \qquad J_5(1) = 0.0003$$

All orders beyond this may be considered negligible.

Using these data, a vector diagram will be plotted in a manner similar to Figs. 12–1 and 12–2. To this end, (12–14) is rewritten with the values of the Bessel functions for $\Phi_v = 1$ substituted and all terms above $J_3(1)$ neglected. In addition, conversion to the exponential form as in the preceding section is carried out so that the complete factor multiplying the carrier is immediately evident. Thus,

$$M(t) = \begin{bmatrix} \text{Real} \\ \text{part} \\ \text{of} \end{bmatrix} A_c \epsilon^{i\omega_c t} \Big[0.7652 - 0.4401 \epsilon^{i\left(\pm\omega_v t - \frac{\pi}{2}\right)}$$
$$- 0.1149 \epsilon^{\pm i2\omega_v t} + 0.0196 \epsilon^{i\left(\pm 3\omega_v t - \frac{\pi}{2}\right)} \Big].$$

The vector diagram of the factor multiplying the carrier is plotted in Fig. 12–3 for selected points in the cycle of the modulating wave. The sequence of events occurring between $\omega_v t = 0$ and $\omega_v t = 2\pi$ is fairly evident from the figure. Three pairs of side frequencies are sufficient in this particular instance to yield good results in the sense that the magnitude of the multiplying vector is very nearly unity over the signal cycle.

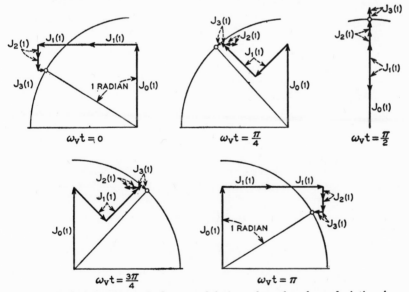

FIG. 12–3 Vector diagrams of phase modulation when the phase deviation is one radian; different diagrams corresponding to different points in the cycle of the sinusoidal modulating wave

Consideration of Fig. 12–3 gives some notion as to why it is that the larger the phase deviation Φ_v becomes, the greater the number of required side frequencies. If Φ_v becomes very large, the resultant vector revolves around the origin a number of times, producing a complicated motion that requires the addition of many vectors.

A study of Fig. 12–3 gives an indication as to why the phase characteristics of the transmitting medium, associated networks, and circuits are so important in this type of modulation. Errors in phase of the various side frequencies result in errors of addition which in turn cause errors in the phase of the resultant multiplier. Finally, these errors are converted into distortion terms at the output of the system.

It is instructive to note that (12–14) reduces to (12–7) as $\Phi_v \to 0$. This reduction may be verified by considering the series definitions (Ref. 23, p. 355) of the Bessel functions in terms of their argument.

Average Power

An important practical consideration is the fact that the average power in a phase-modulated wave is constant. This is true, in general, with two provisions. One is that the spectrum of the modulating wave be continuous. The other is that any discrete components of the modulating wave stem from an ensemble of sinusoids the frequencies of which are all incommensurable with one another and with the carrier frequency.

The foregoing can be readily verified for the case of a sinusoidal modulating wave (Problems 1 and 2). The modulated wave is given by (12–14) and may be thought of as being either a voltage across a resistance or a current flowing through a resistance. In either case, if the sinusoidal carrier and modulating waves are incommensurable, Parseval's theorem enables one to show that the average power is proportional to the sum of the squares of the individual Fourier components of the modulated wave. Consider a unit resistance so that the average power, using (12–14), is given by

$$P = \frac{A_c^2}{2} \sum_{-\infty}^{\infty} J_n^2(\Phi_v) = \frac{A_c^2}{2}. \qquad (12\text{--}15)$$

This result was obtained by noting that the bilateral infinite sum is identically equal to unity for all values of the argument; the identity follows from the properties of Bessel functions (Ref. 23, p. 379).

FREQUENCY MODULATION

In the expression $M(t) = A_c \cos \theta(t)$, frequency modulation is by definition that type of modulation in which the instantaneous frequency is equal to the constant frequency of the carrier plus a time-varying component that is proportional to the magnitude of the modulating wave.

Expression for a Frequency-Modulated Wave

Let $V(t)$ represent the modulating wave and K_1 the factor of proportionality. K_1 is a design constant and, for example, is measured in radians per volt if the modulating wave is expressed in volts. It follows that the instantaneous radian frequency, ω_i is given by

$$\omega_i = \frac{d}{dt}\,\theta(t) = \omega_c + K_1 V(t)$$

and upon performing the integration to get $\theta(t)$,

$$\theta(t) = \int_{-\infty}^{t} \omega_i\,dt = \int_{-\infty}^{t} [\omega_c + K_1 V(t)]\,dt = \omega_c t + \Phi_c + K_1 \int^{t} V(t)\,dt. \qquad (12\text{--}16)$$

The constant Φ_c in the right member of (12–16) represents the initial phase angle of the unmodulated carrier since; if $V(t)$ is always zero, we require that $\theta(t) = \omega_c t + \Phi_c$. The lower limit of the definite integral in (12–16) is omitted because it contributes nothing to the argument. The two additional terms which are added to $\theta(t)$ when a lower limit is specified prove to be equal and opposite and so their sum is always zero.

The result of substituting (12–16) into (12–1) is

$$M(t) = A_c \cos \left[\omega_c t + \Phi_c + K_1 \int^{t} V(t)\,dt\right], \qquad (12\text{--}17)$$

which is consistent with the development in Chapter 3, for example, (3–3). The initial phase angle Φ_c could very well be carried along in the treatment to follow; but since the power spectrum of the resulting expressions will not be affected and since it may easily be introduced into the final answers if desired, Φ_c usually will be considered to be zero.

Sinusoidal Modulating Wave. To facilitate comparisons we set

$$K_1 V(t) = -\,\Delta\omega_c \sin \omega_v t \qquad (12\text{--}18)$$

so that in accordance with (12–16)

$$\omega_i = \frac{d}{dt}\,\theta(t) = \omega_c - \Delta\omega_c \sin \omega_v t. \qquad (12\text{--}19)$$

That is, $\Delta\omega_c/2\pi$ is the frequency deviation and represents the plus or minus peak variation from the unmodulated carrier frequency, f_c. Upon integrating (12–19), we have

$$\theta(t) = \omega_c t + \frac{\Delta\omega_c}{\omega_v} \cos \omega_v t \qquad (12\text{--}20)$$

and when (12–20) is substituted in (12–1), we get

$$M(t) = A_c \cos \left[\omega_c t + \frac{\Delta\omega_c}{\omega_v} \cos \omega_v t\right], \qquad (12\text{--}21)$$

an expression for the modulated wave. Since (12–21) is of the same form as (12–4), the spectrum of (12–21) is displayed by substituting $\Delta\omega_c/\omega_v$ for Φ_v in (12–14), viz.,

$$M(t) = A_c \sum_{n=-\infty}^{\infty} J_n\left(\frac{\Delta\omega_c}{\omega_v}\right) \cos\left[(\omega_c + n\nu_v)t + \frac{n\pi}{2}\right]. \qquad (12\text{–}22)$$

Comparison of Phase Modulation and Frequency Modulation

The following table gives the expression for the phase-modulated and frequency-modulated waves that have been developed up to this point.

Type of Modulation	Modulating Wave	Resulting Expression
(a) Phase	$KV(t)$	$M(t) = A_c \cos\left[\omega_c t + KV(t)\right]$
(b) Frequency	$K_1 V(t)$	$M(t) = A_c \cos\left[\omega_c t + K_1 \int^t V(t)\,dt\right]$
(c) Phase	$\Phi_v \cos \omega_v t$	$M(t) = A_c \cos\left[\omega_c t + \Phi_v \cos \omega_v t\right]$
(d) Frequency	$-\Delta\omega_c \sin \omega_v t$	$M(t) = A_c \cos\left[\omega_c t + \dfrac{\Delta\omega_c}{\omega_v} \cos \omega_v t\right]$

The relation between the two types of modulation can be conveniently compared by examining the expressions (a) through (d). In (d) the modulating wave was chosen so that the trigonometric multiplier appearing in the argument of the resulting expression is similar to that appearing in (c). This was done so that the previous development which displayed the spectrum of a phase-modulated wave would apply directly to the frequency-modulated wave of (d). Comparison of the resulting expression in (c) and (d) will show that the quantity $\Delta\omega_c/\omega_v$ in (d) stands in the same position as Φ_v in (c).

Thus, the phase deviation in the frequency-modulated signal of (d) is equal to the modulation index. That is, when a sinusoidal modulating wave produces a frequency-modulated wave, the phase deviation equals the ratio of the frequency deviation to the frequency of the modulating signal. It follows, therefore, that the phase deviation is inversely proportional to the modulating frequency, provided $\Delta\omega_c$ is a constant.

Illustrative Example. The relation between phase and frequency modulation is further emphasized by an examination of Fig. 12–4. In (a) of Fig. 12–4, the means (mentioned in Chapter 3) by which a phase modulator may be used to obtain a frequency modulator is indicated. A phase modulator is here defined as a device that, in response to an input signal (in this case a time-voltage function v_0), produces at its output a signal v_1 as follows:

$$v_1 = A_c \cos\left(\omega_c t + k_0 v_0\right) \qquad (12\text{–}23)$$

where A_c is a constant and k_0 a design constant of the phase modulator measured in radians per volt.

It is only necessary to cause v_0 to include the applied signal as an integral in order for (12–23) to represent frequency modulation. This can be ac-

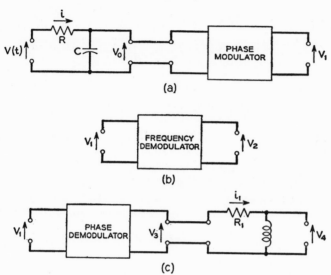

(a)

(b)

(c)

Fig. 12–4   Use of a phase modulator and demodulator to generate and detect frequency modulation

complished conveniently by inserting a simple network, as shown, between $V(t)$ and v_0. If i is the current flowing in the resistor whose resistance is R, then

$$v_0 = \frac{1}{C} \int^t i \, dt.$$

If R is very large compared to the reactance of the capacitance C over the frequency range of interest, then

$$i = \frac{1}{R}; \quad \text{and as} \quad R \to \infty, \quad v_0 \to \frac{1}{RC} \int^t V(t) \, dt$$

which, when substituted in (12–23), yields

$$v_1 = A_c \cos \left[\omega_c t + \frac{k_0}{RC} \int^t V(t) \, dt \right]. \tag{12–24}$$

This is the same as (12–17) when $K_1 = k_0/RC$ and $\Phi_c = 0$. The condition that $R \to \infty$ implies a large loss in the RC network, but this can be overcome by gains included in the constant k_0.

The modulated wave given by (12–24) is now impressed upon a frequency demodulator. It is assumed in Fig. 12–4 that a voltage $v_1 = E_1 \cos \theta(t)$

impressed upon the frequency demodulator by definition will produce a voltage v_2 at its output which is given by $k_1 \dfrac{d}{dt} \theta(t)$, that is, proportional to the time derivative of the time-varying phase angle $\theta(t)$. The factor k_1 is a design constant measured in volts per radian per second.

When the signal of (12–24) is applied to the input of this demodulator,

$$\theta(t) = \omega_c t + \frac{k_0}{RC} \int^t V(t)\, dt$$

and

$$v_2(t) = k_1 \omega_c + \frac{k_0 k_1}{RC} V(t). \tag{12–25}$$

In (12–25), $k_1 \omega_c$ is a constant voltage usually not of interest and removable by means of a simple blocking capacitor. The second term is the desired signal multiplied by a constant controllable by the design of the system.

In Fig. 12–4, (c) indicates how a phase demodulator may be used to obtain the wanted signal (original modulating wave) from the frequency-modulated signal v_1 of (12–24). By definition, the phase demodulator, (c) of Fig. 12–4, is assumed to supply an output voltage, v_3, which is proportional to the phase deviation of the input signal from the unmodulated carrier. That is, in (c) of Fig. 12–4, if

$$v_1 = A_c \cos [\omega_c t + \Phi(t)],$$

then by definition

$$v_3 = k_3 \Phi(t)$$

where k_3 is a design constant measured in volts per radian.

In (12–24) which represents the actual wave applied to the detector input, the phase angle $\Phi(t)$ is

$$\Phi(t) = \frac{k_0}{RC} \int^t V(t)\, dt$$

and, therefore,

$$v_3 = \frac{k_3 k_0}{RC} \int^t V(t)\, dt. \tag{12–26}$$

It is now necessary to differentiate v_3 with respect to time. This can be done, for example, by means of the $R_1 L$ network shown. Again R_1 is assumed very large compared to the reactance. The relations applying are

$$v_4 = L \frac{di_1}{dt}$$

and, if $R_1 \to \infty$, $i_1 \to \dfrac{v_3}{R_1}$. It then follows that

$$v_4 = \frac{L}{R_1} \frac{dv_3}{dt}$$

and substituting from (12–26)

$$v_4 = \frac{Lk_0k_3}{R_1RC} V(t). \tag{12–27}$$

That is, v_4 is the desired signal multiplied by a constant, depending upon the system design.

EXPRESSIONS FOR FREQUENCY–MODULATED WAVES RESULTING FROM COMPLEX MODULATING WAVES

So far the treatment and discussion of the spectrum of a frequency-modulated wave have been restricted to the case of a single, sinusoidal modulating wave. Now, the spectra of a few common but more complex modulating signals will be examined. Only when the index of modulation is very small is the principle of superposition applicable and then only approximately.

Ensemble of Sinusoidal Modulating Waves

Let

$$V(t) = \sum_{v=1}^{v} A_v \cos (\omega_v t + \theta_v)$$

so that

$$\sum_{1}^{v} \int^{t} A_v \cos (\omega_v t + \theta_v) \, dt = \sum_{1}^{v} \frac{A_v}{\omega_v} \sin (\omega_v t + \theta_v)$$

and, whence,

$$\mathrm{FM} = M(t) = A_c \sin \left[\omega_c t + \theta_c + K_1 \sum_{1}^{v} \frac{A_v}{\omega_v} \sin (\omega_v t + \theta_v) \right]. \tag{12–28}$$

Let (12–28) be shortened to

$$M(t) = A_c \sin (C + \sum_{1}^{v} B_v \sin W_v) \tag{12–29}$$

where $C \equiv \omega_c t + \theta_c$, $B_v \equiv K_1 \dfrac{A_v}{\omega_v}$, and $W_v \equiv \omega_v t + \theta_v$. This can also be written as

$$M(t) = \begin{bmatrix} \text{Imag.} \\ \text{part} \\ \text{of} \end{bmatrix} A_c (\exp iC) \left(\exp i \sum_{1}^{v} B_v \sin W_v \right). \tag{12–30}$$

From (12–12) and (12–13) or any reference on Bessel functions

$$\epsilon^{ix \sin \theta} = \sum_{-\infty}^{\infty} J_n(x) \epsilon^{in\theta} \quad \text{or} \quad \epsilon^{ix \cos \theta} = \sum_{-\infty}^{\infty} i^n J_n(x) \epsilon^{in\theta} \tag{12–31}$$

so that (12–30) can be written in the form

$$M(t) = A_c \sum_{n_v = -\infty}^{\infty} \left[\prod_{v=1}^{v} J_{n_v}(B_v) \right] \sin \left(C + \sum_{v=1}^{v} n_v W_v \right). \tag{12–32}$$

For purposes of illustration, if

$$M(t) = \sin(\omega_c t + A_1 \sin \omega_1 t + A_2 \sin \omega_2 t),$$

(12–32) becomes

$$M(t) = \sum_{m=-\infty}^{\infty} \sum_{n=-\infty}^{\infty} J_m(A_1) J_n(A_2) \sin(\omega_c + m\omega_1 + n\omega_2)t. \quad (12\text{–}33)$$

The resulting side frequencies (12–32) represent all possible combinations of $\omega_c \pm m(\omega_1) \pm n(\omega_2) \pm p(\omega_3) \ldots$, et cetera, where m, n, p, $\ldots$ each take on the values 0, ± 1, ± 2, ± 3, $\ldots$. The magnitude of each side frequency is proportional to the product of v Bessel functions where v is the number of discrete components in the modulating wave.

Contrary to the situation in amplitude modulation where superposition holds, the host of new side-frequency components affords clear evidence that superposition does not hold in this type of modulation. An exception appears when the modulation index becomes very small, in which case superposition holds to a first approximation. Under these conditions the essential side frequencies are $\omega_c \pm \omega_1$, $\omega_c \pm \omega_2$, et cetera.

These points are illustrated by Fig. 12–5. In that figure, it is assumed that two sinusoidal waves are caused to frequency-modulate a sinusoidal carrier, first, individually and then simultaneously. Since in this example the magnitudes of the important side frequencies are symmetrical about the carrier, only the components on one side of the carrier are shown. Obviously new components appear when both waves are applied. It is also apparent that the magnitudes of the components that appeared when the modulating waves were applied individually are now changed.

Unsymmetrical Modulating Wave

Equation (12–32) gives an appearance of symmetry that is deceiving. Since any modulating wave may be broken down into its Fourier components, casual examination of the previous expressions for the modulated wave might lead one to conclude that the resulting side frequencies would always be symmetrical about the carrier. Such is not the case. It turns out, as might be expected intuitively, that the energy in the spectrum tends to concentrate around the frequencies that the instantaneous frequency concept would predict.

Thus, if the instantaneous frequency has a particular value during a large part of the cycle of the modulating wave, it will be found that the power contributed by side-frequency components tends to be concentrated in components having nearly that instantaneous frequency. This is because different terms of (12–32) may be of the same frequency; and when they are combined, their phases have to be taken into account.

To show the effect of unsymmetrical components, an example has been computed using a modulating wave consisting of two sine waves having

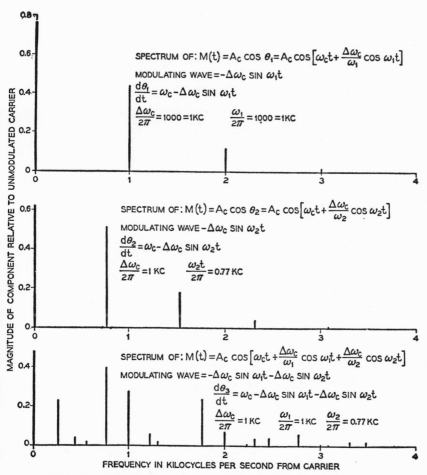

FIG. 12-5 Spectra showing the failure of superposition in frequency modulation

frequencies that are in the ratio of two to one. The results are shown in Fig. 12–6. The modulating waves are so phased as to result in a large dissymmetry and the results produced are quite evident. It should be pointed out, however, that the resulting components do not bear a simple phase relation to one another, and only the magnitude of each component is shown on Fig. 12–6.

Square Modulating Wave

In equation (12–32), when the frequencies ω_c, ω_1, ω_2, ω_3, et cetera, are incommensurable with one another, then each term is separate. When the modulating frequencies are related through some simple factor, then many of the separate components will be of the same frequency. This will be

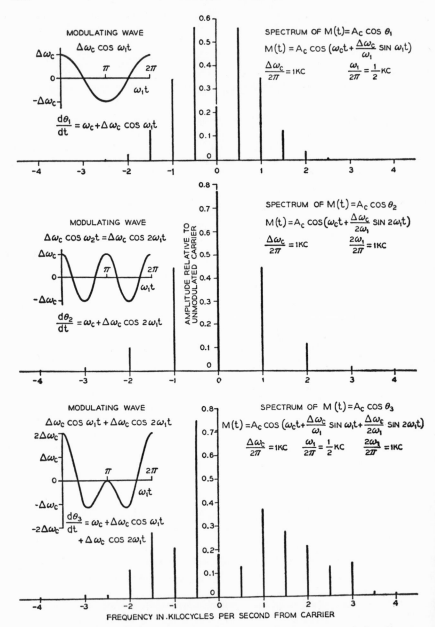

FIG. 12–6　Spectra of frequency-modulated waves illustrating symmetrical and unsymmetrical arrays of side frequencies

the case, for instance, when the frequencies of the modulating wave are the successive terms of a Fourier expansion of a periodic signal function.

In these instances it may be easier to proceed directly rather than to substitute in the formal expression given by (12–32). A case in point is the square modulating wave treated by van der Pol in Reference 5.

In this case the equation for the modulated wave,

$$\text{FM} = M(t) = \sin\left(\omega_c t + \Phi_c + K_1 \int^t V(t)\,dt\right) \quad (12\text{–}34)$$

will be written

$$M = \sin(C + S) = \sin C \cos S + \cos C \sin S \quad (12\text{–}35)$$

where $C \equiv \omega_c t + \Phi_c$ and $S \equiv K_1 \int^t V(t)\,dt$. Expand $\cos S$ and $\sin S$ into a Fourier series, viz.,

$$\cos S = \sum_0^\infty a_n \cos n\Psi + b_n \sin n\Psi \quad (12\text{–}36)$$

and

$$\sin S = \sum_0^\infty A_n \cos n\Psi + B_n \sin n\Psi. \quad (12\text{–}37)$$

Then,

$$M = \frac{1}{2} \sum_0^\infty (b_n + A_n) \cos(C - n\Psi) - (b_n - A_n) \cos(C + n\Psi)$$
$$+ (a_n - B_n) \sin(C - n\Psi) + (a_n + B_n) \sin(C + n\Psi). \quad (12\text{–}38)$$

Let $K_1 V(t)$ be a square wave of amplitude Ω and period $1/f_1$ so centered about the origin of reference $t = 0$ as to be an even function of time and of magnitude Ω when $t = 0$. Then $\Omega/2\pi$ is the frequency deviation in cycles per second. Ω/ω_1 (which equals the ratio of the frequency deviation to the fundamental frequency of the modulating wave) will be designated m.

With these restrictions $\sin S$ and $\cos S$ are odd and even functions respectively of t, and we have

$$S = m\omega_1 t, \qquad -\frac{1}{4f_1} < t < \frac{1}{4f_1}, \quad (12\text{–}39)$$

$$S = m(\pi - \omega_1 t), \quad \frac{1}{4f_1} < t < \frac{3}{4f_1}, \quad (12\text{–}40)$$

$$B_n = 4f_1 \int_0^{\frac{1}{4f_1}} \sin m\omega_1 t \sin n\omega_1 t\,dt + 4f_1 \int_{\frac{1}{4f_1}}^{\frac{1}{2f_1}} \sin m(\pi - \omega_1 t) \sin n\omega_1 t\,dt, \quad (12\text{–}41)$$

$$a_n = 4f_1 \int_0^{\frac{1}{4f_1}} \cos m\omega_1 t \cos n\omega_1 t\,dt + 4f_1 \int_{\frac{1}{4f_1}}^{\frac{1}{2f_1}} \cos m(\pi - \omega_1 t) \cos n\omega_1 t\,dt, \quad (12\text{–}42)$$

and

$$a_0 = \frac{\sin m\dfrac{\pi}{2}}{m\dfrac{\pi}{2}} \quad (12\text{–}43)$$

where

$$\sin S = \sum_{1}^{\infty} B_n \sin n\omega_1 t \quad \text{and} \quad \cos S = \sum_{0}^{\infty} a_n \cos n\omega_1 t. \quad (12\text{--}44)$$

Since (12–38), because of the restrictions of the problem, reduces to

$$M = \frac{1}{2} \sum_{0}^{\infty} (a_n + B_n) \sin (C + n\Psi) + (a_n - B_n) \sin (C - n\Psi), \quad (12\text{--}45)$$

when (12–41) and (12–42) are combined and integrated, and using (12–43) we are able to write

$$M(t) = \sum_{-\infty}^{\infty} \left(1 + \frac{n}{m}\right)^{-1} \frac{\sin \dfrac{(m-n)\pi}{2}}{\dfrac{(m-n)\pi}{2}} \sin (\omega_c t + \Phi_c + n\omega_1 t). \quad (12\text{--}46)$$

When (12–46) is compared to the result that obtains with a sinusoidal modulating wave, both are similar in that, in either case, side frequencies occur above and below the carrier (Fig. 12–7) at separations corresponding to multiples of the signaling frequency. It is of interest to notice what happens to (12–46) when m, the ratio of the frequency deviation to the fundamental frequency of the applied square wave, is an integer. When m is an integer, either all the odd-order or all the even-order side frequencies are absent, depending upon whether m is odd or even, except the pair corresponding to $m = n$; and the amplitude of each member of this pair is half the amplitude of the unmodulated carrier.

BAND-WIDTH CONSIDERATIONS

Even with a sinusoidal modulating signal, the expression for a frequency-modulated wave shows that theoretically an infinitely wide band is required. Practically, the band width required depends on the modulation index and is given by twice the frequency deviation, namely, $2 \Delta f$, provided $f_1 \ll \Delta F$, and by $2f_1$ if $\Delta F \ll f_1$; assuming an appropriate detector. It is the larger of the two that determines an approximate lower bound to the band-width occupancy.

In practical applications with conventional detectors, the occupied band usually includes most of the significant range of the spectrum of the modulated wave. Then the inclusion of a filter to attenuate everything outside of this range causes only a very small amount of nonlinear distortion of the recovered signal.

This is illustrated by Fig. 12–8 which shows the side frequencies on one side of the carrier for a plurality of frequency-modulated waves corresponding to a fixed sinusoidal modulating wave and different modulation indices. The maximum frequency deviation is held constant at 75 kilocycles per second and the modulating frequency is varied. It can be seen that the major portion of the energy is included inside the band of frequencies within the frequency deviation plus the frequency of the modulating wave. If, however, extremely high quality is desired, then with conventional systems it may be necessary to increase the band width.

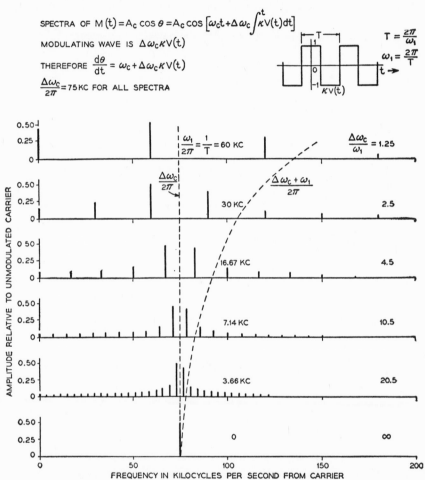

FIG. 12–7   Spectra of constant-deviation, frequency-modulated waves produced by a square modulating wave as the period of the square wave is varied

Figure 12–7 depicts the spectra produced by a square modulating wave as the repetition rate of the square wave is varied. The maximum deviation is fixed at 75 kilocycles per second. For large modulation indices, the energy concentrates within a band equal to the frequency deviation plus the fundamental frequency of the modulating wave. Again, for really high-quality reproduction, a somewhat larger band width is indicated.

When the fundamental or keying frequency of the symmetrical, square modulating wave becomes very small and consequently the modulation index becomes very large, the spectrum of the frequency-modulated wave approaches a two-band spectrum, one band centered at the carrier frequency plus the frequency deviation, and the other at minus the frequency

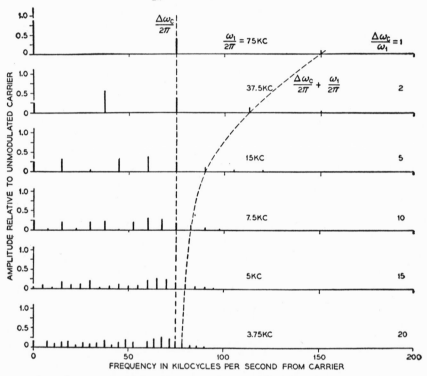

FIG. 12–8 Spectra of constant-deviation, frequency-modulated waves produced by varying the frequency of a sinusoidal modulating wave

deviation. For a sufficiently small keying frequency this gives the appearance of a two-line spectrum because all of the components having significant amplitude are concentrated in two very narrow bands, too narrow to show graphically. This tendency is illustrated in the bottom chart of Fig. 12–7 which corresponds to a very large integral value of the modulation index.

References

1. John R. Carson, "Notes on the Theory of Modulation," *Proceedings of the Institute of Radio Engineers*, New York, Vol. 10, February 1922, pp. 57–64.
2. E. H. Armstrong, "A Method of Reducing Disturbances in Radio Signaling by a System of Frequency Modulation," *Proceedings of the Institute of Radio Engineers*, New York, Vol. 24, May 1936, pp. 689–740.
3. J. G. Chaffee, "Detection of Frequency Modulated Waves," *Proceedings of the Institute of Radio Engineers*, New York, Vol. 23, May 1935, pp. 517–540.
4. Balth van der Pol, "The Fundamental Principles of Frequency Modulation," *Proceedings of the Institution of Electrical Engineers*, London, Vol. 93, Part 3, 1946, pp. 153–158.
5. Balth van der Pol, "Frequency Modulation," *Proceedings of the Institute of Radio Engineers*, New York, Vol. 18, July 1930, pp. 1194–1205.
6. W. L. Everitt, "Frequency Modulation," *Transactions of the American Institute of Electrical Engineers*, New York, Vol. 59, November 1940, pp. 613–625.
7. John R. Carson and Thornton C. Fry, "Variable Frequency Electric Circuit Theory with Application to the Theory of Frequency Modulation," *The Bell System Technical Journal*, New York, Vol. 16, No. 4, October 1937, pp. 513–540.
8. *Frequency Modulation*, a book edited by Alfred N. Goldsmith, Arthur F. Van Dyck, Robert S. Burnap, Edward T. Dickey, and George M. K. Baker, and published by *RCA. Review*, Princeton, N. J., Vol. 1, January 1948. The book contains a large collection of papers relative to frequency modulation and a very extensive appended bibliography.
9. August Hund, *Frequency Modulation*, McGraw-Hill Book Co., Inc., New York, 1942.
10. Stanford Goldman, *Frequency Analysis, Modulation and Noise*, McGraw-Hill Book Co., Inc., New York, 1948.
11. Members of the Staff of the Department of Electrical Engineering of Massachusetts Institute of Technology, *Applied Electronics*, John Wiley and Sons, Inc., New York, 1943, pp. 703–715.
12. F. E. Terman, *Radio Engineers' Handbook*, McGraw-Hill Book Co., Inc., 1943.
13. Hans Roder, "Amplitude, Phase, and Frequency Modulation," *Proceedings of the Institute of Radio Engineers*, New York, Vol. 19, No. 12, December 1931, pp. 2145–2176.
14. Murray G. Crosby, "Communication by Phase Modulation," *Proceedings of the Institute of Radio Engineers*, New York, Vol. 27, No. 2, February 1939, pp. 126–136.
15. S. W. Seeley, "Frequency Modulation," *RCA Review*, New York, Vol. 5, No. 4, April 1941, pp. 468–480.
16. Murlan S. Corrington, "Variation of Band Width with Modulation Index in Frequency Modulation," *Proceedings of the Institute of Radio Engineers*, New York, Vol. 35, No. 10, October 1947, pp. 1013–1020.
17. Murray G. Crosby, "Carrier and Side Frequency Relations with Multitone Frequency or Phase Modulation," *RCA Review*, New York, Vol. 3, No. 1, July 1938, pp. 103–106.
18. N. L. Harvey, N. Leifer, and N. Marchand, "The Component Theory of Calculating Radio Spectra with Special Reference to Frequency Modulation," *Proceedings of the Institute of Radio Engineers*, New York, Vol. 39, June 1951, pp. 648–652.

19. W. A. Cawthra and W. E. Thompson, "Bandwidth of a Sinusoidal Carrier Wave, Frequency Modulated by a Rectangular Wave and Half-Sine-Wave Build-Up," *Proceedings of the Institution of Electrical Engineers*, London, Vol. 98, Part 3, January 1951, pp. 69–74.
20. Frederick S. Woods, *Advanced Calculus*, Ginn and Company, Boston, New Edition, 1934.
21. E. L. Ince, *Ordinary Differential Equations*, Dover Publications, New York, 1944.
22. Eugene Jahnke and Fritze Emde, *Tables of Functions with Formulas and Curves*, Dover Publications, New York, Fourth Edition, 1945.
23. E. T. Whittaker and G. N. Watson, *A Course of Modern Analysis*, The Macmillan Company, New York, 1943.

Problems

1. Let a phase-modulated wave flowing in a unit resistance be represented by

$$M(t) = A_c \cos [\omega_c t + \theta_c + KV(t)].$$

Assume that $KV(t) = A_v \sin (\omega_v t + \theta_v)$ and that $\dfrac{\omega_c}{\omega_v} = \dfrac{f_c}{f_v} = x$, where $2x$ is any positive integer.

Prove that the average power dissipated in the resistance is given by

$$\overline{M^2(t)} = \frac{1}{2} A_c{}^2 \left(1 + J_{-2x}(2A_v) \cos 2(\theta_c - x\theta_v) \right).$$

2. In Problem 1, if $2x$ is not a positive integer, prove that the average power is given by $\dfrac{1}{2} A_c{}^2$.

3. Assume that a modulating wave, $A_v \cos (\omega_v t + \theta_v)$, frequency-modulates $A_c \cos (\omega_c t + \theta_c)$ and that the maximum resulting phase and frequency deviations are $\Delta\Phi$ and Δf, respectively. Show that $\Delta\Phi$, the maximum phase deviation in degrees, is $\dfrac{360}{2\pi} \left[\dfrac{\Delta f}{f_v} \right]$ where f_v is the cyclic frequency of the modulating wave.

4. Write the first 13 terms, that is, carrier and 6 pairs of side frequencies, of cos $(C + A \cos V)$ and sin $(C + A \sin V)$ where $C = \omega_c t + \theta_c$ and $V = \omega_1 t + \theta_1$.

5. Two zero resistance generators the voltages of which are given by cos $[(\omega_c + \Omega)t + \theta_c]$ and cos $[(\omega_c - \Omega)t + \theta_c]$ are alternately connected to a unit resistance. Each is connected at regular intervals for a period π/Ω. At $t = 0$ the first has been connected for an interval of $\pi/2\Omega$ seconds. At $t = \pi/2\Omega$ the first is disconnected and the second connected, et cetera.

What is the current $M(t)$ that flows in the unit resistance? Expand $M(t)$ so as to show the amplitude, frequency, and phase of the individual side-frequency components. Why does this result differ from (12–46)? Describe the difference between the instantaneous phase of the keyed wave flowing in the unit resistance and the phase of cos $(\omega_c t + \theta_c)$.

6. Given: a carrier wave $e = A_c \cos \omega_c t$ where the radian frequency ω_c is 10^8 radians per second.

TIME IN SECONDS

This carrier wave is phase-modulated by the modulating wave $V(t)$ shown above. One volt of signal on the phase-modulator input causes a positive phase deviation of 10 radians. Plot a curve showing the difference in cycles per second between the instantaneous frequency of the resulting phase-modulated wave and the frequency of the unmodulated carrier as a function of time in seconds.

7. In Problem 6 let the carrier wave be frequency-modulated by $V(t)$. Assume that one volt of signal on the input to the frequency modulator increases the frequency 20,000 cycles per second. Plot a curve showing the difference between instantaneous phase and the phase of the unmodulated carrier as a function of time in seconds. Assume the phase difference is zero at $t = 0$.

8. A modulating wave is one volt for $0 < t < 0.001$ second and is zero elsewhere. The carrier frequency is 100 megacycles per second. In a frequency-modulated system the design is such that one volt corresponds to 20 kilocycles per second increase in frequency. Sketch the phase displacement relative to the unmodulated carrier for the period $0 < t < 0.002$.

9. A modulating wave $\cos \omega_1 t$ frequency-modulates a sinusoidal carrier $\cos \omega_c t$, and the resulting frequency-modulated wave is applied to the input of an ideal band-pass filter (no phase distortion in the pass band). Assume that $\omega_c/2\pi$ is the mid-band frequency. Determine the ratio of the greatest to the least instantaneous positive value of the envelope of the signal at the output of the filter for filter pass bands of ω_1/π, $2\omega_1/\pi$, and $3\omega_1/\pi$, and modulation indices of 0.4 and 1.0.

CHAPTER 13

FREQUENCY MODULATORS AND DEMODULATORS

Quite a variety of methods have been described in the literature (Refs. 1 to 22)* for the generation and detection of frequency-modulated waves. As mentioned in Chapter 12, conversion from a phase modulator to a frequency modulator and vice versa is relatively simple. Demodulators can be similarly converted. Furthermore, as regards nomenclature, angle modulation that is neither pure phase modulation nor pure frequency modulation is often called frequency modulation.

MODULATORS

Types of frequency modulators in common use fall into two classes. In the first, Class I, a modulating wave is integrated and then applied to a phase modulator which, in turn, is followed by a frequency deviation multiplier. In the second, Class II, there is a direct variation of the frequency of an oscillation generator, for example, by the variation of a capacitance or inductance.

Class I

Numerous schemes have been devised for obtaining the required phase modulation in Class I modulators. Some are based upon the use of reactance tubes, variable capacitors, and cathode-ray tubes with shaped plates. A particularly simple and practical modulator of this type (Ref. 18) is based upon the use of a saturable-core pulse generator in which the position of the pulses is varied by the introduction of the modulating wave as a variable bias. By this means the desired phase modulation and (through the selection of a harmonic of the resulting pulse train) a first step of frequency multiplication are accomplished in a single operation. The latter is possible because the pulse train is rich in harmonics.

Important in all these circuits is the fact that the carrier frequency may be easily tied back to a crystal-controlled frequency standard. A frequency modulator that is representative of this class is depicted in Fig. 13–1.

* The references cited are listed at the end of each chapter according to the number used in the text.

Because of its historic interest and illustrative value, this circuit will be described in detail. Historically, it is the original arrangement used by Armstrong (Ref. 20) in his famous experiments with frequency modulation.

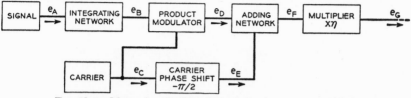

FIG. 13-1   Means for obtaining large-index frequency modulation

Assume (Fig. 13-1) that the modulating wave, e_A, is a sinusoidal wave of radian frequency ω_1, viz.,

$$e_A = A_1 \cos \omega_1 t. \tag{13-1}$$

The function of the integrating network (Fig. 13-1) is to produce a voltage, e_B, as follows:

$$e_B = \int^t A_1 \cos \omega_1 t \, dt = \frac{A_1}{\omega_1} \sin \omega_1 t. \tag{13-2}$$

The carrier supply is designed to produce a sinusoidal wave, e_C, of radian frequency ω_c, namely,

$$e_C = A_c \cos \omega_c t. \tag{13-3}$$

The carrier supply goes to a product modulator (Fig. 13-1) along with e_B, so that, generated in the output of the modulator, is their product multiplied by a constant k, that is,

$$e_D = k e_B e_C = \frac{A_1 A_c k}{\omega_1} \sin \omega_1 t \cos \omega_c t. \tag{13-4}$$

The carrier is also transmitted through a phase shifter that delivers a voltage e_E given by

$$e_E = A_c \cos \left(\omega_c t - \frac{\pi}{2} \right) = A_c \sin \omega_c t. \tag{13-5}$$

An adding network (Fig. 13-1) produces an output voltage, e_F, which is the sum of e_D and e_E, thus,

$$e_F = e_D + e_E = A_c \left[\sin \omega_c t + \frac{kA_1}{\omega_1} \sin \omega_1 t \cos \omega_c t \right] \tag{13-6}$$

$$= A_c \sqrt{1 + \frac{k^2 A_1^2}{\omega_1^2} \sin^2 \omega_1 t} \sin \left[\omega_c t + \tan^{-1} \frac{kA_1}{\omega_1} \sin \omega_1 t \right] \tag{13-7}$$

$$= A_c \sin \left[\omega_c t + \frac{k_1 A_1}{\omega_1} \sin \omega_1 t \right], \text{ provided } \frac{kA_1}{2\omega_1} \ll 1, \tag{13-8}$$

whereas (13-6) separates exactly into

$$e_F = A_c \left[\sin \omega_c t + \frac{kA_1}{2\omega_1} \cos (\omega_c + \omega_1)t - \frac{kA_1}{2\omega_1} \cos (\omega_c - \omega_1)t \right]. \tag{13-9}$$

Although the right-hand sides of (13–8) and (13–9) are approximately the same, they are not equal; and this illustrates the presence of a small amount of amplitude modulation.

The signal, represented approximately by (13–8), is transmitted through a frequency multiplier (Fig. 13–1) which is merely a harmonic producer, and a desired harmonic is selected by filtering. As an incidental but important function, the harmonic producer also removes, through its nonlinear limiting action, most of any small amplitude modulation associated with the phase-modulation process. The result is e_G wherein the instantaneous frequency has been multiplied by a suitable integer, viz.,

$$e_G = A_c \sin \left[n\omega_c t + \frac{nk_1 A_1}{\omega_1} \sin \omega_1 t \right]$$

$$= A_c \sin \left[\omega_C t + \frac{\Delta\omega_C}{\omega_1} \sin \omega_1 t \right] \tag{13–10}$$

where $\omega_C = n\omega_c$ and $\Delta\omega_C = nk_1 A_1$.

Equation (13–10) is the frequency-modulated wave sought. The modulation index can be controlled by the choice of n and other design factors. It is interesting to observe in (13–10) that multiplication of the instantaneous frequency multiplies the modulation index by the same factor. Theoretical considerations have shown that the distortion inherent to the production of a phase-modulated wave by the process represented by (13–8) is principally odd-order products of modulation. In practical designs the total distortion amounts to about 5 per cent when the peak phase departure is plus or minus 25 degrees.

Sometimes it is not convenient to obtain a sufficiently large modulation index by direct multiplication of the phase-modulated wave in (13–8). As an alternative, the resulting signal can be moved downward in the frequency spectrum after the first multiplication. This is accomplished by modulating the signal in a product modulator with a suitably placed carrier and selecting the difference frequency, a process that does not alter the modulation index. Then, starting with the difference frequency, the multiplication process is repeated.

Class II

The theoretical treatment of Class II, the class of frequency modulators that involve a direct variation of frequency, is more complicated and requires some caution (Ref. 19). In practice, modulators of this class are widely used and with excellent results. However, in this case, stabilization of the center frequency is somewhat more complicated and usually requires a form of negative feedback for purposes of automatic control. Another scheme, also in this class, involves the direct application of the modulating wave to the grid return leads of a suitably designed multivibrator. This scheme is especially useful for obtaining frequency modulation when the carrier frequency is below one megacycle per second and the frequency deviations are a large percentage of the carrier.

DEMODULATORS

As mentioned previously, a pure frequency-modulated wave is devoid of variation in amplitude. In practice, the frequency-modulated wave that arrives at the detector input after passing over the transmission medium ordinarily displays considerable variation in amplitude. Typical reasons for this may be traced to the limited band width; unstable attenuation in the medium; transmission distortion varying as a function of frequency; interference caused by noise; crosstalk from other systems; and crosstalk from other channels of the same system.

Limiter

To reduce amplitude variations, a very important device termed a limiter is normally used ahead of the frequency-modulation detector. A limiter might, for example, be a sequence of very strongly overloaded vacuum tubes or transistors. Thus, all that is preserved of the input signal after passing through the limiter is the time distribution of its axial crossings, or zeros. This is, however, equivalent to having a very large number of samples of the modulated wave over the cycle of the modulating wave. According to the sampling principle, there is more than enough information to define the modulating wave.

Discriminator

Usually the output from the limiter is filtered in order to suppress harmonics of the carrier and their associated side frequencies. The result is applied to a discriminator which is a device the output wave of which has instantaneous values proportional to the corresponding values of the instantaneous frequency of its input wave. This represents a recovery of the original modulating wave, and, in practice, the filter at the output of the limiter is ordinarily a part of the discriminator circuit.

Ideal Discriminator

An ideal discriminator would produce an output proportional to the variation in instantaneous frequency and would be absolutely insensitive to variations in the amplitude of the applied wave. Most practical discriminators are, in some measure, sensitive to amplitude variations of the signal, and it is for this reason that the limiter is so important in removing these amplitude variations. In a conventional demodulator, it is only through the removal of amplitude variations in the frequency-modulation detector that frequency modulation achieves its full noise advantage. The ratio detector of Seeley (Ref. 10) goes a long way in making the output of the discriminator independent of the amplitude of the incoming modulated wave.

Simple Discriminators

Probably the commonest form of discriminator is the type which applies the incoming wave (after it has been passed through a limiter followed by a band-pass filter) to a conversion network the output of which includes not only a frequency-modulated wave but, in addition, the wanted signal in the form of an amplitude-modulated wave. Next, this amplitude-modulated wave is applied to an envelope detector (Chap. 10) which produces the desired signal in its output. The envelope detector is insensitive to frequency modulation.

Two of these simple discriminators are shown in Fig. 13-2. In a most elementary form, it is an idealized inductor L in the plate circuit of a pentode. The frequency-modulated wave e applied to the grid is

$$e = A_c \cos\left[\omega_c t + k_1 \int^t V(t)\,dt\right] \qquad (13\text{-}11)$$

where time zero is so chosen as to make the initial phase angle of the un-modulated carrier zero.

The current i, in the plate circuit of the pentode, is assumed to be equal to the transconductance g_m of the tube multiplied by the grid voltage, e. It is also assumed that the resistance in L, the inductive plate load, is negligible, that the pentode is linear, and that the load impedance of the detector circuit is negligible. Under these conditions, the plate current i is

$$i = eg_m = A_c g_m \cos\left[\omega_c t + k_1 \int^t V(t)\,dt\right]. \qquad (13\text{-}12)$$

The voltage e_L is

$$e_L = -L\frac{di}{dt} = A_c g_m L[\omega_c + k_1 V(t)] \sin\left[\omega_c t + k_1 \int^t V(t)\,dt\right]. \qquad (13\text{-}13)$$

The voltage e_0 in the output of an ideal envelope detector would be equal to the envelope of the expression for e_L, that is,

$$e_0 = A_c g_m L[\omega_c + k_1 V(t)]. \qquad (13\text{-}14)$$

The first term is a d-c or fixed current term and the second is the desired signal.

In the foregoing example, conversion from frequency modulation to amplitude modulation was accomplished by differentiating the input signal. Since the total frequency swing of the carrier is usually only a small percentage of the total carrier frequency, the sensitivity of a detector of this type is very low.   Accordingly, it is usual to increase this sensitivity, as in (b) of Fig. 13–2, by using a more complicated network such as an antiresonant arm in the plate circuit of the pentode.   Static character-istics of both circuits are shown in (c) of Fig. 13–2.

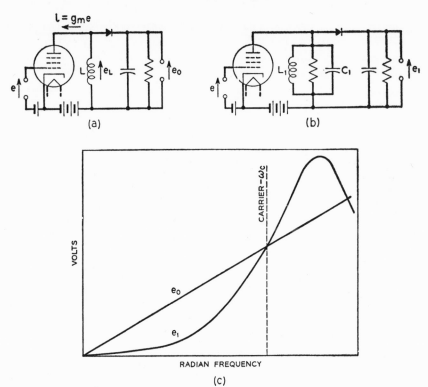

Fig. 13–2   Simple frequency-modulation detectors

In the case of (b) in Fig. 13–2, curvature of the static characteristic, as well as increased sensitivity, is evident.   Results of theoretical studies of the generalized response of a network to a frequency-modulated wave have been given by van der Pol (Ref. 19) and also by Carson and Fry (Ref. 21). It is shown that the resulting response is equal to the product of the applied voltage and the transfer characteristic of the network at the instantaneous frequency; plus a correction series that depends, first, upon the higher derivatives of the steady-state transfer characteristic with respect to fre-quency and, second, upon the derivatives of the variable input frequency with respect to time.

If the transfer characteristic is a linear function of frequency, the cor-rection series vanishes, and the so-called *quasi-stationary* or instantaneous frequency analysis is valid. On the other hand, even if there is nonlinearity in the steady-state characteristic, the instantaneous frequency analysis gives a close approximation to the true state of affairs, provided the modulator index is large; the error being of the order of the reciprocal of the modulation index.

Analytically, the characteristic of (b) in Fig. 13–2 may be handled, as implied previously, by expanding the static characteristic in a power series about the operating point. While a phase characteristic is assigned, for large modulation indices, phase distortion in the conversion network is negligible compared with the distortion arising from higher order terms in the series expansion. Accordingly, by substituting the expression for instantaneous frequency in the expansion, the output signal can be computed. Such an analysis will not be carried out here.

Balanced Detectors

Balanced detectors (examples are shown in Figs. 13–3 and 13–4) have two very important properties: *first*, they reduce distortion by providing a balance for all even-order distortion; and *second*, they reduce residual amplitude modulation. The first property is a familiar one and will not be discussed further. The second results from the fact that, with carrier alone on the detector, a change in amplitude causes an equal effect on both sides of the detector; and since the voltages are subtracted in the output, no effect is produced. This balance is, of course, somewhat upset by the presence of a signal and, therefore, some amplitude modulation will be detected with a signal present. The balanced detector complements the limiter and helps to offset its imperfections.

In Fig. 13–3, (a) is an example of a balanced detector. The two circuits, one for each branch, are tuned to slightly different frequencies and are differentially connected.

Another interesting and widely used balanced detector (Fig. 13–4) operates on the principle that the voltage across the secondary of a tuned transformer is in quadrature with the primary voltage at resonance and departs from the quadrature relationship nearly linearly on both sides of resonance. The voltages E_1, E_2, E_3, and E_4 are defined in (a) of Fig. 13–4 and a vector diagram showing the relative magnitudes and phases of E_3 and E_4 appears in (b) of Fig. 13–4. The circuit is designed so that the magnitude of the primary voltage E_1 is twice the magnitude of E_2. Thus,

$$E_1 = 2E_2. \qquad (13\text{--}15)$$

It is assumed further that resonance occurs at the carrier frequency; that E_2 is 90 degrees ahead of E_1 at this frequency; and that the departure from the quadrature relationship is some constant k multiplied by $\Delta\omega_c$. For a physically realizable network this relation is, of course, only approximate. Expressing these facts symbolically in conventional complex notation gives

$$E_2 = \frac{E_1}{2}\, \epsilon^{\, i\left(\frac{\pi}{2} + k\,\Delta\omega c\right)} = \frac{E_1}{2}\, \epsilon^{\, i\left(\frac{\pi}{2} + \theta\right)}, \qquad (13\text{-}16)$$

as indicated by the vector diagram in Fig. 13-4.

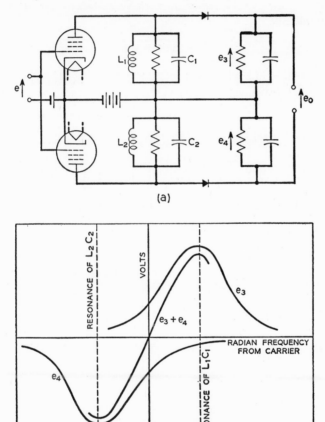

(a)

(b)

Fig. 13-3 Balanced frequency-modulation detector

It is assumed further that the rectifiers are perfect and the load of no consequence so that

$$e_1 = E_3 \quad \text{and} \quad e_2 = E_4. \qquad (13\text{-}17)$$

Now

$$E_3 = E_1 + E_2, \quad E_4 = E_1 - E_2, \quad \text{and} \quad e_0 = e_1 - e_2. \qquad (13\text{-}18)$$

By the law of cosines and using (13–18) and (13–15) it follows that

$$e_1 = E_3 = \sqrt{E_1{}^2 + E_2{}^2 - 2E_1E_2 \cos\left(\frac{\pi}{2} + \theta\right)} = E_1\sqrt{1.25 + \sin\theta} \quad (13\text{–}19)$$

and

$$e_2 = \sqrt{E_1{}^2 + E_2{}^2 - 2E_1E_2 \cos\left(\frac{\pi}{2} - \theta\right)} = E_1\sqrt{1.25 - \sin\theta} \quad (13\text{–}20)$$

and consequently

$$\frac{e_0}{E_1} = \sqrt{1.25 + \sin\theta} - \sqrt{1.25 - \sin\theta}. \quad (13\text{–}21)$$

The relation (13–21) is plotted in (c) of Fig. 13–4. Actually, the apparent linearity is deceptive, since the curve falls off as θ increases and is in error

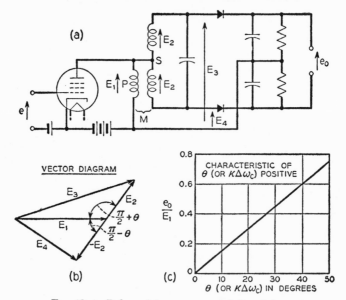

Fig. 13–4   Balanced frequency-modulation detector

by 5.5 per cent at 40 degrees as compared with a line of the same slope at the origin, and by 8 per cent at 50 degrees. Better linearity can be obtained by deliberately overcoupling the transformer and causing the voltages E_1 and E_2 to vary somewhat with frequency.

Other Types

Many other types of detectors for frequency modulation have been proposed and used. One of these, known as frequency-meter type, has recently (Ref. 22) been included in a monitoring instrument. In this type of detector, a pulse of uniform shape is generated every time the input wave passes through zero, and the area under each of these pulses is independent of the rate of occurrence. Thus, the integrated area under a sequence of these pulses is a direct measure of the instantaneous frequency. Another type of detector is based upon feedback and a homodyne detector. The homodyne detector is a product amplitude-demodulator and is supplied with two inputs. One is the incoming signal and the other is the output of a local high-quality frequency modulator at about the same frequency as the incoming signal. After passing through a low-pass filter, the homodyne detector output goes to the input of the local-frequency modulator where it operates to hold the local-modulator frequency in step with the frequency of the incoming signal. Thus, the input to the local modulator (the output of the homodyne detector) will be a direct measure of the modulation. In fact, it is the desired message.

References

1. Murray G. Crosby, "Reactance-Tube Frequency Modulators," *RCA Review*, New York, Vol. 5, July 1940, pp. 89–96.
2. C. F. Schaeffer, "Frequency Modulator," *Proceedings of the Institute of Radio Engineers*, New York, Vol. 28, February 1940, pp. 66–67.
3. A. K. Wing and J. E. Young, "A Transmitter for Frequency Modulated Broadcast Service Using a New Ultra-High-Frequency Tetrode," *RCA Review*, New York, Vol. 5, January 1941, pp. 327–336.
4. L. L. Koros and R. F. Schwartz, "Transistor Frequency Modulator Circuit," *Electronics*, New York, Vol. 24, July 1951, pp. 130–132, 134.
5. E. G. Hopkins, "Beam-Deflection Phase Modulator Valve," *A.W.A. Technical Review*, Vol. 9, No. 1, 1951, pp. 53–66.
6. Stuart W. Seeley, Charles N. Kimball, and Allen A. Barco, "Generation and Detection of Frequency-Modulated Waves," *RCA Review*, New York, Vol. 6, January 1942, pp. 269–286.
7. F. M. Bailey and H. P. Thomas, "Phasitron FM Transmitter," *Electronics*, New York, Vol. 19, October 1946, pp. 108–112.
8. John Ruston, "A Simple Crystal Discriminator for FM Oscillator Stabilization," *Proceedings of the Institute of Radio Engineers*, New York, Vol. 39, July 1951, pp. 783–788.
9. Hans Roder, "Theory of the Discriminator Circuit for Automatic Frequency Control," *Proceedings of the Institute of Radio Engineers*, New York, Vol. 26, May 1938, pp. 590–611.
10. S. W. Seeley, "The Ratio Detector," *RCA Review*, New York, Vol. 8, June 1947, pp. 201–236.
11. John L. Stewart, "A General Theory for Frequency Discriminators Containing Null Networks," *Proceedings of the Institute of Radio Engineers*, New York, Vol. 40, January 1952, pp. 55–57.
12. B. D. Loughlin, "The Theory of Amplitude-Modulation Rejection in the Ratio Detector," *Proceedings of the Institute of Radio Engineers*, New York, Vol. 40, March 1952, pp. 289–296.
13. J. G. Chaffee, "Application of Negative Feedback to Frequency Modulation Systems," *Proceedings of the Institute of Radio Engineers*, New York, Vol. 27, May 1939, pp. 317–331.

14. M. K. Zinn, "Transient Response of an FM Receiver," *The Bell System Technical Journal*, New York, Vol. 27, No. 4, October 1948, pp. 714–731.
15. F. B. Bramhall and L. A. Smith, "Nation-Wide Frequency-Modulated Telegraph Network," *Transactions of the American Institute of Electrical Engineers*, New York, Vol. 70, April 1951, pp. 373–378.
16. J. P. Chisholm, E. F. Buckley, and G. W. Farnell, "A Multichannel PAM–FM Radio Telemetering System," *Proceedings of the Institute of Radio Engineers*, New York, Vol. 39, January 1951, pp. 36–43.
17. J. G. Chaffee, "Frequency Modulation Terminal Equipment for Transcontinental Relay Systems," *Electrical Engineering*, New York, Vol. 70, October 1951, pp. 880–883.
18. L. R. Wrathall, "Frequency Modulation by Nonlinear Coils," *Bell Laboratories Record*, New York, Vol. 24, March 1946, pp. 102–105.
19. Balth van der Pol, "The Fundamental Principles of Frequency Modulation," *Proceedings of the Institution of Electrical Engineers*, London, Vol. 93, Part 3, 1946, pp. 153–158.
20. E. H. Armstrong, "A Method of Reducing Disturbances in Radio Signaling by a System of Frequency Modulation," *Proceedings of the Institute of Radio Engineers*, New York, Vol. 24, May 1936, pp. 689–740.
21. John R. Carson and Thornton C. Fry, "Variable Frequency Electric Circuit Theory with Application to the Theory of Frequency Modulation," *The Bell System Technical Journal*, New York, Vol. 16, No. 4, October 1937, pp. 513–540.
22. C. A. Cady, "A Frequency Monitor for Television Video Transmitters," *The General Radio Experimenter*, Cambridge, Massachusetts, Vol. 23, No. 4, September 1948, pp. 1–6.

Problems

1. A phase-modulated wave is produced by integrating the modulating wave and causing the integrated wave to amplitude-modulate $\cos \omega_c t$ in an ideal balanced product modulator the output of which is also supplied with a quadrature carrier component. The resultant output contains both amplitude and phase modulation.

   Assume the modulating wave is $\cos \omega_v t$. Show that the residual amplitude-modulation in the output of the modulator which would be detected by an envelope detector is composed of components that are even harmonics of the modulating frequency, that is components corresponding to the fundamental and all odd harmonics of the modulating frequency are absent.

2. In Problem 1, what is the phase deviation of the phase-modulated wave if the total amplitude modulation never exceeds one-tenth of one per cent of the unmodulated carrier?

3. If $M(t) = A_c \cos \omega_c t + A_1 \cos (\omega_c + \omega_v)t$, what is ω_i, the deviation of the instantaneous radian frequency from ω_c expressed as a function of time? In particular, what is ω_i for $A_1/A_c = 0.1$, 0.95, 1.0, 1.05, and 10 respectively?

4. A pulse carrier, $A_u \Sigma \dfrac{\sin m \dfrac{\pi}{2}}{m \dfrac{\pi}{2}} \cos m\omega_u t$, perturbs a phase-modulated wave

   $\cos [\omega_c t + kV(t)]$. The essential components of $V(t)$ are confined to the radian frequency range $0 < \omega_v < \omega_2$. A_u is restricted to the range $3 < A_u < 10$ and

ω_u to $0 < \omega_u < \dfrac{\omega_2}{10}$. The interfering pulse carrier is amplitude-modulated by $V_1(t)$ and duration-modulated by $V_2(t)$, where $V_1(t)$ and $V_2(t)$ are two independent modulating waves each restricted in frequency to essential components greater than zero and less than ω_u 20π.

How can the perturbed phase-modulated wave be treated so that a replica of $V(t)$ may be recovered with negligible distortion and negligible interference from the modulated pulse carrier? Assume distortionless transmission over a high-frequency channel that has a band width of $200\omega_2$.

CHAPTER 14

NOISE AND INTERFERENCE IN FM SYSTEMS

Although other systems may be more efficient, frequency modulation represents a simple and convenient way of exchanging band-width occupancy for improved signal-to-noise ratio. As in other systems which permit this type of exchange, the threshold effect is very pronounced for large improvements.

When the peak noise exceeds the peak unmodulated carrier, the zeros of the desired modulated wave change in number as well as position; or, in terms of a limiter, a phenomenon occurs which is commonly referred to as "breaking through" the limiter. When noise, characterized by a uniform power-density spectrum and random phases exceeds about 1/20 (13 decibels below) the average signal power, it is found in practice that breaking through the limiter begins to be noticeable.

For large modulation indices, the threshold is a critical function of the signal-to-noise ratio at the input to the limiter. At noise levels appreciably above this critical value, the signal-to-noise ratio rapidly deteriorates and becomes worse than the performance of an ordinary amplitude-modulation system.

The analysis of a frequency-modulation system at high noise levels is fairly complex and will not be treated here. Papers by S. O. Rice and F. L. H. M. Stumpers (Refs. 1 and 2)[*] deal with this topic in considerable detail.

RESISTANCE NOISE

The analysis will be limited to low noise levels, a situation commonly encountered in systems of communication and of considerable practical importance. Resistance noise will be assumed.

General Approach

It will be shown that frequency modulation can be used to drive the noise still lower by occupying a wider band in the transmission medium and, of course, by using a larger index of modulation in order to utilize

[*] The references cited are listed at the end of each chapter according to the number used in the text.

this wider band.   As a practical illustration of the advantage of frequency modulation, a comparison will be made with familiar systems of amplitude modulation, assuming the same noise-power density (noise power per cycle per second) at the detector inputs.

The signal-to-noise ratio at the output of a system will be defined as the ratio of the average power of a sinusoidal signal at a specified modulation level to the average noise power in the absence of a modulating wave. This definition of signal-to-noise ratio is commonly used in specifying the performance of telephone and program channels and is justified by the fact that noise is most serious when the signal is absent or at a low level. It turns out, as shown by other investigators, that, for low noise levels, the noise in the output of either an amplitude-modulation detector or a frequency-modulation detector is essentially independent of whether a modulating wave is present.   It is, of course, true that, for other types of messages which might use frequency modulation, the received noise may also be important when the wanted signal is present.

Amplitude Modulation

When an amplitude-modulated sinusoidal carrier is written as a function of time, we have (from Chapter 9)

$$M(t) = A_c[1 + kV(t)] \cos (\omega_c t + \Phi_c), \qquad (9\text{--}1)$$

and if $V(t) = A_v \cos (\omega_v t + \theta_v)$, the modulated wave is

$$M(t) = A_c[1 + kA_v \cos (\omega_v t + \theta_v)] \cos (\omega_c t + \Phi_c), \qquad (14\text{--}1)$$

and the average carrier power is

$$P_c = \frac{1}{2} A_c{}^2 \qquad (14\text{--}2)$$

in a circuit of one-ohm resistance.

When the foregoing wave is applied to an ideal amplitude-modulation detector, the output will be a signal voltage, e_s, proportional by a factor m to the modulation $kA_cA_v \cos (\omega_v t + \theta_v)$.   That is, an ideal amplitude-modulation detector merely translates the spectrum of each sideband, with or without inversion, to its original location.   Therefore,

$$e_s = mkA_cA_v \cos (\omega_v t + \theta_v), \qquad (14\text{--}3)$$

and the signal power S_0 from the detector is

$$S_0 = \frac{1}{2} m^2 k^2 A_c{}^2 A_v{}^2 = m^2 k^2 A_v{}^2 P_c \qquad (14\text{--}4)$$

where for convenience a one-ohm output circuit is assumed.

We recall that equation (14–3) may be obtained by multiplying (14–1) by $2m \cos (\omega_c t + \Phi_c)$ and rejecting the d-c term and the high-frequency terms falling above the essential frequency range of the modulating wave. This rejection can be provided by a low-pass filter at the detector output. Such a filter would pass all frequencies up to B with uniform attenuation and no distortion and essentially suppress all higher frequencies.

It is also assumed the detector would be preceded by an ideal band filter that transmits frequency components from $f_c - B$ to $f_c + B$ without loss and highly attenuates frequency components above and below. The noise-power density at the input to the detector is uniform and equal to n watts per cycle per second. Since (Ref. 1) the random, uncorrelated components will add on a power basis, the noise power at the input to the detector is $2Bn$. By using Parceval's theorem (since there is no correlation between the noise in the two sidebands), we deduce that the noise power at the output of the low-pass filter is

$$N_0 = m^2 2Bn. \tag{14-5}$$

Hence,

$$\frac{S_0}{N_0} = k^2 A_v{}^2 \frac{P_c}{2Bn} \tag{14-6}$$

where kA_v is recognized as the modulation factor.

Thus, the average signal-to-average noise power at the output of the detector is proportional to the square of the modulation factor. With 100 per cent modulation, the signal-to-noise ratio at the output is given by the ratio of average carrier power to average noise power at the input to the detector, that is,

$$\left[\frac{S_0}{N_0}\right]_{AM} = \frac{P_c}{2Bn}. \tag{14-7}$$

Frequency Modulation

Frequency modulation of a sinusoidal carrier by a sinusoidal modulating wave may be represented by (from Chapter 13):

$$M(t) = A_c \sin\left[\omega_c t + \frac{F}{f_v} \sin \omega_v t\right]. \tag{13-10}$$

Here F is the cyclic frequency deviation, f_v is the cyclic modulating frequency, and the instantaneous frequency (defined as the time rate of change of the argument) is given by

$$\omega_i = \omega_c + 2\pi F \cos \omega_v t$$
$$= \omega_c + \omega_F \cos \omega_v t \tag{14-8}$$

where ω_F is the angular frequency deviation.

Signal Output. The frequency detector is assumed to be ideal in every respect. For example, it does not recognize the presence of amplitude modulation, it is distortionless, and it is noise-free. When the wave of (13–10) is demodulated by the frequency detector, the voltage at the output of the low-pass filter, that is, the output of the detector, is given by

$$e_s = m\omega_F \cos \omega_v t \qquad (14\text{–}9)$$

where m is a factor of proportionality. The corresponding average output power in a one-ohm circuit is

$$S_0 = \frac{m^2 \omega_F{}^2}{2}. \qquad (14\text{–}10)$$

Sum of Two Sinusoids. At this point it will be helpful to recall the resultant of two sinusoids of different frequencies, as expressed by

$$R = A \cos \alpha + B \cos \beta. \qquad (14\text{–}11)$$

Set $\dfrac{B}{A} \equiv x$ and $\alpha - \beta \equiv \gamma$. Then,

$$\begin{aligned}
R &= A \cos \alpha + B \cos \alpha \cos \gamma + B \sin \alpha \sin \gamma \\
&= A[(1 + x \cos \gamma) \cos \alpha + (x \sin \gamma) \sin \alpha] \\
&= A\sqrt{1 + 2x \cos \gamma + x^2} \cos (\alpha - \theta) \qquad (14\text{–}12)
\end{aligned}$$

where

$$\theta = \tan^{-1} \frac{x \sin \gamma}{1 + x \cos \gamma}. \qquad (14\text{–}13)$$

If α and β are replaced by $\alpha - \dfrac{\pi}{2}$ and $\beta - \dfrac{\pi}{2}$, (14–11) and (14–12) become

$$R = A \sin \alpha + B \sin \beta$$

and

$$R = A\sqrt{1 + 2x \cos \gamma + x^2} \sin (\alpha - \theta), \qquad (14\text{–}14)$$

respectively, where θ is still given by (14–13).

Let $A = A_c$, $\alpha = \omega_c t$, and $\beta = (\omega_c + \omega_n)t$. Then, by noting that $\gamma = -\omega_n t$ and by using (14–14) and (14–13), we may write

$$R = A_c\sqrt{1 + 2x \cos \omega_n t + x^2} \sin [\omega_c t - \theta] \qquad (14\text{–}15)$$

where from (14–13),

$$\theta = \tan^{-1} \frac{-x \sin \omega_n t}{1 + x \cos \omega_n t}. \qquad (14\text{–}16)$$

Also,

$$\omega_i = \text{instantaneous radian frequency}$$

$$= \omega_c - \frac{d\theta}{dt}$$

$$= \omega_c + x\omega_n \frac{x + \cos \omega_n t}{1 + 2x \cos \omega_n t + x^2} \tag{14-17}$$

$$= \omega_c + \omega_n \frac{1}{1 + \dfrac{\dfrac{1}{x} + \cos \omega_n t}{x + \cos \omega_n t}} \tag{14-18}$$

$$= \omega_c + \omega_n - \omega_n \frac{\dfrac{1}{x^2} + \dfrac{1}{x} \cos \omega_n t}{1 + \dfrac{1}{x^2} + \dfrac{2}{x} \cos \omega_n t}. \tag{14-19}$$

Equation (14-15) is exact and may be regarded as a sinusoid that has been both amplitude-modulated and angle-modulated. If this wave goes to an ideal frequency demodulator, such as a balanced linear discriminator tuned to $\omega_c/2\pi$, the output will be proportional to the deviation of the instantaneous frequency from the carrier, as expressed by the last two right-hand terms of (14-19).

When x is a positive real, the factor multiplying ω_n in (14-18) is greater or less than $\frac{1}{2}$ as x is greater or less than unity, and varies over a modulating cycle depending on x. The factor may be written $F(x,\omega_n t)$ and satisfies $F(1/x,\omega_n t) = 1 - F(x,\omega_n t)$. As x varies from small to large values, the change in instantaneous frequency approaches $\omega_n/2\pi$. As x approaches unity from above or below, there is at $x = 1$ a reversal in the polarity of the angle modulation. With increasing x, this means $B = xA_c$ grabs control when x exceeds unity.

This transfer of control is indicated by the following consideration. When the sum of two sinusoids is expressed as a single sinusoid with a variable amplitude and variable argument (14-15), an examination of the amplitude factor will show that, provided $x \neq 1$, the radicand never goes through zero regardless of the possible values of $\cos \gamma$. Thus all the zeros of (14-15) must be included in the sinusoidal factor. Incidentally, the factors A and B can always be made positive by an appropriate choice of the origin of reference or by a suitable choice of the arguments of the sinusoids.

Noise Output. Assume here, as previously, that the carrier is not modulated when the noise is to be evaluated, and that uncorrelated noise is uniformly distributed in frequency over the frequency range accepted at the detector input. Assume further that the band of noise may be replaced by a large number of sinusoidal elements, each of amplitude ΔN and unrelated in phase and frequency. For exact representation of the noise wave, the sampling principle specifies the least number of sinusoidal elements conforming to this specification.

Since $x = \dfrac{\Delta N}{A_c} \ll 1$, if we combine equations (14–13) and (14–14), the sum of a particular incremental noise sinusoid and the unmodulated carrier may be written to a first approximation in the form

$$R = A_c \sin \omega_c t + \Delta N \sin \left[(\omega_c + \omega_n)t + \Phi_n \right]$$
$$\approx A_c \sqrt{1 + 2x \cos (\omega_n t + \Phi_n)} \, \sin \left[\omega_c t + x \sin (\omega_n t + \Phi_n) \right]. \quad (14\text{–}20)$$

This is in the same form as (13–10). The instantaneous frequency is given by

$$\omega_i \approx \omega_c + \frac{\Delta N}{A_c} \omega_n \cos (\omega_n t + \Phi_n) \qquad (14\text{–}21)$$

which is in the same form as (14–8).

Equation (14–20) represents a composite wave consisting of the unmodulated carrier plus an incremental noise component, and the instantaneous frequency of this wave is given by (14–21). When the composite wave is applied to the same frequency demodulator, amplitude modulation may be ignored, and the incremental output noise voltage e_n will be

$$e_n = m \frac{\Delta N}{A_c} \omega_n \cos (\omega_n t + \Phi_n). \qquad (14\text{–}22)$$

The incremental noise power dN_n in the assumed one-ohm output circuit is given by

$$dN_n = \frac{m^2}{2} \left[\frac{\Delta N}{A_c} \right]^2 \omega_n^2. \qquad (14\text{–}23)$$

Since x is small and consequently the frequency deviation is small, it may be assumed, to a rough approximation, that superposition applies. Accordingly, the net noise may be approximated by finding the separate noise output corresponding to each incremental component at the input and evaluating their sum.

If df is an elementary width of band that includes the frequency represented by the sinusoid of amplitude ΔN, then, for a one-ohm load resistance,

$$\Delta N = \sqrt{2n \, df} \qquad (14\text{–}24)$$

where n is the uniform noise density in watts per cycle per second and ΔN is in volts. The factor $\sqrt{2}$ appears because ΔN is the amplitude of the sinusoid. When we place the right-hand member of (14–24) in (14–23), we have

$$dN_n = m^2 \frac{\omega_n^2}{A_c^2} n \, df. \qquad (14\text{–}25)$$

It is important to note that, in the absence of signal, the output frequency of the interfering noise is the same frequency as the absolute value of the difference between the original noise frequency and the carrier frequency. Although average noise power output is independent of modulation for the type of noise and modulating wave assumed, as the modulation varies, noise components are contributed by different parts of the spectrum.

Also, (14–22) provides the basis for the familiar statement that frequency modulation yields a triangular noise spectrum, since the angular frequency ω_n appears as a factor in the differential noise output voltage. That is, the magnitude of the incremental noise voltage at the output increases linearly with the frequency difference of the interfering component from the carrier.

The average output noise power N_0 is closely approximated by

$$N_0 = \int dN_n = \int_{-B}^{B} m^2 \frac{\omega_n^2}{A_c^2} n \, df = \frac{8\pi^2 m^2}{3A_c^2} nB^3. \tag{14–26}$$

Since $P_c = \dfrac{A_c^2}{2}$, (14–26) may be written

$$N_0 = \frac{4\pi^2}{3} \frac{m^2}{P_c} nB^3. \tag{14–27}$$

Signal-to-Noise Ratio. On the basis of the previous assumptions, the signal-to-noise ratio at the output of a frequency-modulation system is given by dividing (14–10) by (14–27), viz.,

$$\left[\frac{S_0}{N_0}\right]_{\text{FM}} = 3\left[\frac{F}{B}\right]^2 \frac{P_c}{2Bn}. \tag{14–28}$$

The last factor on the right in (14–28) is recognized as the ratio (at the input of the detector) of the average carrier power to the average noise power in the pair of noise sidebands immediately above and below the carrier. The signal-to-noise ratio at the output of the detector is proportional to the square of the ratio of the frequency deviation to the band width of the output filter.

Thus, it is seen that the signal-to-noise ratio may be increased indefinitely by increasing the frequency deviation F, so long as "break through" of the limiter does not occur. However, as F is increased, the band width of the transmission medium must be increased to minimize distortion, and thus a wider band of noise is accepted. Hence, for a given transmitter power and a specified medium there is a limit to F and, therefore, to the improvement.

In amplitude modulation the output signal and noise powers are proportional to the incoming signal and noise. In a frequency-modulation system, when the frequency deviation is large compared with the frequency of the modulating wave, and when the signal-to-noise ratio at the input to the detector is substantially less than one, the signal-to-noise ratio at the output is large. When the signal and noise at the input are equal, the output is very noisy. If now the noise is gradually increased, once the noise substantially exceeds the unmodulated carrier, the noise "grabs" or takes over, and the wanted signal is badly distorted and soon deleted.

One of the reasons for noise reduction with increasing band-width occupancy is that small noise perturbations tend to alter the modulated wave in a way that the receiver chooses to ignore. In the absence of noise, the many side-frequency components of the modulated wave are individually of just such amplitude and phase as to cause large deviations in the instantaneous frequency during a modulating cycle. In the absence of signal, because the noise components are random, small, and uncorrelated, their maximum effect in changing the instantaneous frequency is small.

Component parts of the demodulator do not account fundamentally for noise reduction. They are merely aids in realizing more closely an ideal frequency demodulator which is sensitive only to frequency modulation. For example, the function of the limiter is to wipe off amplitude modulation, whereas the dual function of a balanced linear discriminator is to make pure amplitude modulation nugatory and to produce an output that is proportional to the deviation of the instantaneous frequency from the carrier.

Other equally effective alternatives would serve as well. If we assume large signal-to-noise ratios and perfect transmission, the theoretical possibility of signal-to-noise improvement by frequency modulation requires, first, the production of a frequency-modulated wave whose frequency deviation exceeds $B/\sqrt{3}$ and, second, detection by a sufficiently exact frequency demodulator.

Comparison of Amplitude and Frequency Modulation

The signal-to-noise ratios already developed allow at least one direct comparison between amplitude and frequency modulation. This is on the basis of the same carrier power, the same noise-power density at the detector input, and full modulation. The comparison is obtained by dividing (14–28) by (14–7) which gives

$$\frac{\left[\dfrac{S_0}{N_0}\right]_{FM}}{\left[\dfrac{S_0}{N_0}\right]_{AM}} = 3\,\frac{F^2}{B^2}. \tag{14–29}$$

For this case it is obvious that frequency modulation, in exchange for band-width occupancy, can provide much better transmission than amplitude modulation.

On the basis of the same peak power at the transmitter, single-sideband modulation, as shown in Chapter 9, has an eight-to-one noise advantage over conventional amplitude modulation. It is also true, however, that, when peak power is the basis of comparison, frequency modulation provides another four-to-one advantage over amplitude modulation beyond

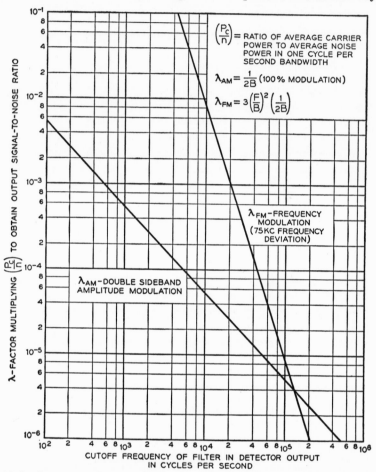

Fig. 14–1 Output signal-to-noise ratios of a double-sideband, amplitude-modulation detector and a frequency-modulation detector (75 kilocycle-per-second frequency deviation); cutoff of output low-pass filter varied; noise-power density at detector inputs constant

that shown by (14–29). Therefore, if the peak power delivered by transmitter is the same, the noise performance of frequency modulation as compared to single sideband is

$$\frac{\left[\dfrac{S_0}{N_0}\right]_{\text{FM}}}{\left[\dfrac{S_0}{N_0}\right]_{\text{SSM}}} = \frac{3}{2}\frac{F^2}{B^2}. \tag{14–30}$$

Figures 14–1 and 14–2 show some of the foregoing relationships.   In these figures the factor λ is the ratio of carrier-power to noise-power density.

In Fig. 14–1 the noise performance is shown as a function of the cutoff in cycles per second of the low-pass filter located in the output of the sys-

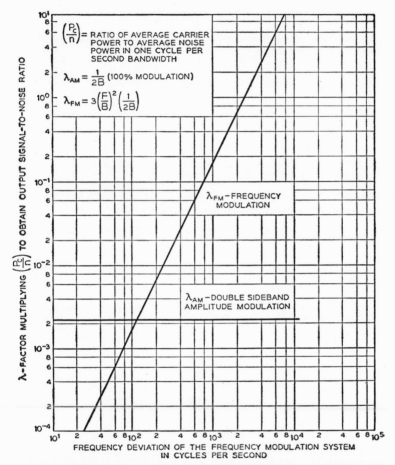

Fig. 14–2   Output signal-to-noise ratios of a double-sideband, amplitude-modulation detector and a frequency-modulation detector; output low-pass filter cutoff, 200 cycles per second; deviation of frequency-modulated wave varied; noise power density at detector input constant

tem.   It is evident that the frequency-modulation system improves at a logarithmic rate three times that of the amplitude-modulation system as the cutoff frequency of the output filter is reduced.

For a fixed frequency deviation of 75 kilocycles per second as shown, for example, in Fig. 14–1, the performance of the frequency-modulation system is much better in the range of interest for broadcast purposes.   For

$B = 15,000$ cycles per second, the improvement ratio is seventy-five to one, or 18.8 decibels. It is of interest to note that the noise performances are equal when $B = \sqrt{3} \, F$ or, in the case shown, when $B = 130$ kilocycles per second.

In Fig. 14–2 the factor λ is plotted as a function of the frequency deviation. This has no effect on an amplitude-modulation system, but has a substantial effect on a frequency-modulation system. There is a 6-decibel or four-to-one improvement in the ratio of signal power to noise power for each two-to-one increase in the frequency deviation, provided B is held constant (at 200 cycles per second for the example illustrated by Fig. 14–2).

Large Noise Theory

As mentioned previously, a high noise level exceeding the improvement threshold, as evidenced by breaking through the limiter, requires an entirely different type of analysis. References 1 and 2 treat this problem and demonstrate that the output noise of a frequency-modulation system increases sharply at a critical noise level and, finally, as the input noise is further increased, a saturation effect prevents further increase in output noise. It is also shown that any signal in the presence of high noise tends to be suppressed.

DE–EMPHASIS

General Theory

In many systems of communication the magnitude of the modulating wave varies statistically as a function of frequency. For example, in voice and many other types of signals, the energy at the upper end of the signal spectrum is a great deal less than at the lower end. To take advantage of this, at the transmitting end the signal is first passed through a network that leaves the low signal frequencies unaffected but increases the higher signal frequencies. This process is called pre-emphasis.

In order to restore the signal components to their proper relationship, the inverse process is carried out at the receiver. This is called de-emphasis. As a result, the output signal is not appreciably altered by the addition of pre-emphasis and de-emphasis networks. However, even though the signal is unaffected, noise will be affected because the de-emphasis network is in the significant noise path.

In practice, de-emphasis is usually accomplished by a simple resistor-capacitor combination in the signal path of the demodulator. The circuit employed in many frequency-modulation receivers appears in Fig. 14–3. A time constant τ of 75 microseconds is commonly used for broadcast reception. As compared with no pre-emphasis, in practice pre-emphasis of the signals to match the network of Fig. 14–3 may require that the modulation level of the transmitter at low frequencies be reduced. In the treatment to follow, this factor will be ignored. The signal used for comparison purposes will be a sinusoidal modulating wave at a low frequency not appreciably affected by pre-emphasis. At this frequency it will be assumed that the modulation level is the same as with no pre-emphasis.

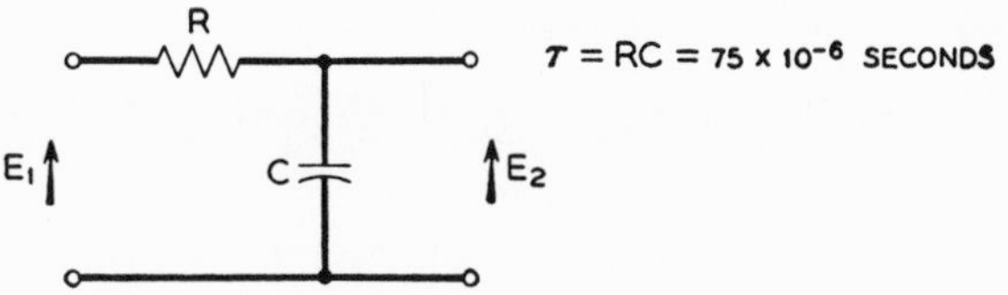

FIG. 14–3   Simple de-emphasis network

The transmission characteristic of the network of Fig. 14–3 may be regarded as given by

$$\frac{E_2}{E_1} = \frac{\dfrac{1}{iC\omega}}{R + \dfrac{1}{iC\omega}} = \frac{1}{i\omega\tau + 1} \tag{14-31}$$

where ω is the radian frequency of an assumed demodulated noise component and $\tau = RC$. The square of the absolute value of this ratio, namely,

$$\left|\frac{E_2}{E_1}\right|^2 = \frac{1}{1 + \omega^2\tau^2} \tag{14-32}$$

is of particular interest.

The technique now involves application of (14–32) to expressions for the incremental noise voltage squared. The phase angle of the transmission characteristic is of no concern since the phases of the noise components representing resistance noise are random and the integration is on a voltage squared or power basis. Integration of the new expressions for the incremental output noise then gives the noise with the de-emphasis network in the demodulator output. Because of the shape of the noise spectrum in a frequency modulation system, the de-emphasis network is particularly effective for this type of modulation.

Amplitude Modulation

Without de-emphasis

$$N_0 = 2m^2n \int_0^B df = m^2 2Bn. \tag{14-33}$$

With de-emphasis

$$[N_0]_d = 2m^2n \int_0^B \frac{df}{1 + 4\pi^2\tau^2f^2}$$

$$= \frac{m^2n}{\pi\tau} \tan^{-1} 2\pi B\tau. \tag{14-34}$$

The improvement in the ratio of average signal power to average noise power due to de-emphasis is given by

$$\frac{N_0}{[N_0]_d} = \frac{2\pi B\tau}{\tan^{-1} 2\pi B\tau}, \tag{14-35}$$

and with the aid of (14-6) we obtain

$$\left[\frac{S_0}{N_0}\right]_{AM-D} = [k^2 A_v^2]\left[\frac{P_c}{2Bn}\right]\left[\frac{2\pi B\tau}{\tan^{-1} 2\pi B\tau}\right]. \tag{14-36}$$

The first factor on the right is the modulation factor squared; the second, the ratio at the detector input of average carrier power to average noise power; and the third, the improvement factor due to de-emphasis. With complete modulation, $k^2 A_v^2 = 1$ and

$$\left[\frac{S_0}{N_0}\right]_{AM-D} = \left[\frac{P_c}{2Bn}\right]\left[\frac{2\pi B\tau}{\tan^{-1} 2\pi B\tau}\right]. \tag{14-37}$$

The improvement factor due to de-emphasis will be designated ψ_{AM}, viz.,

$$\left[\frac{S_0}{N_0}\right]_{AM-D} = \psi_{AM}\left[\frac{S_0}{N_0}\right]_{AM}. \tag{14-38}$$

The factor ψ_{AM} for a de-emphasis time constant of 75 microseconds is shown in Fig. 14-4 for a variable low-pass filter cutoff. Consideration of ψ_{AM} for small angles shows that ψ_{AM} approaches unity as B approaches zero. It is of interest to note the rate at which the improvement factor increases for large cutoff frequencies, and this may be done by expanding the inverse tangent in an infinite series, viz.,

$$\tan^{-1} x = \frac{\pi}{2} - \frac{1}{x} + \frac{1}{3x^3} - \frac{1}{5x^5} + \cdots, \quad x^2 > 1.$$

With this substitution,

$$\psi_{AM} = \frac{2\pi B\tau}{\dfrac{\pi}{2} - \dfrac{1}{2\pi B\tau} + \cdots}, \quad 2\pi B\tau > 1. \tag{14-39}$$

As B becomes very large,

$$\lim_{B \to \infty}, \quad \psi_{AM} \to 4B\tau. \tag{14-40}$$

Thus, when the band width of the low-pass filter is large, the improvement is proportional to the band width used.

Frequency Modulation

Without de-emphasis

$$N_0 = \frac{8m^2 n\pi^2}{A_c^2}\int_0^B f^2\, df = \frac{8\pi^2 m^2}{3A_c^2} nB^3 = \frac{m^2 n}{P_c}\frac{4\pi^2 B^3}{3}. \tag{14-26}$$

With de-emphasis

$$[N_0]_d = \frac{8m^2n\pi^2}{A_c^2} \int_0^B \frac{f^2\,df}{1 + 4\pi^2\tau^2f^2} = \frac{m^2n}{P_c\tau^2}\left[B - \frac{1}{2\pi\tau}\tan^{-1}2\pi B\tau\right] \quad (14\text{-}41)$$

and

$$\psi_{\mathrm{FM}} = \frac{N_0}{[N_0]_d} = \frac{(2\pi B\tau)^3}{3[2\pi B\tau - \tan^{-1}2\pi B\tau]}. \quad (14\text{-}42)$$

Also

$$\lim_{B \to 0}, \quad \psi_{\mathrm{FM}} \to 1 \quad (14\text{-}43)$$

and

$$\lim_{B \to \infty}, \quad \psi_{\mathrm{FM}} \to \frac{(2\pi B\tau)^2}{3}. \quad (14\text{-}44)$$

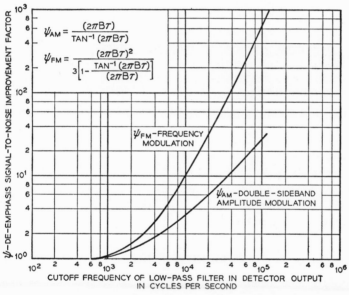

Fig. 14-4   Improvement in output signal-to-noise ratios of a double-sideband, amplitude-modulation detector and a frequency-modulation detector for a de-emphasizing time constant τ of 75×10^{-6} second; cutoff frequency of output low-pass filter varied; noise-power density at detector inputs constant

Thus, when B is very small, the improvement factor due to de-emphasis reduces to unity. When B is large, the improvement factor is proportional to B^2 instead of B as in the case of amplitude modulation. For purposes of comparison both ψ_{FM} and ψ_{AM} were plotted on Fig. 14-4.

The signal-to-noise ratio is given by

$$\left[\frac{S_0}{N_0}\right]_{\mathrm{FM-D}} = \psi_{\mathrm{FM}}\left[\frac{S_0}{N_0}\right]_{\mathrm{FM}} \quad (14\text{-}45)$$

where the factors on the right are given by (14-42) and (14-28).

INTERFERENCE BETWEEN SIMILAR SYSTEMS

In general, it works out that a wide-band frequency-modulation system is relatively immune to interference from other systems for exactly the same reason that explains the noise improvement. Compared on the basis of crosstalk between adjacent channels in the spectrum, frequency modulation also has the further advantage that the crosstalk is less intelligible and, therefore, less distracting. Compared with amplitude modulation, the interchannel crosstalk is less, and a broadcast transmitter requires less power to cover a given area.

The tendency of frequency modulation to favor the strongest signal affects intersystem interference in an important way. Imagine two stations spaced geographically and operating on the same frequency. Consider that a receiver is carried from one to the other of these stations. With a large-index frequency-modulation system, the mid-range region within which the two signals are both heard is relatively small, much smaller than for an amplitude-modulation system. According to studies made by the British Broadcasting Corporation (Ref. 12), a separation ratio of 30 decibels between the signals from two stations causes no perceptible interference in the output of a receiver, whereas, when the ratio falls to 10 decibels, the interference completely ruins intelligence.

The channel-grabbing characteristic can produce some annoying effects if the receiver is located between two transmitters operating at the same frequency. When fading conditions exist, it may so happen that the receiver will switch from one signal to the other, depending on their relative field intensity at the receiver.

IMPULSE NOISE

As already mentioned, resistance noise may be regarded as having a uniform power-density spectrum over the radio-frequency acceptance band but random phases. Although impulse noise has a uniform power-density spectrum, the components are so phased that at certain times they all add. Hence, the magnitude of impulse noise increases in proportion to the accepted band width.

The foregoing discussion implies that the carrier power required to reach the improvement threshold will be greater for impulse noise, and this is indeed the case. Fortunately, however, it becomes less necessary for the signal to override impulse noise because the duration of the impulse is short. Even though the signal may be completely eliminated by noise for a brief interval, the degradation is likely to be slight.

The magnitude of the interference produced in the output of the receiver is determined by the change in instantaneous frequency. The change in instantaneous frequency caused by an impulse is limited by the band width of the intermediate-frequency path to something not much larger than the frequency deviation. The duration of the interruption to signal reception in the output of the receiver is also determined essentially by the band width of the intermediate-frequency path. With a broadcast system using a frequency deviation of 75 kilocycles per second, this duration is only 13 microseconds. The acoustic effect of such a short interruption would be extremely small. Since impulse noise originating in man-made sources is not uncommon, this characteristic of frequency modulation is very important.

The possibilities of reducing the effects of high values of impulse noise are not limited to frequency modulation. A good amplitude limiter in a wide-band intermediate-frequency stage achieves much the same result for an amplitude-modulated receiver. Such a limiter is described in Reference 13, and a similar principle has been utilized in other experimental receivers.

DISTORTION IN FREQUENCY MODULATION

In the usual forms of frequency-modulation receiver, too narrow a band in the high-frequency circuits will cause nonlinear distortion. Similarly, phase irregularities in the transmission path may also produce nonlinear distortion because the component vectors then add improperly. Fading, even in the microwave range, may be a source of serious distortion inasmuch as such effects in the radio-frequency propagation path may introduce severe phase variations. Multipath transmission, with consequent selective fading, will be a source of severe distortion if the selective fades are so deep that they cause breaking through the limiter. Reasons for the distortion are fairly obvious when the steady-state transmission characteristic is considered.

Phase distortion in a frequency-modulation system can so rotate the side frequencies that frequency modulation is transformed into amplitude modulation. When this occurs ahead of the receiver limiter, the amplitude modulation is eliminated. No equalizer can restore the frequency modulation after limiting. The effect varies as an even function of the phase distortion. Second-order distortion varies as an odd function and can be minimized by equalization of opposite side frequencies. Odd-order products of distortion cannot be improved in this way.

References

1. S. O. Rice, "Statistical Properties of a Sine Wave Plus Random Noise," *The Bell System Technical Journal*, New York, Vol. 27, No. 1, January 1948, pp. 109–157.

2. F. L. H. M. Stumpers, "Theory of Frequency-Modulation Noise," *Proceedings of the Institute of Radio Engineers*, New York, Vol. 36, September 1948, pp. 1081–1092.

3. Murlan S. Corrington, "Frequency-Modulation Distortion Caused by Common and Adjacent Channel Interference," *RCA Review*, New York, Vol. 7, December 1946, pp. 522–560.

4. Murray G. Crosby, "Frequency-Modulation Noise Characteristics," *Proceedings of the Institute of Radio Engineers*, New York, Vol. 25, April 1937, pp. 472–514.

5. Stanford Goldman, "Frequency-Modulation Noise and Interference," *Electronics*, New York, Vol. 14, August 1941, pp. 37–42.

6. L. Riebman, "Distortion in Linear Passive Networks," *Proceedings of the Institute of Radio Engineers*, New York, Vol. 39, June 1951, pp. 692–697.

7. R. M. Wilmotte, "Reduction of Interference in FM Receiver by Feedback Across the Limiter," *Proceedings of the Institute of Radio Engineers*, New York, Vol. 40, January 1952, pp. 34–36.

8. Murray G. Crosby, "Frequency-Modulation Propagation Characteristics," *Proceedings of the Institute of Radio Engineers*, New York, Vol. 24, 1936, pp. 898–913.

9. L. B. Arguimbau and J. G. Granlund, "Sky-Wave FM Receiver," *Electronics*, New York, Vol. 22, December 1949, pp. 101–103.

10. D. G. Lindsay, "A Dual-Diversity Frequency-Shift Receiver," *Proceedings of the Institute of Radio Engineers*, New York, Vol. 39, June 1951, pp. 598–612.

11. Murray G. Crosby, "The Service Range of Frequency Modulation," *RCA Review*, New York, Vol. 4, No. 3, January 1940, pp. 349–371.

12. "Frequency-Modulation Tests," British Broadcasting Company, *Wireless World*, London, Vol. 52, October 1946, pp. 316–320.

13. James F. Lamb, "A Noise Silencing I. F. Circuit for Superheterodyne Receivers," *QST*, West Hartford, Connecticut, February 1936, p. 11.

Problems

1. A sinusoidal carrier $\cos \omega_c t$ plus resistance noise goes to a distortionless filter having a pass band that is essentially limited to frequencies ranging from $f_c - B$ to $f_c + B$. The ratio of carrier to noise is large. The output of the filter goes to a quiet linear amplifier the output of which is divided into two independent parts. One goes to an ideal product-demodulator, the other to an ideal frequency-demodulator. Included in the output of each demodulator is a low-pass filter capable of passing without distortion all frequencies less than B cycles per second.

   Is there any way the noise out of the product-demodulator can be modified so as to approximate closely, at all instants of time, the noise out of the frequency demodulator?

2. In Problem 1 assume the carrier frequency is very high and replace the frequency-demodulator by an ideal envelope-detector. What is the difference between the noise out of the envelope-detector and the noise out of the product-demodulator?

3. A phase-modulation system and an amplitude-modulation system are equally vulnerable to resistance noise when transmission is over the same medium. The amplitude-modulation system transmits the carrier and both sidebands. The loss over the medium is independent of frequency, and the carrier power is the same in the two cases. The peak phase deviation with PM is 20 degrees. What is the percentage peak modulation with AM?

4. Frequency modulation without de-emphasis results in a received noise power which varies as the cube of the band width when the interference is resistance noise due to thermal agitation. Explain.

5. Assume a frequency-demodulator as shown including a limiter preceded by an ideal band-filter that accepts without loss a band of 150 kilocycles per second and attenuates completely outside this band. The frequency of the unmodulated carrier is in the center of this band. Assume also an ideal, 10-kilocycle-per-second, low-pass filter in the output. The ratio of average carrier power to total average noise power at A is 40 decibels. Assume resistance noise. Assume the input is a frequency-modulated wave that has been modulated by a sinusoidal signal. The frequency deviation of the frequency-modulated wave is 50 kilocycles per second.

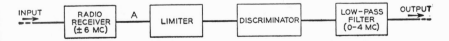

(a) What is the ratio in the output of average signal power to average noise power expressed in decibels?

(b) What is the ratio in (a) if a simple resistor-capacitor de-emphasis network whose time constant is 100 microseconds is used in the output of the demodulator?

6. In Problem 5 assume that the limiter and frequency-demodulator are replaced by an ideal, double-sideband, amplitude-modulation demodulator and that the signal is replaced by an amplitude-modulated carrier that has been 100 per cent modulated by a sinusoidal modulating wave. Assume also that the average carrier power to total average noise power is 40 decibels. What is the ratio in decibels of average signal power to average noise power in the output of the demodulator?

7. It is desired to transmit 20-kilocycle-per-second program channels using pulse-code modulation over an existing frequency-modulation radio system. The radio system has a low-pass or base band, that is, a video pass-band of 120 kilocycles per second, and may be frequency-modulated ± 240 kilocycles per second. The receiver band width (at intermediate frequencies) is 480 kilocycles per second. Under nonfading conditions the signal-to-noise ratio (ratio of average powers) as measured at the output of the intermediate-frequency amplifier is 53 decibels. For purposes of computation it may be assumed that the peak video noise is 13 decibels above the root-mean-square video noise.

(a) If a 30-decibel fading margin is to be allowed, how many pulse-code-modulation channels each having 529 linear quantum steps may be transmitted over a single-link radio system without errors due to noise? Describe the code used.

(b) Suppose the system is to be extended to ten identical links. If a fade of 30 decibels may occur in any or all links at the same time, and complete freedom of instrumentation is afforded, how many program channels may be transmitted? Describe briefly the code and necessary instrumentation.

8. Consider a radio receiving system as shown:

The radio receiver accepts without loss a frequency band 12 megacycles per second wide and attenuates completely outside the pass band. The unmodulated carrier is centered in the pass band of the receiver. The output low-pass filter has the characteristic of an ideal structure, cutting off at 4 megacycles per second. Assume that the only noise is resistance noise and that the ratio of average carrier power to average noise power is 50 decibels at point A. The received signal is a frequency-modulated wave deviated by a television signal and the instantaneous peak-to-peak frequency excursion is 8 megacycles per second.

(a) What is the ratio of peak-to-peak output signal to average noise signal? (Ratio in decibels of the average power in a sinusoidal signal, the root-mean-square value of which is equal to the peak-to-peak video signal, to the average noise power in the absence of modulation.)

(b) What theoretical noise improvement could be realized by using simple pre-emphasis and de-emphasis RC networks with a time constant of 0.5 microsecond?

CHAPTER 15

PULSE–MODULATION ESSENTIALS

Pulse modulation as distinct from *pulse-code modulation* will be adopted as a designation for unquantized pulse modulation. Familiar examples are pulse-amplitude modulation (PAM), pulse-duration modulation (PDM), and pulse-position modulation (PPM). Any of these may be quantized, and, in terms of present nomenclature, they then come under the heading of pulse-code modulation.

Certain operating features are essentially the same for any pulse system. These are reviewed in the present chapter, and the review will provide background material for use in subsequent chapters.

SAMPLING

In a pulse-modulation system, the message information is transmitted intermittently rather than continuously. A series of discrete pulses (unquantized code elements) rather than a continuously changing wave carries the specification of the message. When the message is not already made up of values arranged in a discrete time sequence, it must be reduced to this form before transmission. Sampling affords a means for representing a continuously varying wave by a series of single values. Sampling is important, but it may be only a preliminary step in a pulse-modulation process.

The sampling principle has been treated in Chapter 4. For the present purpose, it will suffice to recall one conclusion. This is that successive instantaneous measurements of magnitude made upon a continuous message wave, such as speech, at the rate of $2B$ measurements per second (where B is the significant band width of the message in cycles per second) provide enough information for reconstruction of the original wave.

With PAM, PDM, and PPM systems, one pulse normally specifies each sample of the message wave. In these cases, the minimum number of pulses is $2B$ per second per channel.

MULTIPLEXING

Characteristic of pulse modulation is the comparative ease with which channels may be multiplexed by time division as distinguished from fre-

quency division. Multiplexing by time division simplifies instrumentation, since relatively simple synchronous switches or gating circuits replace
the modulators, demodulators, carrier generators, and band-pass filters
ordinarily employed in a frequency-division system. Many of the terminal operations can be common to a plurality of channels.

The foregoing discussion is not intended to suggest that, for all multiplex transmission, pulse modulation with time division is preferred when
all factors are considered. In any practical application a final choice will
be influenced by many factors pertaining to the particular situation.

Numerous combinations and variations of the pulse modulating process
are possible. One example is a time-division system wherein individual
pulses are modulated in different ways by several independent modulating
waves. If it were permissible to widen the band, each pulse of a PPM
array might, in addition, be independently amplitude-modulated and also
independently varied in duration. This triply modulated pulse train could
then be made to amplitude-modulate a frequency-modulated wave. This
frequency-modulated wave could have been generated by letting another
triply modulated pulse train frequency-modulate a sinusoidal carrier. In
this way a total of six messages might be impressed upon one wave by this
complicated process of multidimensional modulation.

It is not suggested that the foregoing illustrative example is either practical or efficient. However, other combinations might find practical application, particularly in conjunction with appropriate nonlinear operations.
In any event, it should be appreciated that useful systems are not limited
to the ones enumerated.

Method of Operation

Conventional multiplexing of channels in time division is accomplished
at the transmitting terminal by feeding pulses from the channel equipment to a common output circuit, and by controlling the generation of
individual pulses so that pulses for different channels fall within successive
and recurrent intervals of time. This is illustrated by the three-channel
PPM system shown in schematic form at the top of Fig. 15–1. This schematic represents only one of many alternative arrangements and is described only to illustrate the basic operations involved in multiplexing
position-modulated pulses.

In Fig. 15–1, (b) depicts the relative times of occurrence of the pulses
for the individual channels and also the multichannel array obtained after
interleaving the individual channel pulses. The positions occupied by
unmodulated pulses are indicated by solid lines, and the positions occupied
by pulses modulated to the maximum extent are indicated by dotted lines.
Marker pulses are used for synchronization. In this example, the marker
pulses are of greater duration than the channel pulses. The interval oc-

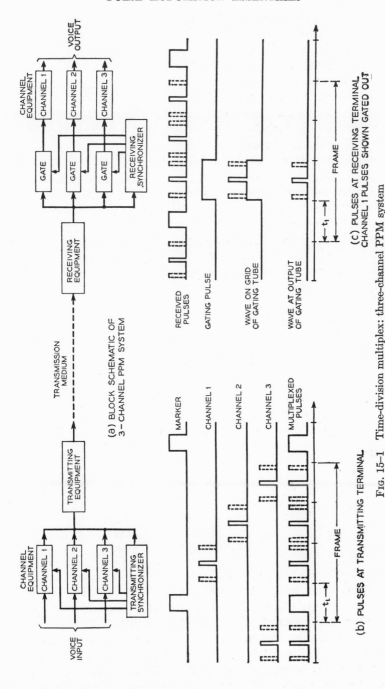

(a) BLOCK SCHEMATIC OF 3–CHANNEL PPM SYSTEM

(b) PULSES AT TRANSMITTING TERMINAL

(c) PULSES AT RECEIVING TERMINAL CHANNEL 1 PULSES SHOWN GATED OUT

FIG. 15–1 Time-division multiplex: three-channel PPM system

cupied by one complete set of pulses (in this case a marker pulse and one pulse for each message channel) is called a *frame*.

The timing of each channel pulse is controlled by a synchronizer. Usually the synchronizer includes a plurality of synchronized pulse generators that control certain synchronized operations. As indicated in Fig. 15–1, and as is usually the case, the available time is divided equally among all channels. Thus, if the duration of a frame is T seconds and if the number of similar channels (including the marker pulse) is N, the frame time allotted to a particular channel is T/N seconds.

At the output of the block labelled "receiving equipment" in (a) of Fig. 15–1, multiplexed pulses are recovered in approximately their original form. From the receiving equipment they go to electronic circuits, called *gates*, which separate them and route them to the proper channel equipment. This is done by timing the "open" and "closed" intervals of the gates so that a particular channel gate is open only when the pulses that should pass this gate are being received. Operation of the gates is controlled by pulses from the synchronizer.

Gate Circuits

There are several varieties of gate circuits. A simplified form of one in common use appears in Fig. 15–2. In this circuit, pulses from the receiving equipment are combined with rectangular pulses from the synchronizer

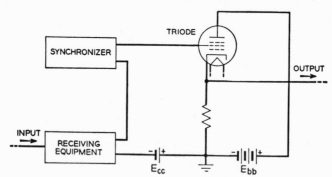

FIG. 15–2 Gate circuit, simplified drawing

and impressed upon the grid of a triode along with a negative biasing voltage. Pulses from the synchronizer are of positive polarity. Their magnitudes are slightly below the negative biasing voltage so that, by themselves, they cannot drive the triode into its conducting condition. Pulses from the receiving equipment likewise are of positive polarity and, in the case of either PPM or PDM systems, their magnitude is about equal to that of the synchronizing pulses. Under these conditions, the triode becomes conductive only during intervals when pulses from the receiving equipment and from the synchronizer are simultaneously impressed upon the grid of the triode.

Thus, the gate is open only when a pulse from the synchronizer is present. When the triode is in the conducting condition, its cathode voltage is very nearly proportional to its grid voltage. As a result, the pulses at the output of the gate have almost the same shape as those from the receiving equipment. This is illustrated in (c) of Fig. 15–1.

The same type of gate may be used with PAM systems. Here the magnitude of the pulse from the synchronizer must be great enough to make the triode conducting when the superimposed PAM pulse has its least magnitude.

Two-Channel System

When a system has only two channels, it is possible to use a simpler method of gating at the cost of a 6-decibel signal-to-noise penalty. Positive pulses are transmitted for one channel and negative pulses for the other. Therefore, gates may be used that separate pulses on the basis of differences in polarity rather than differences in times of occurrence.

A gate of this type might consist of a germanium diode connected between the output of the receiving equipment and the input of the channel equipment. Two diodes, one for each channel, would be connected into the circuit in opposite directions. Since diodes are essentially conducting in one direction only, positive pulses would pass through one of the diodes and negative pulses through the other. This method of gating simplifies the instrumentation and is applicable to two-channel PDM and PPM as well as PAM systems.

CONVEYING THE INFORMATION OF THE SAMPLES TO THE DISTANT RECEIVER

In (a) of Fig. 15–1 there is shown a block marked "transmitting equipment" at the input to the transmission medium, and another block marked "receiving equipment" at the output of the medium. The operations that must be performed by these blocks of equipment depend not only upon the nature of the transmitting medium but also upon the frequency allocation.

In the simplest case the transmission medium might consist of a pair of wires or a coaxial cable, and the allotted frequency band might occupy the low end of the range, starting at zero cycles per second. The transmitting equipment would then include a low-pass filter to restrict the frequency components of the multiplexed pulses. Similarly, the receiving equipment would include another low-pass filter to attenuate high-frequency noise and other out-of-band interference. After filtering, the incoming pulses would be amplified and fed to gate circuits.

In other situations the allotted frequency band is in a relatively high-frequency region. This would be true when the pulses are transmitted by radio. The transmitting equipment of (a) in Fig. 15–1 then includes a modulator for translating the pulses to their allotted band. When a single sideband is transmitted, the result is to shift the spectrum of the train of pulses to its desired location in the radio spectrum. If double-sideband amplitude modulation is used, the required band width is doubled; and if frequency modulation is used, the band-width occupancy might be even greater.

A long transmission system will, in general, include repeaters at various intermediate points. These may be either linear amplifiers or circuits that perform the dual function of amplifying and reshaping the pulses. The latter type of repeater is employed chiefly in PDM and PPM systems, wherein a noise reduction and an improvement in the interference threshold of the system are realized by reshaping or regenerating the pulses.

At the receiving terminal, signals are fed to the receiving equipment indicated in (a) of Fig. 15–1, where they eventually are demodulated so that the pulses once again occupy a band at the lower extreme of the frequency range.

A METHOD OF SCALING WHEREBY TIME DIVISION IS REGARDED AS A SCALE MODEL OF A SINGLE–CHANNEL SYSTEM

Assume that noise in the transmission medium has the properties of resistance noise. Suppose further that the ratio of average signal power to average noise power at the output of the system and band-width occupancy in the transmission medium have been specified in terms of a one-channel system. Then the transmission of N channels over the same medium while maintaining the specified signal-to-noise ratio in each channel involves several modifications. The band-width occupancy is increased N-fold, the time available to transmit each pulse is divided by N, the peak power of each pulse is multiplied by N, each frame contains N pulses, and the average transmitted power is increased N-fold. This treatment assumes that the in-band loss over the high-frequency transmission path is independent of the number of channels and ignores synchronization.

SYNCHRONIZATION

Although most pulse systems require synchronization, Chapter 20 describes a type of system which operates with nonsynchronized pulses. Chapter 19 goes into a more advanced treatment of additional features and problems relating to synchronized systems and synchronized networks.

An altogether different system of synchronization is described in Chapter 20 which offers a solution to the problem of two-way multichannel synchronous transmission between a central station and a plurality of mobile stations.

Apart from repeaters, in any system of synchronized transmission we will be concerned with two synchronizers, one at each end. This is because a great many of the terminal operations must be controlled and timed to a nicety by a synchronizer. For example, synchronizing equipment at the transmitting terminal controls the generation of marker and channel pulses so that they occur in proper sequence and at exactly the right times. At the receiving terminal, the operation of gates must be synchronized with the incoming pulses.

There are two basic types of receiving synchronizers which have been termed *start-stop* and *long-time*. Synchronizing methods used at the transmitting terminal are substantially independent of those which might be adopted for the receiving terminal.

Synchronization at the Transmitting Terminal

The over-all operation of a pulse-modulation system is controlled at the sending end by a master oscillator or, where stability requirements are not too stringent, by a free-running multivibrator. Through the use of appropriate circuits, pulses derived from the waves generated by the oscillator or multivibrator are utilized to drive the sampling circuits, marker generator, and other circuits.

Consider, for example, a three-channel PAM system whose pulse train has the form shown in (a) of Fig. 15–3. During each frame interval, four control pulses are supplied in succession to four paths at the output of the synchronizer. One path goes to the marker generator and the others to sampling circuits for the three channels. The pulses are equally spaced and of like duration.

There are various ways of timing the generation of control pulses. One that is highly accurate utilizes a master oscillator with a frequency so chosen that there is one cycle of oscillation for each pulse to be transmitted.

The control pulses might also be generated by a ring circuit driven by a master oscillator. In this arrangement the ring circuit constitutes a multistage device wherein each stage may be in either an "on" or an "off" condition, with only one stage in the "on" condition at a time. For the system depicted in (a) of Fig. 15–3, the ring circuit would have four stages. At the output of each stage, one pulse is produced every four cycles of the oscillator wave. These pulses might be fed through pulse-shaping circuits, and the resulting pulses of substantially rectangular shape and proper duration would then go to the four paths mentioned previously.

In a system where the timing requirements are lenient, a multivibrator is permissible. It might operate at the rate of one cycle per frame, which corresponds to 8,000 cycles per second in the three-channel PAM system

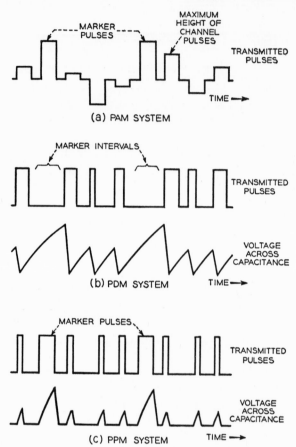

FIG. 15–3 Start-stop synchronization for several three-channel systems

of Fig. 15–3. The four channel pulses required per frame could be derived from the multivibrator wave through use of a resistor-capacitor timing circuit. A description of this type of circuit appears in the next section.

Start-Stop Synchronization

Method of Operation. With the start-stop method, synchronization is usually maintained on a per frame basis. At the expense of increased errors in timing, the same principle may be applied by taking several frames at a time. In a many-channel telephone system (10,000 channels, for example), the synchronizing interval might be a fraction of a frame.

Assume synchronization is on a per frame basis. The method involves transmitting something, in addition to the message-bearing pulses, to serve as a time mark within each frame interval so that gates may be made to open and close at the proper times at the receiving terminal. In some cases, the necessary time mark is established by transmitting a special pulse, or "marker," per frame. In other cases, a marker space may be used: that is, an interval in which a pulse is omitted.

Problem of Marker Identification. When marker pulses are used, they must differ from the message-bearing pulses in some recognizable way. Various wave forms are possible, but the choice is restricted to some extent by the following considerations: *first*, pulse systems frequently employ repeaters to reshape the pulses at various points along the route, and the marker pulse preferably should be capable of being handled conveniently by the repeaters in the same way as the other pulses; *second*, the marker pulse should not be of shorter duration than the other pulses or the required band width will be increased; and *third*, to simplify instrumentation, it is advantageous to make the interval allotted to a marker pulse equal to that allotted to any other pulse.

Figure 15–3 depicts three examples of markers that might meet system requirements. A three-channel system is assumed, but the same types of pulses are suitable for systems with larger numbers of channels.

Identification of a Marker by Its Magnitude. The scheme shown in (a) of Fig. 15–3 applies to a PAM system where the marker is identified by making its magnitude exceed that of the other pulses. It is relatively easy to isolate this marker. For example, the incoming pulses could be fed to the grid of a vacuum tube that is biased beyond cutoff by an amount just in excess of the maximum magnitude of the other pulses, so that these pulses never are able to drive the tube conducting. Since a marker pulse is able to drive the tube conducting, a pulse is produced in the plate circuit whenever a marker is impressed on the grid. How this pulse is used to synchronize other operations will be explained presently.

Identification of a Marker by Its Absence. In (b) of Fig. 15–3 is shown a method which applies to a PDM system; a marker interval is shown instead of a marker pulse. The description to follow represents one way of identifying a marker interval. Basically the method utilizes the charging time of a resistor-capacitor circuit to measure the duration of the intervals between successive duration-modulated pulses. One terminal of the capacitor is tied to ground and the other is connected through a resistor to a relatively high-voltage, positive, d-c supply. At the beginning of each duration-modulated pulse, a circuit is activated which throws a low impedance across the capacitor and thus allows it to discharge. The low impedance is removed after the lapse of an interval that is short compared to the interval between successive duration-modulated pulses, at which time the capacitor starts to charge again. The charging continues until the beginning of the next duration-modulated pulse, when the cycle of operations repeats.

The time constant of the resistor-capacitor circuit is so chosen that, during the normal charging interval, the voltage across the capacitor rises to an assigned value equal, for example, to one-fourth of the d-c supply voltage. During the marker interval, the voltage reaches a considerably higher value. The ungrounded terminal of the capacitor is connected to a suitably biased vacuum tube, so that this tube is driven conducting, and a pulse is generated in its plate circuit during each marker interval. The voltage across the capacitor is shown by the lower curve of (b) in Fig. 15–3.

Identification of a Marker by Its Duration. Part (c) of Fig. 15–3 applies to a PPM system, and in this case the marker pulse is distinguished by making its duration several times longer than that of the other pulses. At the receiving terminal the marker pulse may be separated from the other pulses essentially by the method just described for a PDM system. The capacitor is allowed to charge during the time of occurrence of each pulse, and the capacitor is discharged during the intervening intervals. Consequently, the capacitor voltage reaches its highest value during the time of occurrence of a marker pulse. This is illustrated by the lower curve of (c) in Fig. 15–3.

Generation of Control Pulses. After the marker pulses have been separated from the message-bearing pulses, they are used to control the operation of the synchronizing circuit at the receiving terminal. The function of this circuit is to open and close channel gates in proper sequence. This requires circuits that, in effect, measure off pre-assigned time intervals starting from the marker pulse and cause gates to operate at the ends of these intervals. The charge (or discharge) time of a resistor-capacitor (RC) circuit is sometimes employed for this purpose.

In a three-channel system, for example, there would be three RC circuits, all having different time constants. During the time of occurrence of the marker pulse, low-impedance shunts are automatically connected across the capacitors to bring their voltages practically to ground potential. Then, at the end of the marker pulse, the shunts are simultaneously removed, allowing the capacitors to charge through resistors connected to a positive d-c supply of relatively high voltage.

The time constant of one RC circuit is so chosen that the voltage across the capacitor reaches a pre-assigned value at the beginning of the gating interval for channel 1. The voltages across the other two capacitors reach the same value at times corresponding to the beginning of the gating intervals for channels 2 and 3. Each capacitor is connected to a circuit that generates a pulse as soon as the voltage across the capacitor reaches the above-mentioned value. The circuits are so designed that the duration of each pulse is equal to a gating interval. The pulses thus generated are fed to the appropriate channel gates.

Noise Considerations. It is characteristic of start-stop synchronization that noise, received along with the marker, increases the channel noise in a PPM system. This occurs because the edges of the received pulses do not rise in zero time, but are somewhat sloping. The exact position in time of the edge of a received pulse is regarded as the time at which the magnitude of the pulse passes through a pre-assigned value. This might, for example, correspond to half the peak value. When noise is added to the sloping edge of a pulse, the cross-over time is advanced or retarded, depending upon the polarity of the noise. Thus, as a result of noise, the apparent position in time of a marker pulse will "jitter" from frame to frame.

In a PPM system the value of signal represented by a channel pulse is proportional to and measured by the interval between the channel pulse and the marker. Jitter of the marker changes this time interval and thus translates noise associated with the marker pulse into channel noise. Similarly, noise causes the channel pulses to jitter independently of the marker. Since these jitter effects are uncorrelated, and because the edges of the marker and channel pulse have equal slopes, the total noise power at the output of a channel will be doubled.

Jitter of the marker pulse is of less consequence in PAM systems due to the fact that the magnitude of the wanted signal represented by a channel pulse is determined by the magnitude of the pulse rather than by its time of occurrence. In PDM systems, the signal magnitude represented by a channel pulse is determined only by the interval between its leading and trailing edges. Both edges will jitter, thereby contributing to the total noise, but the effect of marker-pulse noise may be minimized.

Long-Time Synchronization

Derivation of the Synchronizing Frequency. With long-time synchronization, the timing operations are controlled by a sinusoidal component obtained by filtering the received pulse train with a filter having a very narrow pass band. To elucidate this principle, consider a three-channel PPM system in which four pulses are transmitted per frame, a marker pulse being used for reasons to be given shortly. The marker pulse has the same duration as the channel pulses and is position-modulated at a 4-kilocycle-per-second rate. The pulse train has the form shown in (a) of Fig. 15–4. A frequency component of this sequence of pulses is the sinusoidal wave shown on the lower curve of (a) in Fig. 15–4. When 8,000 frames per second are transmitted, the frequency component of interest is $4 \times 8,000$ cycles per second. Now, if the pulses are fed to a filter with a pass band centered at 32 kilocycles per second, the output of the filter will be the sinusoidal wave shown in (a) of Fig. 15–4, but displaced in relation to the same component at the input by the phase shift of the filter.

Generation of Control Pulses. After the phase of this derived sinusoidal wave is suitably corrected, it drives a four-stage ring circuit. Successive

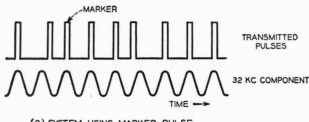

(a) SYSTEM USING MARKER PULSE
POSITION-MODULATED AT 4 KC RATE

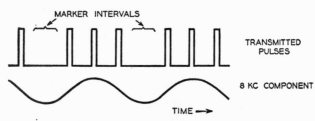

(b) SYSTEM USING MARKER INTERVAL
INSTEAD OF MARKER PULSE

FIG. 15–4   Long-time synchronization for three-channel PPM systems

stages of the ring circuit are switched to the "on" condition at the rate of one switching operation per cycle of the driving oscillation. Pulses from the first stage operate a gate for the marker pulse, and pulses from stages 2, 3, and 4 operate gates for channels 1, 2, and 3 respectively. Since there is nothing to distinguish one cycle from another, there is only one chance in four that the timing of the gates would be correct if nothing further were done. To make this method of synchronization automatic, an additional circuit serves to bring the pulses from the ring circuit into proper time relationship with the channel pulses.

This requires two steps. *First*, an indicator is needed to determine whether or not the system is in synchronization. *Second*, during intervals when the system is not in synchronization, the time relationship between the ring circuit pulses and the incoming channel pulses must be changed automatically and progressively until the proper relationship is found. This action will be termed "hunting."

Indicator Circuit. A marker pulse is provided as part of the method for achieving the first step. This marker pulse is modulated, at the transmitting terminal, by a 4-kilocycle sinusoid in the same way that the channel pulses are modulated by the speech waves.   Each voice-input circuit (Fig. 15–1) is provided with a low-pass filter which attenuates 4-kilocycles, thereby insuring that the marker pulse is the only one that can ever be modulated at this rate.

When the system is in synchronization, each marker pulse passes through its gate and into receiving channel equipment similar to that for the voice circuits.   At the output of this particular channel equipment is a narrow band-pass filter that freely passes 4-kilocycles.

Under operating conditions, a 4-kilocycle sinusoid appears at the output of the filter.   When the system is out of synchronization, the filter output is substantially zero because channel pulses instead of marker pulses are passed by the marker gate.   The 4-kilocycle wave is rectified, and this rectified current controls a relay which turns on the "hunting" circuit whenever the system is out of synchronization.

Hunting Circuit.   While the hunting circuit is in action, it periodically causes the four-stage ring to skip one step and thus establishes in succession the four possible relationships between the received pulses and those generated by the ring.   The circuit operates at a comparatively slow rate, say ten times per second, so that the relay will have time to function.   As soon as synchronization is restored, the relay operates to turn off the hunting circuit.

Hunting action may also be secured by an oscillator operating at a frequency a few cycles per second greater (or less) than the 32-kilocycle wave. The four-stage ring is driven by this oscillator, which is allowed to run freely at times when hunting action is required.   But as soon as synchronization is established, the oscillator is made to lock in with the received 32-kilocycle wave and thus maintain the proper relationship between the received pulses and those generated by the ring circuit.

Avoiding the Necessity for a Hunting Circuit.   The necessity for a hunting circuit may be avoided by utilizing a lower frequency component of the received pulses.   This frequency must be equal to or less than the frame frequency.   For example, in the case of the three-channel PPM system the synchronizing frequency would be 8 kilocycles per second or lower.

One way to obtain this frequency is to use a marker interval, (b) of Fig. 15–4, in place of a marker pulse.   An 8-kilocycle component is obtained by applying the received pulses to the input of a narrow band-pass filter.   Aside from the phase shift introduced by the filter, this component is phased with respect to the pulses as indicated on the lower curve of (b) in Fig. 15–4 and is caused to drive a pulse generator.   This pulse generator produces short pulses at the rate of 8,000 per second.   These pulses operate gate-generating circuits in a manner similar to that described for the resistor-capacitor start-stop synchronization system.

It should be noted that there are other ways of providing an 8-kilocycle component in the pulse train. For example, making the marker pulse wider than the channel pulses also produces this component.

Sources of Error. In the foregoing illustrative example, the use of the 8-kilocycle synchronizing frequency instead of a 32-kilocycle frequency, has the significant disadvantage that it increases the timing errors. A 1-degree error in the phase of the 8-kilocycle wave results in the same timing error in the synchronizing operations as a 4-degree error in the 32-kilocycle wave. Requirements for the band-pass filter, phase-correcting network, and pulse-generating circuit are proportionally more stringent. Accordingly, application of this method is generally restricted to systems with a relatively small number of channels.

Another possible source of error, in the long-time synchronization method, is that caused by sidebands that appear around the 8- or 32-kilocycle synchronizing frequency when the pulses are position-modulated. If the band-pass filter does not cut off sharply enough, a portion of these sidebands will pass through, mix with the synchronizing frequency, and produce timing errors. To minimize this effect, low-frequency suppression networks are used in the channel transmitting equipment to prevent the transmission of signal frequencies below a certain value. Then the width of the pass band of the synchronizing-frequency filter is limited to this same value or less on either side of the synchronizing frequency.

Noise-Considerations. Noise accumulated from the transmission medium also mixes with the synchronizing frequency to produce errors. However, the width of the band occupied by the interfering noise is equal to that of the synchronizing-frequency filter, which should and can be comparatively narrow. This means that the channel noise is increased only a trivial amount by noise from the synchronizing circuit. In PPM systems, long-time synchronization has a noise advantage of nearly three decibels over start-stop synchronization for this reason. Although described previously in relation to a PPM system, the same synchronizing methods are applicable to PAM and PDM systems.

CHAPTER 16

PULSE–AMPLITUDE MODULATION

Amplitude-modulated pulses are old, much older than amplitude-modulated sinusoids. However, the complete and exact analysis of pulse-amplitude modulation is comparatively new; only within the last fifteen years has it been thoroughly understood in its most general form. Current interest lies in its application to time-division multiplex systems, instrumentation, and other electronic fields. An advanced treatment of time-division systems given in Reference 1,* by W. R. Bennett, is clearly presented and comprehensive. References 2 to 4 provide additional background. Before entering upon a detailed treatment of pulse-amplitude modulation, its salient features will be summarized.

Amplitude-modulated pulses are usually multiplexed by time division or phase discrimination. Once the essential frequency ranges of the simultaneous, independent, and unquantized modulating waves are specified, a minimum band width (Ref. 1) equal to the sum of the message bands will theoretically be required if there is to be no interchannel interference. The ratio of average signal to average noise power in the output of each message channel can, in principle, be made independent of band-width occupancy, provided this occupancy equals or exceeds that minimum band. Also, this ratio equals the theoretical ratio for a corresponding multichannel, frequency-divided, single-sideband, suppressed-carrier system. The foregoing conclusions pertaining to noise assume that the average signal power applied to the medium is fixed and that the noise has the properties of resistance noise.

When peak instead of average power is controlling, the situation is different. In this case, whenever the band width occupied by a PAM system exceeds the theoretical minimum, the resulting signal-to-noise ratio is less. Also, the wider the band, the smaller the ratio. Accordingly, for a specified signal-to-noise ratio at the output of the system, more peak power is required as the band is widened. Although a wider band implies a larger signal power, other requirements are eased. This follows since the over-all transmission requirements and practical tolerances tend to become un-

---

* The references cited are listed at the end of each chapter according to the number used in the text.

reasonably severe unless the occupied band is considerably wider than the theoretical minimum.

Unlike PDM or PPM, PAM is not able to reduce small noise perturbations in exchange for increased band-width occupancy. It does, however, have the advantage of simplicity.

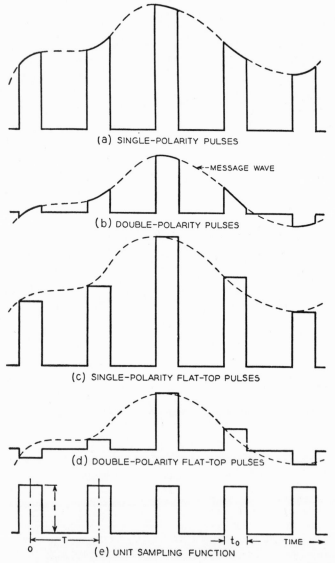

(a) SINGLE-POLARITY PULSES

←—MESSAGE WAVE

(b) DOUBLE-POLARITY PULSES

(c) SINGLE-POLARITY FLAT-TOP PULSES

(d) DOUBLE-POLARITY FLAT-TOP PULSES

(e) UNIT SAMPLING FUNCTION

FIG. 16–1   Idealized pulse shapes for pulse-amplitude modulation (PAM)

MODULATION METHODS

Objective

A primary function of the modulation process is to convert the message wave into a series of amplitude-modulated pulses. More often than not, the message wave is sampled at regular intervals. The result is a series of pulses proportional in magnitude to the sampled values. The wave form of these pulses depends upon the instrumentation. Four idealized pulse shapes are shown in Fig. 16–1. The message wave is represented by dotted lines and the corresponding amplitude-modulated pulses by solid lines.

Production of Single-Polarity, Amplitude-Modulated Pulses

The pulses in (a) of Fig. 16–1 are of positive polarity and of the type produced by the sampling circuit in Fig. 16–2. In this circuit, the message wave from the voice-input circuit and the rectangular pulses from the synchronizer are combined with a negative biasing voltage and impressed

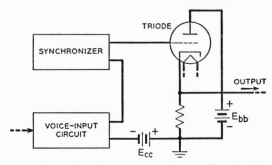

FIG. 16–2 Simplified drawing of a sampling circuit

upon the grid circuit of a triode. Sufficient biasing voltage is applied so that the message wave alone cannot drive the tube into a conducting condition. Pulses from the synchronizing circuit are of constant amplitude and positive polarity. The synchronizing pulses are large enough to drive the triode well into its conducting region even when the message wave is at its most negative value.

Accordingly, the tube is conductive when synchronizing pulses are present and is nonconductive when they are absent. The output of this sampling circuit is the voltage across the cathode resistor. When the tube is nonconductive, the cathode-resistor voltage is zero; and when the tube is conductive, the cathode-resistor voltage is accurately proportional to the grid voltage. Since the grid voltage during each conductive interval changes by an amount equal to the change in the message voltage, the tops of the pulses have the same shape as the message wave.

Production of Double-Polarity, Amplitude-Modulated Pulses

The pulses shown in (b) of Fig. 16–1 differ from those shown in (a) in that their magnitudes may be positive or negative and are defined with reference to magnitude zero. They might be obtained from a balanced sampler or by adding to the pulses from the sampling circuit of Fig. 16–2 a train of rectangular, negative pulses of such amplitude as just to cancel out the pulses from the sampling circuit when the message voltage is zero. The required negative pulses may be derived from pulses generated by the synchronizing circuit. For example, when positive pulses from a synchronizer are impressed upon the grid of a triode, negative pulses appear in the plate circuit.

Production of Flat-Top, Amplitude-Modulated Pulses

The pulses shown in (c) of Fig. 16–1 are flat-topped. Their amplitudes are proportional to the values of the message wave at times coinciding with the leading edges of the pulses. Generation of the pulses may be facilitated by the use of "holding" circuits. In such a circuit, a capacitor is charged to a voltage equalling that of the message wave at the sampling time. Then the capacitor is disconnected from any path through which it could lose its charge.

Voltage across the capacitor is fed to the input of a sampling circuit similar to the one shown in Fig. 16–2. In this case voltage from the capacitor replaces the voltage from the voice-input circuit. An appropriately timed pulse from the synchronizer makes the triode in the sampling circuit conductive, thus producing a pulse across the cathode resistor. Since the voltage across the capacitor is constant during this interval, the generated pulse is flat-topped. At the end of the pulse, the capacitor is discharged and thereby made ready to repeat a similar set of operations.

The double-polarity, flat-top pulses shown in (d) of Fig. 16–1 differ from those in (c) only in that their amplitudes are unbiased. They might be derived by adding a train of rectangular, negative pulses to the type shown in (c) of Fig. 16–1.

SPECTRA OF AMPLITUDE-MODULATED PULSES

Unit Sampling Function

Time zero may be so chosen that the unit sampling function shown in (e) of Fig. 16–1 is given by

$$U = k \sum_{m=-\infty}^{\infty} \frac{\sin mk\pi}{mk\pi} \cos m\omega_c t \qquad (16\text{–}1)$$

where $k = t_0/T$ is the ratio of the duration of a pulse to the interval between centers of successive pulses, and $\omega_c = 2\pi f_c = 2\pi/T$ is the fundamental frequency of the pulse train in radians per second.

Double-Polarity, Amplitude-Modulated Pulses

The double-polarity pulses of (b) in Fig. 16–1 are obtained by multiplying the message wave, $V(t) \equiv V$, by the unit sampling function. If $V(t) = A_v \cos (\omega_v t + \theta_v)$,

$$M_1(t) = UV$$

$$= kA_v \sum_{-\infty}^{\infty} \frac{\sin mk\pi}{mk\pi} \cos [(m\omega_c + \omega_v)t + \theta_v]$$

$$= kA_v \cos (\omega_v t + \theta_v) + kA_v \sum_{1}^{\infty} \frac{\sin mk\pi}{mk\pi} \cos [(m\omega_c \pm \omega_v)t \pm \theta_v].$$

$$(16\text{–}2)$$

In equation (16–2) the two plus and two minus signs go together.

Since an arbitrary band-limited modulating wave $V(t)$ may be represented by $\sum_{v=0}^{\infty} A_v \cos (\omega_v t + \theta_v)$, the spectrum of the train of double-polarity, amplitude-modulated pulses is proportional to the modulating wave and to the upper and lower sidebands of this wave around $\omega_c/2\pi$ and its harmonics. Since superposition (Chaps. 9 and 10) applies in this and all essential cases to follow, $V(t)$ may be regarded as a single sinusoid without loss of generality.

Single-Polarity, Amplitude-Modulated Pulses

The single-polarity pulses in (a) of Fig. 16–1 may be formed by adding UK, where K is a suitable factor, to the pulse train of (b) in Fig. 16–1. Thus,

$$M_2(t) = M_1(t) + Kk \sum_{-\infty}^{\infty} \frac{\sin mk\pi}{mk\pi} \cos m\omega_c t. \qquad (16\text{–}3)$$

Double-Polarity, Flat-Top Pulses

The double-polarity, flat-top pulses of (d) in Fig. 16–1 may be expressed analytically by the following procedure. When a modulating wave is sampled at regular intervals, the samples approach closer and closer to flat-top pulses as the sampling interval is progressively shortened. In the limit, the pulses are differentially short, and, for our purposes, expression (16–2) for the resulting amplitude-modulated pulses reduces to

$$M_3(t) = A_v \frac{d\tau}{T} \sum_{-\infty}^{\infty} \cos [(m\omega_c + \omega_v)t + \theta_v] \qquad (16\text{–}4)$$

when t_0 is replaced by $d\tau$, a differentially small interval.

Double-polarity, flat-top pulses, as in (d) of Fig. 16–1, may be regarded as an ensemble of a large number of trains of differentially short pulses side by side; that is, as the sum of a large number of trains of short pulses wherein each successive train of recurrent pulses is delayed by an additional interval $d\tau$. Assume that the leading edge of a flat-top pulse occurs at time zero and that its duration is t_0 seconds. The entire collection of short pulses, delayed by amounts ranging from zero to t_0, then add to determine the complete pulse. The desired sequence of flat-top pulses is obtained by summing the contributions of all of the trains of short pulses over the range zero to t_0. Accordingly, (16–4) is replaced by

$$M_4(t) = \frac{A_v}{T} \sum_{-\infty}^{\infty} \int_0^{t_0} \cos\left[(m\omega_c + \omega_v)(t - \tau) + \theta_v\right] d\tau$$

$$= kA_v \sum_{-\infty}^{\infty} \frac{\sin k\pi \dfrac{m\omega_c + \omega_v}{\omega_c}}{k\pi \dfrac{m\omega_c + \omega_v}{\omega_c}} \cos\left[(m\omega_c + \omega_v)\left(t - \frac{t_0}{2}\right) + \theta_v\right] \quad (16\text{–}5)$$

where as previously $k = t_0/T$.

The variable factor of the sinusoidal term corresponding to $m = 0$ in (16–5) is

$$\frac{\sin \omega_v \dfrac{t_0}{2}}{\omega_v \dfrac{t_0}{2}} \quad (16\text{–}6)$$

and illustrates the basic theorem for aperture effect in sampling, referred to in Chapter 4 on pages 40 to 41 and discussed briefly on page 55. The physical interpretation is that the process of clamping instantaneous samples for t_0 seconds introduces a delay of $t_0/2$ seconds and a distortion factor given by $\dfrac{\sin \omega_v \dfrac{t_0}{2}}{\omega_v \dfrac{t_0}{2}}$. The distortion is linear and can be compensated for by an equalizer.

Single-Polarity, Flat-Top Pulses

Single-polarity, flat-top pulses are pictured in (c) of Fig. 16–1. They differ from double-polarity, flat-top pulses by adding to the latter the unit sampling function multiplied by a suitable factor K. This adds a d-c component and components corresponding to the recurrence rate $\omega_c/2\pi$ and its harmonics. The complete expression for the pulses of (c) in Fig. 16–1 is

$$M_5(t) = M_4(t) + Kk \sum_{-\infty}^{\infty} \frac{\sin mk\pi}{mk\pi} \cos m\omega_c t \quad (16\text{–}7)$$

where $M_4(t)$ is given by (16–5).

DEMODULATION METHODS

Pulses generated at the transmitting terminal are multiplexed, conveyed to the receiving terminal, and routed to the proper channel equipment by gating circuits, as described in Chapter 15.   The pulses are then ready to be demodulated, that is, converted back to the same form as the original message wave.

Almost all types of amplitude-modulated pulses are easily demodulated by a low-pass filter, or network, having an appropriately shaped loss-frequency characteristic.   The process amounts to selection of the modulating wave from the modulated pulses.   Network characteristics are determined from the spectrum of the pulses.

Equation (16–2), which applies to double-polarity, amplitude-modulated pulses as distinguished from flat-top pulses, shows that the modulating wave is present.   It is represented by components of the form $kA_v \cos (\omega_v t + \theta_v)$.   Since k does not depend upon the frequency of the modulating wave, the loss-frequency characteristic of the filter should be flat in the pass band for distortionless demodulation.

Above the pass band the filter must introduce enough loss for adequate suppression of other spectrum components.   Suppose the system transmits speech and the highest transmitted frequency is 4 kilocycles per second.   The pass band of the filter that demodulates the pulses then extends from zero to 4 kilocycles.   If transmission is at the Nyquist rate, the value of $\omega_c/2\pi$ corresponds to 8 kilocycles, and the low-pass filter must suppress the first lower sideband extending from 4 to 8 kilocycles per second.   This is impractical because no guard space separates the pass band from the band to be attenuated.

If the pulse recurrence rate is 10 kilocycles per second instead of 8 (while the message frequencies are still restricted to a 4-kilocycle band) the situation is relieved.   Frequencies represented by the lower sideband of the recurrence frequency now fall in a band extending from 6 kilocycles to 10 kilocycles.   Accordingly, the loss of the filter may be increased gradually from 4 to 6 kilocycles per second, since there are no components to be suppressed in this intermediate region.   The filter must also provide suppression above the recurrence frequency to reduce the upper sideband.   Whether suppression of still higher frequency components is required will depend upon system design.

The spectrum of single-polarity, amplitude-modulated pulses shown in (a) of Fig. 16–1 differs from the one for the double-polarity pulses in (b) of Fig. 16–1 merely in that it has added to it the recurrence frequency and its harmonics.   Except at these frequencies where additional suppression is required, a filter designed to demodulate the pulses of (a) would have the same loss-frequency characteristics as the one used for the pulses of (b).   This additional suppression is important because the recurrence frequency and its harmonics are present all of the time, whereas other spectrum components increase and decrease along with the voice wave.   When the amplitudes are comparable, frequency components that are continuously present are much more objectionable than those existing only in the presence of speech. Hence, unmodulated components present in the absence of speech require relatively more suppression.

The flat-top pulse trains of (c) and (d) in Fig. 16–1 are likewise readily demodulated by the method just described.

As previously mentioned, a simple equalizing network is sometimes needed in addition to the low-pass filter. This equalizer makes the in-band loss decrease as the frequency increases in such a manner as to compensate for the aperture effect, namely,

$$\frac{\sin \dfrac{k\pi\omega_v}{\omega_c}}{\dfrac{k\pi\omega_v}{\omega_c}}.$$

The amount of equalization needed is rather small, and may be omitted in some practical applications, especially when the pulses are short. The amount required is greatest when the values of k and ω_v/ω_c are maximum. This occurs when the pulse duration is equal to the recurrence interval and the system is transmitting at the Nyquist rate. Then ω_v assumes its maximum value, namely, half the radian recurrence frequency, ω_c. Under these conditions, the coefficient mentioned above becomes equal to $2/\pi$ at the maximum message frequency, as against unity at zero frequency. This corresponds to a 3.9-decibel increase in loss across the pass band, and, in order for the over-all transmission characteristic of the system to be flat, the equalizer must provide the inverse variation with frequency.

In a working system, the message wave recovered at the output of the low-pass filter may be smaller than required. Accordingly, it may be necessary to pass the message wave through a linear amplifier as a final operation.

INTERCHANNEL CROSSTALK

To illustrate the evaluation of interchannel crosstalk, we shall assume that synchronized switches at the two ends of the system sequentially connect N similar channels to a distortionless line at regular intervals corresponding to $\omega_c/2\pi$ times a second. $T = 2\pi/\omega_c$ is the frame interval, T/N is the amount of frame time allocated to each channel, and t_0 is the duration of each switching connection. The essential frequency range of each channel approaches half the frame frequency.

Let $j = 1, 2, \ldots N$ and assume that a sinusoid

$$e_j = E_j \cos (\omega_v t + \theta_v) \tag{16–8}$$

is present on channel j.

Except for a time displacement that is the same between all adjacent channels, the N switching functions are alike, viz.,

$$U_j = k \sum_{m=-\infty}^{\infty} \frac{\sin mk\pi}{mk\pi} \cos (m\omega_c t - m\Phi_j)$$

$$= k \sum_{-\infty}^{\infty} A_m \cos (m\omega_c t - m\Phi_j) \qquad (16\text{--}9)$$

where $\Phi_j = 2\pi \dfrac{j-1}{N}$ and $A_m = \dfrac{\sin mk\pi}{mk\pi}$.

Let I_j be the line current as a function of time from channel j. Then

$$I_j = e_j U_j. \qquad (16\text{--}10)$$

By writing e_j and U_j as the real part of appropriate imaginary exponentials, it is apparent that

$$I_j = kE_j \sum_{-\infty}^{\infty} A_m \cos [(m\omega_c + \omega_v)t - m\Phi_j + \theta_v]. \qquad (16\text{--}11)$$

Equation (16–11) shows that commutator-type switching at the sending end results in the production of the signal itself (analytically regarded as the upper sideband about zero frequency) and upper and lower sidebands around the switching frequency and each harmonic of the switching frequency.

At the receiving end, the synchronized switching process between channel l and the line may be represented by

$$G_l = k \sum_{-\infty}^{\infty} A_m \cos (m\omega_c t - m\Phi_l) \qquad (16\text{--}12)$$

where k has been made the same as at the sending end and

$$\Phi_l = 2\pi \frac{l-1}{N}.$$

Consider I_{jl} to be the current received in channel l when channel j is active and let it be understood that j and l may be any two of the N channels.

$$I_{jl} = e_j U_j G_l. \qquad (16\text{--}13)$$

Assume an ideal low-pass filter with cutoff $B = \omega_c/4\pi$ in the output of each channel. Also assume that M is the upper bound of $m = 0, \pm 1, \ldots$, and that t_0 and consequently k are small so that A_m can be replaced by unity. Under these conditions the crosstalk is given by

$$\frac{I_{jl}}{I_{ii}} = \frac{1}{1 + 2M} \left[1 + 2 \sum_{1}^{M} \cos 2m\pi \frac{l-j}{N} \right]$$

$$= 1, \text{ if } l = j$$

$$= \frac{\sin \left[(2M+1)\pi \left(\dfrac{l-j}{N} \right) \right]}{(2M+1) \sin \pi \left[\dfrac{l-j}{N} \right]}, \text{ if } l \neq j. \qquad (16\text{--}14)$$

Thus, when $M = \dfrac{N-1}{2}$, the crosstalk is zero. In this case, $N = 2M+1$, and $(2M + 1)B$ is the total band width. If all channels are active, the system transmits N sidebands on zero frequency; N upper and N lower sidebands on f_c, the switching frequency; and N upper and N lower sidebands on the first $\dfrac{N-3}{2}$ harmonics of f_c. In theory, therefore, a system is capable of simultaneously transmitting N channels without mutual interference. The theoretical band-width occupancy of this system is the same as for N single-sideband, amplitude-modulation channels multiplexed by frequency division. It should be noted that equality of the N sidebands and their exact phases account for the suppression of interchannel crosstalk.

Systems with even numbers of channels can also be devised. These would use only upper and lower sidebands of the switching frequency and its harmonics. In fact, complete information for the separation of N channels should be and is contained in any set of N sidebands (Ref. 1).

Useful switching functions (Ref. 1) are not limited to the simple function given by (16–9). Furthermore, with the simple commutator type of switching, as the contact duration t_0 is decreased from its largest value T/N, optimal band widths appear which give better crosstalk suppression than bands somewhat wider or narrower. This means that a particular system must be designed and operated appropriately to realize either little or theoretically zero mutual interference. An essential requirement is a suitable choice of a generalized switching function. It should be noted that the term *interchannel crosstalk* as used here is the same as *intersymbol interference*. This has been discussed in earlier chapters.

SIGNAL–TO–NOISE RATIO

Important in the design of a communication system is its susceptibility to various types of interference that may be encountered in the transmission process. More than any other single factor, signal-to-noise ratio places an upper limit upon the spacing between terminals and repeaters. Furthermore, signal-to-noise ratios tend to determine the kinds and numbers of systems that can operate in the same transmission medium.

The amount of interference that can be tolerated depends upon the type of system, the nature of the message, the character of the interference, the transmission properties of the medium, and many other factors. The treatment here will be limited to PAM systems operating under idealized conditions, and it will be assumed that the interference is resistance noise.

Let N similar channels each occupying a frequency range $0 < f < B$ be multiplexed by time division. Assume a commutator-type system as described in the preceding section. Let N be odd, and assume N sidebands are transmitted. This means that, at the transmitting end, frequencies above NB are attenuated by a low-pass filter. Transmission distortion will be ignored by assuming a distortionless line, uniform transmission, and ideal filters.

Consider that a typical modulating wave, $V(t)$, is multiplied by $\dfrac{T}{t_0\sqrt{N}}$ before it is sampled by the commutator-type switch. Then the average signal power in the N sidebands delivered by this particular channel, and as measured at the output of the transmitting low-pass filter, will be $\overline{V^2(t)}$. This follows from: Theorems I, III, and IV in Chapter 4; recognition that the sidebands are nearly equal, provided t_0 is sufficiently small; and Parceval's theorem. It is assumed that $V(t)$ satisfies the conditions of Theorems III and IV. Moreover, if the N modulating waves are incommensurable and the average channel powers are alike, the total average signal power is N times that of a single channel.

From Theorems I, II, III, and IV in Chapter 4, and (16–13), we find that the ratio of average signal power to average noise power at a particular channel filter output is equal to the ratio at the filter input of the average signal power associated with that particular channel to the input noise power in a band B. The numerical measure of the average input noise power in a band B is Bn, where n is the average noise-power density per cycle per second.

References

1. W. R. Bennett, "Time Division Multiplex Systems," *The Bell System Technical Journal*, New York, Vol. 20, No. 2, April 1941, pp. 199–221.
2. Callahan, Mathes, and Kahn, "Time Division Multiplex in Radio-Telegraphic Practice," *Proceedings of the Institute of Radio Engineers*, New York, Vol. 26, January 1938, pp. 55–75.
3. W. D. Boothroyd and E. M. Creamer, Jr., "A Time Division Multiplex System," *Transactions of the American Institute of Electrical Engineers*, New York, Vol. 68, Part 1, 1949, pp. 92–97.
4. H. L. Krauss and P. F. Ordung, "Distortion and Bandwidth Characteristics of Pulse Modulation," *Transactions of the American Institute of Electrical Engineers*, New York, Vol. 66, 1947, pp. 984–988. This reference is not limited to PAM.

Problems

1. Assume two ideal single-sideband channels with identical transmission characteristics. The two channels are connected to an ideal line so that loss is independent of frequency. The frequency ranges occupied by the two sidebands are distinct and nonoverlapping. At the receiver input, the noise power density is uniform and uncorrelated: for example, resistance noise.

Let S_0 be the effective (that is, root-mean-square) signal at the output of channel 1 and N_0 the effective noise. At the sending end, let the same modulating signal be transmitted over channel 2. At the transmitting end, the two inputs to the two channels are so adjusted that the two receiver outputs are S_1 and S_2, where $S_1^2 + S_2^2 = S_0^2$ and $S_0 > S_1 \geq S_2$. Thus, $S_2 = kS_1$ where $0 < k \leq 1$.

At the receiving end, assume the output of channel 1, namely, S_1 and N_0, is multiplied by a factor u, with $0 < u < \infty$, so that the modified output is uS_1 and uN_0. The effective values of the output from channel 2 are S_2 and N_2, where $N_2^2 = N_0^2$. The two outputs are so combined that the signals add in phase with the result that the effective value of the combined signal output is $S_1 + S_2$.

What is the combined noise output? What is the ratio of the effective value of combined signal to the effective value of the combined noise? What is the value of u for maximum ratio of combined signal to combined noise expressed as a function of k? What is the expression for the corresponding optimum signal-to-noise ratios?

2. Resistance noise is limited by an ideal filter to a band just less than B. Will B samples per second uniquely define the in-phase component of the noise?

3. Assume a four-channel system of the on-and-off commutator switching type. Assume that the on-time is short. Theory shows that four sidebands of equal amplitude are sufficient to convey each message without interchannel crosstalk. With the carriers for channel 1 as a reference, what are the proper phases and frequencies of the carriers for the other three channels?

4. In Problem 3 show that the crosstalk from channel 1 into any other channel is zero.

CHAPTER 17

PULSE–DURATION MODULATION

Pulse-duration modulation (PDM) is sometimes referred to in the literature on the subject (Refs. 1 to 19)* as pulse-length modulation or pulse-width modulation. Pulse-duration modulation is a particular form of pulse-time modulation. It is modulation of a pulse carrier (pulse carrier is defined on page 30 of Chapter 3) in which the value of each instantaneous sample of a continuously varying modulating wave is caused to produce a pulse of proportional duration.

The modulating wave may vary the time of occurrence of the leading edge, the trailing edge, or both edges of the pulse. In any case, the message-bearing signal to be transmitted is composed of discrete values, and each value must be uniquely defined by the duration of a modulated pulse.

Pulse-duration modulation has an advantage analogous to that of frequency modulation. Noise and interference can be reduced at the expense of increasing the band-width occupancy, provided the extraneous disturbances are below the improvement threshold. This advantage is very important in multichannel operations.

When considering different ways of multiplexing channels, time division has simplicity and flexibility in its favor; but systems possessing these advantages require wide bands. The narrower the high-frequency band, the harder it is to make a time-division system work. Even in the PAM case, there is an urge to employ a very wide band to ease the transmission tolerances associated with a specified, interchannel, crosstalk requirement. With PDM, the crosstalk requirements are relaxed by an amount corresponding to the noise advantage associated with the wider band. Thus, if a very wide band is available, multiplexing not only becomes easier; but, in addition, average signal power is conserved.

In PDM, the part of the signal power that carries no information to the receiver is wasted. The amount of power wasted depends upon the maximum extent to which a pulse can be modulated. When the useless part is subtracted from PDM, we have PPM. The power saved represents the fundamental advantage of PPM over PDM.

* The references cited are listed at the end of each chapter according to the number used in the text.

263

MODULATION METHODS

Three ways of modulating pulse duration are illustrated in Fig. 17–1. Solid lines indicate the durations of the unmodulated pulses, and dotted lines show the two extremes for maximum modulation. "Guard interval"

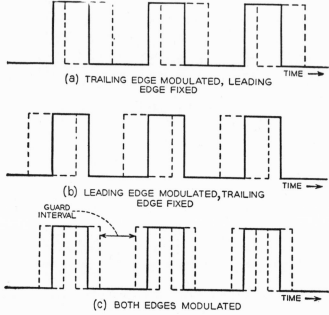

(a) TRAILING EDGE MODULATED, LEADING EDGE FIXED

(b) LEADING EDGE MODULATED, TRAILING EDGE FIXED

GUARD INTERVAL

(c) BOTH EDGES MODULATED

FIG. 17–1   Pulse-duration modulation or PDM

(Fig. 17–1) refers to the minimum interval between the trailing edge of one pulse and the leading edge of the next when the pulses are fully modulated.

There are many schemes for producing duration-modulated pulses. Any particular scheme may be utilized in any one of three ways. For purposes of illustration, Fig. 17–2 depicts a particular procedure wherein the trailing edge alone is modulated. The message or modulating wave is first converted to a series of flat-top, amplitude-modulated pulses, all of maximum duration. A saw-tooth sweep wave, as in (a) of Fig. 17–2, from the synchronizer is then added to the amplitude-modulated pulses, and the combination is applied to the input of a slicer. A slicer has the property that its output is zero whenever its input is below a certain value (referred to as the "control value") and is maximum whenever the input exceeds this value. The amplitude of the saw-tooth wave is slightly greater than the difference between the tops of most negative and most positive amplitude-modulated pulses. This process produces the duration-modulated pulse train shown on the lower curve in (a) of Fig. 17–2.   This method of sampling is called "uniform sampling" because pulse durations are proportional to message-wave values at uniformly spaced sampling times.

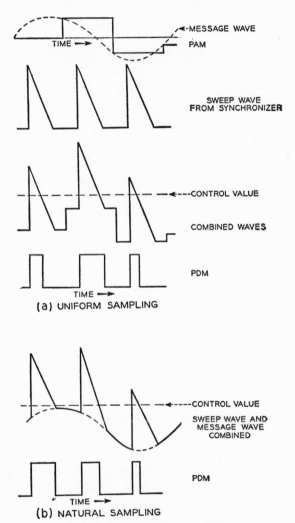

Fɪɢ. 17–2   Generation of PDM

To simplify instrumentation, the same modulation result is sometimes realized without converting the message wave to PAM.   Such a scheme is illustrated in (b) of Fig. 17–2.   The message wave varies during the sweeping process, and the duration of a duration-modulated pulse is proportional to the magnitude of the message wave at the trailing edge of the pulse.

Thus, the time of sampling varies and coincides in time with each trailing edge. Leading edges are fixed and occur at regular intervals.

When this method is used to produce pulses with leading edges modulated, the shape of the saw-tooth wave is reversed. Pulses with both edges modulated can be produced with sweep waves in the form of isosceles triangles.

The sampling associated with any way of modulating pulse duration may be either *uniform* or *natural*. In the case of uniform sampling, if the leading edge is modulated or if both edges are modulated and $\pm kT/2$ is the extreme variation in duration, the sampling information is delayed more than $kT/2$ seconds in carrying out the modulation process.

The illustrations in Fig. 17–2 are for a single-channel system. As an alternative to using one pulse-duration modulator for each channel of a multichannel system, the message waves may be converted to amplitude-modulated pulses, which are then multiplexed by time division, and the combined array converted to duration-modulated pulses in a common-channel modulator. Again, the sampling may be either uniform or natural.

SPECTRA OF DURATION–MODULATED PULSES

The following expressions for the spectra of duration-modulated pulses were taken from unpublished papers by W. R. Bennett. The method of derivation was based on a double Fourier series expansion in two variables, a procedure originally developed by Bennett (Ref. 18) for the purpose of analyzing rectified waves. The method has proven to be highly effective in the systematic and rigorous treatment of certain complicated modulation problems. It is worthy of special attention here and is explained in the following section.

Method of Analysis

Although application of the double Fourier series method of analysis will be described with reference to duration-modulated pulses as illustrated in Fig. 17–2, the general method can be applied to other types of waves.

Natural sampling is assumed. The modulating wave is a single sinusoid represented by $A_v \cos \omega_v t$. The fundamental frequency of the pulses is ω_c radians per second, so that ω_c is equal to 2π times the number of pulses transmitted per second.

In the general case, ω_v and ω_c are incommensurable and the pulse train is nonperiodic. To get around this difficulty, Bennett represented the duration-modulated pulses by the three-dimensional geometrical configuration illustrated in the upper drawing of Fig. 17–3. This diagram represents part of a region in which many walls have been erected, all parallel to each other and of identical shape. The walls rest upon a flat surface that will be referred to as the XOY plane. The positions occupied by the walls are indicated by the shaded areas. All walls are of the same height, their tops are flat, and their sides are perpendicular to the XOY plane.

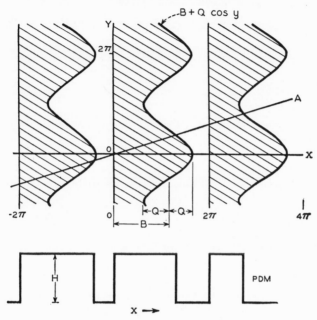

FIG. 17–3   Spectrum analysis by a double Fourier series

The walls are flat on one side; on the other side, their shape is defined, for this example, by the relation

$$x' = B + Q \cos y \qquad (17\text{–}1)$$

where x' is the difference between the two sides of a wall, measured along lines parallel to the X-axis.

B and Q are expressed in units of length. There is one wall (Fig. 17–3) for every 2π units of length along the X-axis. Likewise, there is one complete cycle of $Q \cos y$ for every 2π units of length in the Y-direction.

Now suppose that a plane, perpendicular to the XOY surface and including the origin, is passed through the walls along the line OA in the drawing. When the intersection of this plane with the walls is projected upon a second plane, likewise perpendicular to the XOY surface but including the X-axis, the resulting curve will have the shape shown at the bottom of Fig. 17–3. Here H represents the height of the walls.

If x is considered to represent time instead of distance, the above-mentioned curve may be thought of as a train of duration-modulated pulses with modulated trailing edges. Furthermore, the duration of each pulse is determined by the value of $Q \cos y$ at the end of the pulse rather than its value at uniformly spaced instants, so that the sampling is natural sampling.

In order to represent a given train of duration-modulated pulses by the configuration of Fig. 17–3, x and y must be related to time essentially as follows:

$$x = \omega_c t \qquad (17\text{-}2)$$

and

$$y = \omega_v t. \qquad (17\text{-}3)$$

These relationships have the following significance. For each value of time inserted in (17–2) and (17–3), a point is specified in the XOY plane. The locus of all such points is a straight line passing through the origin and with a slope ω_v/ω_c. This line corresponds to OA in Fig. 17–3.

Now, consider the entire region to be sectioned into elementary squares with edges 2π units long. Then, over an interval corresponding to one second of time, the plane the position of which is specified by OA will traverse $\omega_c/2\pi$ squares in the X-direction. Since ω_c was defined in radians, pulses are generated at the rate of $\omega_c/2\pi$ cycles per second. Similarly, the plane will encounter $\omega_v/2\pi$ squares in the Y-direction, and this corresponds to the pulses being modulated by a message wave having a frequency of $\omega_v/2\pi$ cycles per second.

The quantities B and Q need to be expressed as functions of parameters that define the given train of duration-modulated pulses. B may be specified as a function of k where k is the ratio, in the absence of modulation, of pulse duration to the interval between pulse centers. From Fig. 17–3 it is apparent that

$$B = 2\pi k. \qquad (17\text{-}4)$$

Q may be specified as function of A_v, the amplitude of the sinusoidal modulating wave. In Fig. 17–3, the extreme change in position of the trailing edge from its unmodulated time of recurrence is $2Q$ and the pulse recurrence interval corresponds to 2π. Therefore $\pm \pi$ is a bound to the maximum possible excursion or modulation of a pulse. Let

$$Q = M\pi \qquad (17\text{-}5)$$

define M, which will be called "modulation index" since $\pm M\pi$ is the maximum excursion of the trailing edge from one extreme to the other.

The foregoing discussion has shown how a train of duration-modulated pulses may be represented by a three-dimensional geometrical configuration when the modulating wave is a sinusoid. The next step will explain why this helps in deriving an expression for the spectrum of the pulses. A key to the explanation lies in the following consideration.

If the XOY plane in the configuration of Fig. 17–3 is sectioned into elementary squares with edges 2π units long, the portions of the walls within the different squares are identical. This suggests that the height of the configuration can be expressed as a function of x and y by means of a double Fourier series. The double Fourier series will be designated $F(x, y)$. When, for example, the modulating wave is a sinusoid, a series such as this can be used to represent the pulse train. It is only necessary to replace x and y in the series with the time function given by (17–2) and (17–3). Since the series gives the height of the configuration at any point on the XOY plane, it must also give the height along the particular line OA traced out by these time functions. The double Fourier series may be developed as follows.

The line of intersection of the walls with a plane perpendicular to the XOY plane and including the X-axis has the same form as a train of rectangular pulses, all of equal duration. Now if the plane is kept parallel to the X-axis but moved to a new point of intersection with the Y-axis, a train of rectangular pulses of durations that are all equal is again obtained. Since these pulses are periodic with respect to x, the intersection of the plane with the walls may always be described by a simple Fourier series, written

$$F(x, y_1) = \frac{1}{2} a_0(y_1) + \sum_{m=1}^{\infty} [a_m(y_1) \cos mx + b_m(y_1) \sin mx] \quad (17\text{–}6)$$

where

$$a_m(y_1) = \frac{1}{\pi} \int_0^{2\pi} F(x, y_1) \cos mx \, dx, \quad m = 0, 1, 2, \ldots, \quad (17\text{–}7)$$

$$b_m(y_1) = \frac{1}{\pi} \int_0^{2\pi} F(x, y_1) \sin mx \, dx, \quad m = 1, 2, \ldots, \quad (17\text{–}8)$$

and y_1 is the point of intersection of the plane with the Y-axis.

The values of the coefficients $a_m(y_1)$ and $b_m(y_1)$ depend upon the point of intersection of the plane with the Y-axis, and are therefore functions of y. Since these values are periodic with respect to y in intervals of 2π, they may also be represented by Fourier series. For example, the coefficient $a_m(y_1)$ may be written as follows for all possible values of y:

$$a_m(y) = \frac{1}{2} c_{0m} + \sum_{n=1}^{\infty} [c_{nm} \cos ny + d_{nm} \sin ny] \quad (17\text{–}9)$$

where

$$c_{nm} = \frac{1}{\pi} \int_0^{2\pi} a_m(y) \cos ny \, dy \quad (17\text{–}10)$$

and

$$d_{nm} = \frac{1}{\pi} \int_0^{2\pi} a_m(y) \sin ny \, dy. \quad (17\text{–}11)$$

The coefficient $b_m(y_1)$ likewise may be written as Fourier series. Thus, the coefficient of each term in the original series (17–6) is replaced by a complete Fourier series with y as the variable.

The problem now is to put this double series into a convenient form. The first step is to replace $a_m(y_1)$ in (17–6) with the series given in (17–9), and make similar substitutions for the coefficient $b_m(y_1)$ in (17–6). In the new series, products of trigonometric functions are expanded and like terms collected. The coefficients in this new series then consist of (17–10) and (17–11), along with other coefficients of similar form which are present in the series for $b_m(y_1)$.

The second step is to expand these expressions for the coefficients. For example, in (17–10) the term $a_m(y)$ is replaced by (17–7). Thus,

$$
\begin{aligned}
c_{nm} &= \frac{1}{\pi} \int_0^{2\pi} \left[\frac{1}{\pi} \int_0^{2\pi} F(x, y) \cos mx \, dx \right] \cos ny \, dy \\
&= \frac{1}{\pi^2} \int_0^{2\pi} \int_0^{2\pi} F(x, y) \cos mx \cos ny \, dx \, dy \\
&= \frac{1}{2\pi^2} \int_0^{2\pi} \int_0^{2\pi} F(x, y) \cos (mx + ny) \, dx \, dy \\
&\quad + \frac{1}{2\pi^2} \int_0^{2\pi} \int_0^{2\pi} F(x, y) \cos (mx - ny) \, dx \, dy. \quad (17\text{–}12)
\end{aligned}
$$

Here the coefficient c_{nm} is equated to the sum of two terms. When similar operations are performed on the other coefficients and like terms collected, the double Fourier series reduces to the following expression:

$$
\begin{aligned}
F(x, y) =\ & \frac{1}{2} A_{00} + \sum_{n=1}^{\infty} [A_{0n} \cos ny + B_{0n} \sin ny] \\
& + \sum_{m=1}^{\infty} [A_{m0} \cos mx + B_{m0} \sin mx] \\
& + \sum_{m=1}^{\infty} \sum_{n=\pm 1}^{\pm \infty} [A_{mn} \cos (mx + ny) + B_{mn} \sin (mx + ny)] \quad (17\text{–}13)
\end{aligned}
$$

where

$$
A_{mn} = \frac{1}{2\pi^2} \int_0^{2\pi} \int_0^{2\pi} F(x, y) \cos (mx + ny) \, dx \, dy \quad (17\text{–}14)
$$

and

$$
B_{mn} = \frac{1}{2\pi^2} \int_0^{2\pi} \int_0^{2\pi} F(x, y) \sin (mx + ny) \, dx \, dy. \quad (17\text{–}15)
$$

With x and y replaced by the time functions (17–2) and (17–3), the terms of the double Fourier series (17–13) are subject to the following interpretation:

The first term $\frac{1}{2} A_{00}$ is the d-c component of the pulses. The frequency components of the second term correspond to the frequency components of the modulating wave and its harmonics. The third term separates into frequencies corresponding to the fundamental frequency of the pulses and to harmonics of this frequency. The frequency components of the last term are given by the ensemble of all possible pairs formed by taking the sum and difference of integral multiples of each fundamental.

The double integral (17–14) is proportional to the volume of a solid that occupies one elementary square in Fig. 17–3 and has a shape that is determined by multiplying the height of the wall, namely, $F(x, y)$, evaluated at every point within the square, by the factor $\cos (mx + ny)$. Since the area of the elementary square is $4\pi^2$, A_{mn} is equal to twice the average height of the weighted solid.

Expression (17–15) is subject to the same interpretation, except that the height multiplier in this case is $\sin (mx + ny)$.

To summarize, this general method of spectrum analysis consists of the following operations:

1. The train of duration-modulated pulses is represented by an appropriate three-dimensional configuration as illustrated by Fig. 17–3.
2. The height of the three-dimensional configuration at all points is expressed in terms of a double Fourier series (17–13). The coefficients of the terms in the series are obtained by evaluating the definite integrals (17–14) and (17–15).
3. The final expression for the train of duration-modulated pulses is obtained by replacing x and y in the double series (17–13) by the time functions $(\omega_c t)$ and $(\omega_v t)$, respectively.

When this method of analysis is applied to waves other than duration-modulated pulses, the procedure is the same, but the walls have different shapes. The general method used to determine the shape of the walls can be illustrated as follows.

Consider two planes perpendicular to plane OXY: plane A includes line OA and plane B includes line OX. Consider also the portion of the geometrical configuration in Fig. 17–3 which occupies the elementary square bounded by $x = 0$ to 2π and $y = 0$ to 2π. The shape of the wall within this square is such that, when its intersection with plane A is projected upon plane B, the resulting projection has the shape of a duration-modulated pulse in which the leading edge coincides with the beginning of one cycle of the modulating wave. This follows since line OA crosses the flat side of the wall, which represents the leading edge of the pulse, at the origin where y equals zero. Therefore, this point marks the beginning of one cycle of the modulating wave, $Q \cos y$.

Next, consider the elementary square bounded by $x = 2\pi$ to 4π and $y = 0$ to 2π. The point at which the line OA crosses the flat side of the wall in this square depends upon the slope of OA with respect to the X-axis. The slope of OA is equal to ω_v/ω_c. With the value of slope that was arbitrarily assigned to OA in Fig. 17–3, the crossover occurs at the point where y is approximately equal to $2\pi/3$. Accordingly, the shape of the geometrical configuration above the line OA in this square is the same as the shape of the duration-modulated pulse produced by the modulator when the leading edge of the pulse occurs $2\pi/3$ radians after the beginning of a cycle of the modulating wave. In any other elementary square, the shape of the geometrical configuration above the line OA is related to the shape of the duration-modulated pulses in a similar manner.

Since the walls are identical in all elementary squares, the preceding result may be applied to lines drawn parallel to OA in the elementary square bounded by $x = 0$ to 2π and $y = 0$ to 2π. Thus, the shape of the geometrical configuration along and above any such line in this square corresponds to the shape of a duration-modulated pulse in which the leading edge occurs y'' radians after the beginning of a cycle of the modulating wave. Here y'' is the point of intersection of the line with the Y-axis.

To establish the shape of the geometrical configuration, it is only necessary to determine how the shape of the pulses produced by the modulator varies as a function of y''. Since this relationship defines the shape of the geometrical configuration above any line parallel to OA, the shape of the configuration is defined at all points within the elementary square bounded by $x = 0$ to 2π and $y = 0$ to 2π.

In general, this method of spectrum analysis is applicable to any modulation process wherein the carrier and modulating waves are periodic functions of time. The modulating wave does not have to be a single-frequency wave, as in the preceding example. It may have any form encountered in a physical system so long as it is periodic.

There are several points to be noted in connection with practical applications of this method.

In some cases, it is helpful to express the double Fourier series in complex form, namely,

$$F(x, y) = \sum_{m=-\infty}^{m=\infty} \sum_{n=-\infty}^{n=\infty} K_{mn} \epsilon^{i(mx+ny)} \tag{17–16}$$

where

$$K_{mn} = \frac{1}{4\pi^2} \int_0^{2\pi} \int_0^{2\pi} F(x, y) \epsilon^{-i(mx+ny)} \, dx \, dy. \tag{17–17}$$

In evaluating the integrals (17–14) and (17–15), or (17–17), the area of integration does not need to be a square. Any other shape is permissible, provided the area is $4\pi^2$ and provided the configurations in all elementary areas are identical. The validity of this follows from the fact, previously noted, that each integral represents the volume of an elementary portion of a solid. If a solid is sectioned into a given number of identical parts, the volume of each part is independent of the shape of the part.

When the integrals cannot be solved by analytical methods, any particular component of the double series can be determined by numerical integration. This amounts to finding the average height of the solids mentioned before.

In the preceding discussion, the phase angle of the modulating wave $\cos \omega_v t$ was taken as zero. For phase angles other than zero, y is replaced by

$$y = \omega_v t + \theta \qquad (17\text{-}3a)$$

where θ is in radians.

In the configuration of Fig. 17–3 this is geometrically equivalent to moving the plane from the position indicated by line OA, to another in which it crosses the Y-axis at a distance θ from the origin, while keeping constant its angle with respect to the X-axis. It may be noted that the phase of the sinusoidal modulating wave is significant only when the frequency of the modulating wave and the fundamental frequency of the pulses are commensurable.

The purpose of this section has been to describe Bennett's method of analysis completely enough to allow the reader to apply it to other two-frequency modulation problems. For those interested in the detailed derivation of the spectrum of the pulses shown in Fig. 17–3, the integrals are evaluated in the following section.

Pulses with Trailing Edge Modulated

It turns out that evaluation of the integrals is simplified by expressing them in complex form. However, we wish to express the final series in real instead of complex notation, and for this purpose it is convenient to express the integrals a little differently than in equation (17–17). By combining (17–14) and (17–15),

$$A_{mn} + iB_{mn} = \frac{1}{2\pi^2} \int_0^{2\pi} \int_0^{2\pi} F(x, y) \epsilon^{i(mx+ny)} \, dx \, dy. \qquad (17\text{-}18)$$

Reference to Fig. 17–3 will show that the height of the walls is equal to the constant H for all values of x between 0 and $B + Q \cos y$, and is zero for other values of x up to 2π. Therefore, the preceding integral takes the following form when applied to this particular configuration:

$$A_{mn} + iB_{mn} = \frac{H}{2\pi^2} \int_0^{2\pi} \int_0^{B+Q \cos y} \epsilon^{i(mx+ny)} \, dx \, dy$$

$$= \frac{H}{2\pi^2 im} \int_0^{2\pi} \left[\epsilon^{i(mx+ny)} \right]_0^{B+Q \cos y} dy$$

$$= -\frac{iH}{2\pi^2 m} \int_0^{2\pi} \left[\epsilon^{i(mB+mQ \cos y+ny)} - \epsilon^{iny} \right] dy. \qquad (17\text{-}19)$$

Except for the case where $n = 0$, the term ϵ^{iny} does not contribute to the definite integral. This follows because the term represents trigonometric functions that are periodic with respect to y in intervals of 2π.

Since m appears in the denominator, equation (17–19) is indeterminate for the case where $m = 0$. The cases where m or n is zero have to be considered separately.

Equation (17–19) with the foregoing restriction becomes

$$A_{mn} + iB_{mn} = \frac{-iH}{2\pi^2 m} \epsilon^{imB} \int_0^{2\pi} \epsilon^{imQ \cos v_\epsilon iny} \, dy \qquad (17\text{–}20)$$

and is of the form (Ref. 20)

$$J_n(Z) = \frac{i^{-n}}{2\pi} \int_0^{2\pi} \epsilon^{iZ \cos \Phi} \epsilon^{in\Phi} \, d\Phi$$

where the left member is a Bessel function of the first kind with integer suffix.

When Z is replaced with mQ and Φ with y, we have

$$\int_0^{2\pi} \epsilon^{imQ \cos v_\epsilon iny} \, dy = 2\pi i^n J_n(mQ). \qquad (17\text{–}21)$$

When (17–21) is substituted into (17–20),

$$A_{mn} + iB_{mn} = - \frac{iH}{2\pi^2 m} \epsilon^{imB} 2\pi i^n J_n(mQ).$$

Since $i^n = \epsilon^{in\pi/2}$,

$$A_{mn} + iB_{mn} = - \frac{iH}{\pi m} \epsilon^{i(mB + n\pi/2)} J_n(mQ) \qquad (17\text{–}22)$$

where

$$A_{mn} = \frac{H}{\pi m} J_n(mQ) \sin\left(mB + \frac{n\pi}{2}\right) \qquad (17\text{–}23)$$

and

$$B_{mn} = - \frac{H}{\pi m} J_n(mQ) \cos\left(mB + \frac{n\pi}{2}\right), \qquad (17\text{–}24)$$

valid for all integer values of m and n except zero.

The evaluation of the integral for the special cases where m or n equals zero is straightforward so that it will not be discussed here.

After completing the integrations and combining some of the terms, the coefficients are inserted in the double series (17–13). The symbols x, y, B, and Q are then replaced by their equivalents from equations (17–2), (17–3), (17–4), and (17–5), respectively. As a matter of convenience, the common factor H is set equal to unity. This gives the following series for duration-modulated pulses with trailing edges modulated by natural samples of a sinusoidal modulating wave.

$$F_1(t) = k + \frac{M}{2} \cos \omega_v t + \sum_{m=1}^{\infty} \frac{\sin m\omega_c t}{m\pi}$$

$$- \sum_{m=1}^{\infty} \frac{J_0(m\pi M)}{m\pi} \sin (m\omega_c t - 2m\pi k) \tag{17–25}$$

$$- \sum_{m=1}^{\infty} \sum_{n=\pm 1}^{n=\pm\infty} \frac{J_n(m\pi M)}{m\pi} \sin \left(m\omega_c t + n\omega_v t - 2m\pi k - \frac{n\pi}{2} \right).$$

The symbols in equation (17–25) have been defined in this and the preceding section. The modulating wave is $M \cos \omega_v t$.

Duration-modulated pulses produced from uniform samples of the modulating wave may be similarly analyzed. The walls in the geometrical configuration have a different shape, and the integration is simplified by taking, for the area of integration, a parallelogram with one pair of sides parallel to the Y-axis and the other pair parallel to the line OA. The analysis as given below applies to pulses with trailing edges modulated and uniform sampling.

$$F_2(t) = k - \sum_{n=1}^{\infty} \frac{J_n\left(\dfrac{n\pi M\omega_v}{\omega_c} \right)}{\dfrac{n\pi\omega_v}{\omega_c}} \sin \left(n\omega_v t - \frac{2n\pi k\omega_v}{\omega_c} - \frac{n\pi}{2} \right)$$

$$+ \sum_{m=1}^{\infty} \frac{\sin m\omega_c t - J_0(m\pi M) \sin (m\omega_c t - 2m\pi k)}{m\pi} \tag{17–26}$$

$$- \sum_{m=1}^{\infty} \sum_{n=\pm 1}^{n=\pm\infty} \frac{J_n\left[(m\omega_c + n\omega_v) \dfrac{\pi M}{\omega_c} \right]}{(m\omega_c + n\omega_v) \dfrac{\pi}{\omega_c}} \sin \left[(m\omega_c + n\omega_v)\left(t - \frac{2\pi k}{\omega_c} \right) - \frac{n\pi}{2} \right].$$

Again the modulating wave is $M \cos \omega_v t$ and the symbols have their previous meaning.

The timing of the pulses is such that the leading, or unmodulated, edge of one of the pulses occurs exactly at time $t = 0$. This is true for both types of sampling.

Pulses with Leading Edge Modulated

Obviously pulses with trailing edges modulated become pulses with leading edges modulated when the time scale is reversed. Therefore, to obtain the series expression for the latter pulses, it is only necessary to put a negative sign in front of t in the formulas of the preceding section. For example,

$$F_3(t) = F_1(-t) \tag{17–27}$$

where $F_3(t)$ is the series representing a train of duration-modulated pulses with leading edges modulated and natural sampling. Similarly,

$$F_4(t) = F_2(-t) \qquad (17\text{-}28)$$

where $F_4(t)$ is the series representing a train of duration-modulated pulses with leading edges modulated and uniform sampling.

Since $\cos(-\omega_v t) = \cos \omega_v t$, the modulating wave is the same as before. The timing of the pulses is such that the trailing, or unmodulated, edge of one of the pulses occurs exactly at time $t = 0$. This is true for both types of sampling.

Pulses with Both Edges Modulated

Pulses with both edges modulated may be considered as a combination of two pulse trains, one with leading edges modulated and the other with modulation on the trailing edges. The duration-modulated pulses of the two preceding sections occur in the proper time relationship to one another so that, when they are added together, the required pulses are obtained. Duration-modulated pulses with both edges modulated may be represented by the addition of appropriate formulas from the two preceding sections. That is,

$$F_5(t) = F_1(t) + F_3(t) = F_1(t) + F_1(-t) \qquad (17\text{-}29)$$

where $F_5(t)$ is a series representing a train of pulses with both edges modulated and natural sampling and

$$F_6(t) = F_2(t) + F_4(t) = F_2(t) + F_2(-t) \qquad (17\text{-}30)$$

where $F_6(t)$ is a series representing a train of pulses with both edges modulated and uniform sampling.

DEMODULATION METHODS

Before or in the process of recovering the original modulating wave, advantage should be taken of the noise-reducing properties of duration-modulated pulses. One procedure is to change the received pulses into rectangular pulses by means of a "slicer." The slicer is a circuit that extracts very thin, horizontal segments of the received pulses. Each slice is usually taken about midway between the base and top of the pulse so as to include points on the leading and trailing edges where the absolute value of the slope is a maximum. In practice, a slicer might consist of several appropriately biased vacuum tubes or transistors operating in tandem. The thin segments are then processed to form enlarged pulses of similar shape.

Low-Pass Filter

By far the most common scheme for deriving the wanted signal is to connect the output of the slicer sequentially to low-pass filters, one filter being associated with each channel. Amplification is provided before and after filtering as required. In a multichannel system where the index of modulation is inherently small due to the many channels, the wanted signal is recovered with negligible distortion.

In the case of a single-channel system where the modulation index is likely to be substantial, the amount of distortion may be serious. For example, consider the case of natural sampling and modulation of the trailing edges by a sinusoidal modulating wave. The spectrum is given by (17–25). The wanted component is present and harmonics of the modulating wave are absent. The frequencies of the important in-band distortion components are $\omega_c - 2\omega_v$, $\omega_c - 3\omega_v$, $\omega_c - 4\omega_v$, et cetera. The coefficients of these terms are independent of frequency, but depend upon the magnitude of the modulation index, M.

At low-modulation levels the third order product, $\omega_c - 2\omega_v$, follows a square law with respect to the modulation index; $\omega_c - 3\omega_v$ follows a cube law; and so on. The following table illustrates how these products compare with the message wave at three modulation levels. The tabulated values are the decibel ratios of the coefficient of the last term in (17–25) to the coefficient of the second term.

Modulation Index M in Per Cent	Product	
	$\omega_c - 2\omega_v$	$\omega_c - 3\omega_v$
5	28	60
10	22	48
20	16	36

It is apparent that the modulation index must be small to prevent undue distortion of the message. The permissible distortion depends not only upon the nature of the message but also upon the class of services for which the system is designed. In a multichannel system, the modulation index is inversely proportional to the number of channels.

When regular sampling is used, the output of the low-pass filter (17–26) contains not only the wanted message wave, but its harmonics. With natural sampling these harmonics are missing. As with natural sampling, the other in-band distortion products of the form $\omega_c - n\omega_v$ are present. This would lead one to expect a net deterioration of quality when the sampling is regular instead of natural. Detailed studies show this to be true.

Conversion to PAM

In principle any distortion, aside from that introduced by noise, can be eliminated since a PDM signal has all the information necessary for exact recovery of the modulating wave. Uniform sampling and conversion to PAM followed by a filter can provide exact recovery of the wanted message.

Conversion to PAM may be accomplished by means of a holding circuit. With this arrangement, a capacitor is charged to a voltage proportional to the duration of the duration-modulated pulse, and the voltage is then held at a virtually constant value while a new pulse proportional in magnitude to the voltage across the capacitor is generated.

To allow sufficient time for these operations, alternate pulses are usually fed to separate holding circuits. The conversion process is illustrated, for one of the groups, in Fig. 17–4. As indicated at the top of this figure, the time allotted for the transmission of each pulse is t_1 seconds. Alternate

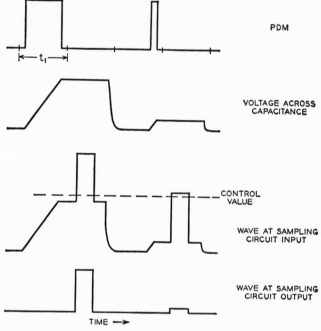

Fig. 17–4   Conversion of PDM to PAM

pulses are omitted from this train so that this represents the series of pulses fed to one of the holding circuits. The voltage across the capacitor is assumed to be substantially zero coincident with the leading edge of a pulse. Thereafter, the voltage is caused to increase almost linearly, until the trailing edge of the pulse is reached. At this time the capacitor is disconnected from any branch of the circuit through which it might lose its charge.

The voltage across the capacitor is then impressed upon the input of a sampling circuit. During the interval immediately following a duration-modulated pulse, while the capacitor voltage is constant, a rectangular pulse from the synchronizing circuit drives the sampler triode conductive.

The voltage at which the triode changes from nonconducting to conducting is labeled "control value" in Fig. 17–4. Since the voltage at the sampling-circuit output is proportional to the capacitor voltage during the conducting interval, the output consists of the amplitude-modulated pulses shown at the bottom of Fig. 17–4.

At the end of the holding interval, a shunt is connected across the capacitor to remove its charge. Coincident with the leading edge of the next pulse, the shunt is removed, and the converter is ready to repeat its sequence of operations.

Except for imperfections of instrumentation, the amplitudes of the amplitude-modulated pulses generated by the above method are precise samples of the original modulating wave. With uniform sampling the modulating wave may be recovered in undistorted form by feeding the amplitude-modulated pulses to the input of an appropriate low-pass filter and equalizer.

With natural sampling, the amplitudes of the amplitude-modulated pulses are not proportional to samples taken at equally spaced instants. Instead, they are proportional to samples taken at times coinciding with the positions of the modulated pulse edges. With the above-mentioned method of detection, this results in distortion of the modulating wave at the receiving terminal. The distortion becomes smaller as the magnitude of the modulating wave decreases. It is also small in a system with a large number of channels.

Although both methods of demodulation have been described with reference to the trailing edge case, they are both applicable in all three modulating schemes.

SIGNAL–TO–NOISE RATIO

Even when the noise is small compared with the wanted signal, the noise manifests itself as jitter in the leading and trailing edges of the recovered pulses. Since the positions of the leading and trailing edges define pulse duration, it is evident that the receiver cannot distinguish between signal modulation and noise. Slopes of the leading and trailing edges influence noise reduction. The absolute value of the slope is proportional to the band width. If the noise has the properties of resistance noise, the reduction in root-mean-square noise current is proportional to the absolute value of the slope.

Inasmuch as noise affects PDM and PPM systems similarly, the treatment of noise will be deferred to Chapter 18. Here it is sufficient to state a fundamental principle common to all pulse systems, namely, that the noise reduction depends upon the ratio of band width utilized to the total band width of the N like channels. When the noise has the properties of resistance noise and is small compared with the signal, an interesting proportionality exists. The ratio of average signal power to average noise power at the output of each channel is proportional to the square of the ratio of the prorated band width gainfully utilized by the channel to the band width of the channel itself. In theory, channel band width would be measured by half the sampling frequency.

As previously mentioned, both leading and trailing edges of the pulses are affected by noise. Noise contributions from the two edges will combine to an extent depending upon their correlation. With resistance noise, the correlation is negligible. Consequently, the signal-to-noise ratio is three decibels poorer than when only one edge is affected, provided the absolute values of the slopes of the two edges are equal at the operating level of the slicer. If the noise is a wave, low in frequency compared with the recurrence rate of the channel pulses, the two noise contributions add almost directly. If the absolute values of the two slopes are equal, the signal-to-noise ratio will be about 6 decibels poorer than when one edge only is affected.

References*

1. "Multi-Channel Pulse Modulation," Details of Army Wireless Station No. 10, *Wireless World*, London, Vol. 52, 1946, pp. 187–192.
2. E. G. James, J. C. Dix, J. E. Cope, C. F. Ellis, and E. W. Anderson, "The Development of the Wireless Set No. 10: An Early Application of Pulse Length Modulation," *The Journal of the Institution of Electrical Engineers*, London, Vol. 94, Part 3A, 1947, pp. 517–527.
3. S. H. Moss, "Frequency Analysis of Modulated Pulses," *Philosophical Magazine and Journal of Science*, London, Vol. 39, 7th Series, 1948, pp. 663–691.
4. M. M. Levy, "Pulse Modulation and Demodulation Theory," *Journal of the British Institution of Radio Engineers*, London, Vol. 7, 1947, pp. 64–83.
5. M. M. Levy, "Some Notes on Pulse Technique," *Journal of the British Institution of Radio Engineers*, London, Vol. 7, 1947, pp. 99–116.
6. S. C. Kleene, "Analysis of Lengthening of Modulated Repetitive Pulses," *Proceedings of the Institute of Radio Engineers*, New York, Vol. 35, 1947, pp. 1049–1053.
7. Ernest R. Kretzmer, "Distortion in Pulse-Duration Modulation," *Proceedings of the Institute of Radio Engineers*, New York, Vol. 35, 1947, pp. 1230–1235.
8. H. J. von Baeyer, "The Basic Principles of Multichannel Transmission with Modulated Pulses," *Brown Boveri Review*, Baden, Switzerland, Vol. 33, March 1946, pp. 65–69.
9. P. Güttinger, "Pulse Time Modulation," *Brown Boveri Review*, Baden, Switzerland, Vol. 33, August 1946, pp. 188–192.
10. F. F. Roberts and J. C. Simmonds, "Multichannel Communication Systems," *Wireless Engineer*, London, Vol. 22, November 1945, pp. 538–549 and December 1945, pp. 576–580.
11. G. G. MacFarlane, "On the Energy Spectrum of an Almost Periodic Succession

---

* Some of the references cited in this chapter are not limited to pulse-duration-modulation.

of Pulses," *Proceedings of the Institute of Radio Engineers*, New York, Vol. 37, October 1949, pp. 1139–1143.

12. Gordon L. Fredendall, Kurt Schlesinger, and A. C. Schroeder, "Transmission of Television Sound on the Picture Carrier," *Proceedings of the Institute of Radio Engineers*, New York, Vol. 34, 1946, pp. 49P–61P.

13. G. G. Gouriet, "Random Noise Characteristics of a Pulse-Length-Modulated System of Communication," *The Journal of the Institution of Electrical Engineers*, London, Vol. 94, Part 3A, 1947, pp. 551–555.

14. E. Fitch, "The Spectrum of Modulated Pulses," *The Journal of the Institution of Electrical Engineers*, London, Vol. 94, Part 3A, 1947, pp. 556–564.

15. G. H. Parks, "A New Method of Wide-Band Modulation of Pulses," *The Journal of the Institution of Electrical Engineers*, London, Vol. 94, Part 3A, 1947, pp. 511–516.

16. C. Louis Cuccia, *Harmonics, Sidebands, and Transients in Communication Engineering*, McGraw-Hill Book Co., Inc., New York, pp. 238 and 315–316.

17. J. C. Lozier, "Spectrum Analysis of Pulse-Modulated Waves," *The Bell System Technical Journal*, New York, Vol. 26, April 1947, pp. 360–387.

18. W. R. Bennett, "New Results in the Calculation of Modulation Products," *The Bell System Technical Journal*, New York, Vol. 12, April 1933, pp. 228–243.

19. C. B. Feldman and W. R. Bennett, "Bandwidth and Transmission Performance," *The Bell System Technical Journal*, New York, Vol. 28, No. 3, pp. 490–595.

20. Eugene Jahnke and Fritz Emde, *Tables of Functions*. Translation published by Dover Press, New York, 1945, p. 149.

Problems

1. (a) In the description of the double Fourier series method of analysis described on pages 266 to 275, suppose that the trailing edges are modulated by uniform instead of natural samples and that the modulating wave being sampled is a square wave instead of $M \cos \omega_v t$. Draw a diagram showing what geometrical configuration would take the place of the one pictured in Fig. 17–3. Make the drawing correspond to the following conditions:

The timing of the modulating wave is such that one cycle of the wave starts precisely at time $t = 0$. The wave is positive during the first half of each cycle and negative during the second half of each cycle. The modulating wave is sampled at times corresponding to the leading edges of the duration-modulated pulses.

The timing of the duration-modulated pulses is such that the leading edge of one pulse occurs exactly at $t = 0$.

The maximum duration of the duration-modulated pulses is $B + Q$ and the minimum duration is $B - Q$, where B is the pulse duration in the absence of modulation. The duration of the duration-modulated pulses is longest for positive samples of the modulating wave and is least for negative samples.

The fundamental radian frequency, ω_v, of the modulating wave is smaller than the fundamental radian frequency, ω_c, of the unmodulated pulses.

(b) Describe, in a few sentences, the additional operations which must be carried out to complete the spectrum analysis of the duration-modulated pulses after the geometrical configuration of (a) has been determined.

(c) Is the preceding analysis valid when ω_v is greater than ω_c?

CHAPTER 18

PULSE–POSITION MODULATION

Pulse-position modulation is a particular form of pulse-time modulation in which the value of each instantaneous sample of a modulating wave is caused to vary the position in time of a pulse relative to its unmodulated time of occurrence. The variation in relative position may be related to the modulating wave in any predetermined unique manner. Compared with pulse-duration modulation, pulse-position modulation conserves signal power and for this reason has aroused considerable interest in recent years (Refs. 1 to 24)*. However, in situations where band width is at a premium, it is less desirable than some other methods, such as pulse-code modulation. Practical applications of PPM systems have been on a modest scale, even though their instrumentation can be extremely simple.

In either pulse-duration modulation or pulse-position modulation the maximum modulating signal must not cause a pulse to enter adjacent allotted time intervals. In telephone systems this requirement leads to a very wasteful use of time space. In fact, almost all of the frame time available for modulation is wasted in almost every frame because many of the busy channels may be expected to be inactive, and most of the rest will be carrying small signal power. Consequently, although pulse-position modulation is more efficient than pulse-duration modulation, both fall short of the theoretical ideal when used for multiplexing ordinary telephone channels.

SPECTRA OF PULSE–MODULATION SYSTEMS

At this point and before proceeding with the treatment of pulse-position modulation, a slightly different way of deriving the spectra will be developed for the purpose of drawing additional general conclusions. This particular method was suggested by J. G. Kreer, Jr., as a means of clarifying the various classifications of pulse modulation.

The modulated waves associated with any type of pulse-modulation system belong to a class of functions that are partially periodic in nature.

---

* The references cited are listed at the end of each chapter according to the number used in the text.

It is characteristic of the functions within this class that they may be divided into equal segments in the independent variable, and within each segment the function is one of a class of single-parameter functions.

Such functions may be conveniently expressed as a series of modulated sinusoidal waves, modulated either in phase or amplitude or both. This is made possible by assuming that each period function is repeated indefinitely and expanding in a Fourier series. The desired series is then obtained by letting the coefficients of the Fourier series vary from period to period in accordance with the modulating wave.

As an example of this procedure, let us consider a pulse-modulation signal in which the unmodulated pulses are ideal rectangular pulses with time of duration t_0, amplitude unity, and repetition period T. That is, the cyclic pulse-carrier frequency f_c is equal to $1/T$, and the corresponding radian frequency ω_c is equal to $2\pi/T$. Assume that the leading edge is modulated with a modulation factor K_1, the trailing edge with a modulation factor K_2, and the amplitude with a modulation factor K_3. The modulated wave may then be described as follows:

$$
\left.
\begin{aligned}
M(t) &= 0, \quad \left(n - \frac{1}{2}\right)T \le t \le nT - \frac{t_0}{2} + K_1 V_1(T_{n_1}) \\
M(t) &= 1 + K_3 V_3(T_{n_3}), \\
&\quad nT - \frac{t_0}{2} + K_1 V_1(T_{n_1}) \le t \le nT + \frac{t_0}{2} + K_2 V_2(T_{n_2}) \\
M(t) &= 0, \quad nT + \frac{t_0}{2} + K_2 V_2(T_{n_2}) \le t \le \left(n + \frac{1}{2}\right)T
\end{aligned}
\right\}
\quad (18\text{-}1)
$$

where $V_1(t)$, $V_2(t)$, and $V_3(t)$ are independent modulating waves, $n = 0$, $\pm 1, \pm 2, \ldots$, and T_{n_1}, T_{n_2}, and T_{n_3} denote the respective times in the nth period that $V_1(t)$, $V_2(t)$, and $V_3(t)$ were sampled. Our immediate interest will be served by setting $V_1(t) = V_2(t) = V_3(t) = V(t)$, and $T_{n_1} = T_{n_2} = T_{n_3} = T_n$. With uniform sampling T_n can be replaced by Tn.

Assume that the modulated wave $M(t)$ may be represented by

$$
M(t) = a_0(n) + \sum_{m=1}^{\infty} a_m(n) \cos m\omega_c t + b_m(n) \sin m\omega_c t \quad (18\text{-}2)
$$

where $a_m(n)$ and $b_m(n)$ are constants over any one period, T, but may vary from period to period. Then we have:

$$
\begin{aligned}
a_0(n) &= \frac{1}{T} \int_{nT - \frac{t_0}{2} + K_1 V(T_n) = c}^{nT + \frac{t_0}{2} + K_2 V(T_n) = d} [1 + K_3 V(T_n)]\, dt \\
&= \frac{1 + K_3 V(T_n)}{T} [t_0 + (K_2 - K_1) V(T_n)], \quad (18\text{-}3)
\end{aligned}
$$

$$a_m(n) = \frac{2}{T} \int_c^d [1 + K_3 V(T_n)] \cos m\omega_c t \, dt$$

$$= \frac{1 + K_3 V(T_n)}{m\pi} \left(\sin m\omega_c \left[\frac{t_0}{2} + K_2 V(T_n) \right] + \sin m\omega_c \left[\frac{t_0}{2} - K_1 V(T_n) \right] \right)$$

$$= \frac{2[1 + K_3 V(T_n)]}{m\pi} \sin m\omega_c \left[\frac{t_0}{2} + \frac{K_2 - K_1}{2} V(T_n) \right]$$

$$\cos m\omega_c \left[\frac{K_1 + K_2}{2} V(T_n) \right], \tag{18-4}$$

and

$$b_m(n) = \frac{2}{T} \int_c^d [1 + K_3 V(T_n)] \sin m\omega_c t \, dt$$

$$= \frac{1 + K_3 V(T_n)}{m\pi} \left(-\cos m\omega_c \left[\frac{t_0}{2} + K_2 V(T_n) \right] \right.$$

$$\left. + \cos m\omega_c \left[\frac{t_0}{2} - K_1 V(T_n) \right] \right)$$

$$= \frac{2[1 + K_3 V(T_n)]}{m\pi} \sin m\omega_c \left[\frac{t_0}{2} + \frac{K_2 - K_1}{2} V(T_n) \right]$$

$$\sin m\omega_c \frac{K_2 + K_1}{2} V(T_n). \tag{18-5}$$

When (18–3), (18–4), and (18–5) are substituted for the appropriate coefficients in (18–2) we obtain:

$$M(t) = \frac{t_0}{T} + \frac{K_2 - K_1 + K_3 t_0}{T} V(T_n) + \frac{K_3(K_2 - K_1)}{T} V^2(T_n)$$

$$+ \sum_{m=1}^{\infty} 2 \left[\frac{1 + K_3 V(T_n)}{m\pi} \right] \sin m\omega_c \left[\frac{t_0}{2} + \frac{K_2 - K_1}{2} V(T_n) \right]$$

$$\left(\cos \left[m\omega_c \frac{K_1 + K_2}{2} V(T_n) \right] \cos m\omega_c t \right.$$

$$\left. + \sin \left[m\omega_c \frac{K_1 + K_2}{2} V(T_n) \right] \sin m\omega_c t \right)$$

$$= \frac{t_0}{T} + \frac{K_2 - K_1 + K_3 t_0}{T} V(T_n) + \frac{K_3(K_2 - K_1)}{T} V^2(T_n)$$

$$+ \sum_{m=1}^{\infty} 2 \left[\frac{1 + K_3 V(T_n)}{m\pi} \right] \sin m\omega_c \left[\frac{t_0}{2} + \frac{K_2 - K_1}{2} V(T_n) \right]$$

$$\left(\cos \left[m\omega_c t - m\omega_c \frac{K_1 + K_2}{2} V(T_n) \right] \right). \tag{18-6}$$

It should be noted that, by using a proper set of clamped samples, (18–6) applies to either uniform or natural sampling.

The first three terms in (18–6) may be regarded as an amplitude-modulated zero-frequency carrier. The remaining terms are familiar in form and each is recognized to be a combination of an amplitude- and phase-modulated sinusoid. The frequencies of these sinusoids are f_c and its harmonics.

From (18-6) it follows that K_3 and $(K_2 - K_1)$ contribute amplitude modulation only, and $(K_1 + K_2)$ contributes phase modulation only. It follows from (18-1) that position modulation of the center of the pulses is proportional to $(K_1 + K_2)$, whereas duration modulation of the pulses is proportional to $K_2 - K_1$.

When $K_1 = K_2$ and $K_3 = 0$, for example, we have PPM; and if $K_1 = K_2$ and $K_3 \neq 0$, we have both PPM and PAM. It is interesting to note (18-6) that, as $(K_1 + K_2)$ contributes pure phase modulation, the corresponding modulating wave is not $V(t)$ but the clamped samples of $V(t)$. The modulating wave that amplitude-modulates f_c and its harmonics is more difficult to describe, but in many cases of interest it may not differ appreciably from the clamped samples of $V(t)$.

In contrast to the methods of Chapter 17, note especially that equation (18-6) holds for an arbitrary $V(t)$. Even so, it does not display the spectrum of the modulated wave $M(t)$. Instead, it expresses $M(t)$ as the sum of a series of modulated carriers, the carrier frequencies being 0, f_c, $2f_c$, $3f_c$, et cetera. It is possible to extend the analysis to display the spectrum, but this extension is so tedious that it would have to be justified for a particular problem.

MODULATION METHODS

Position-modulated pulses may be produced in many ways. One is to derive them from duration-modulated pulses. The modulating wave is sampled and converted to duration-modulated pulses as explained in Chapter 17. In carrying out this process, either uniform or natural sampling is permissible. The duration-modulated pulses then go to a circuit that generates a rectangular pulse of short duration each time the modulated edge of a duration-modulated pulse passes through a specified value. The position-modulated pulses thus produced are all of equal duration.

Another simple way of producing position-modulated pulses is to pass the modulating wave and a sinusoid having a frequency that is equal to the sampling rate through a miniature, highly nonlinear inductance. The nonlinear inductance forms the primary winding of a transformer. The desired position-modulated signal appears upon rectification of the transformer output. In the absence of a modulating wave, the output is the unmodulated pulse train.

This is an example of natural sampling, and the time of appearance of the position-modulated pulse represents the instant that the modulating wave was, in effect, sampled. With special miniature transformers of this type, termed "kick" coils, the duration of the position-modulated pulses might be as short as a microsecond. If shorter pulses are desired, the ensemble of pulses may be subjected to a differentiating and clipping process.

SPECTRA OF PPM

The results of a spectrum analysis of pulse-position modulation will be given for the case of channel pulses that are position-modulated by a sinusoidal input. The unmodulated pulses will be represented by the unit sampling function expressed as an even function of time, viz.

$$U = k \sum \frac{\sin mk\pi}{mk\pi} \cos m\omega_c t \qquad (18\text{-}7)$$

where $k = t_0/T$ with t_0 as the duration of a pulse, and with $T = 2\pi/\omega_c$ as the unmodulated pulse repetition period or frame interval.

When a sum is bilateral and both limits infinite, as in (18-7), the limits will be omitted. Likewise, if the variable that assumes all possible positive and negative integral values including zero is obvious, it will not be indicated.

The modulating wave is represented by

$$V(t) = A_v \sin \omega_v t. \qquad (18\text{-}8)$$

Let

$$k_1 V(t) = M \sin \omega_v t \qquad (18\text{-}9)$$

where $\pm MT/2$ is the maximum excursion of a pulse from its unmodulated time of recurrence.

If PPM denotes the representation of the unit pulses position-modulated by $A_v \sin \omega_v t$, then

$$\text{PPM} = \sum\sum a_{mn} \cos (m\omega_c + n\omega_v)t \qquad (18\text{-}10)$$

where a_{mn} depends on whether the sampling is uniform or natural. The following values of a_{mn} were obtained by the double Fourier series method.

Uniform Sampling

$$a_{mn} = k(-)^n \frac{\sin\left[m + n\dfrac{\omega_v}{\omega_c}\right]k\pi}{\left[m + n\dfrac{\omega_v}{\omega_c}\right]k\pi} J_n\left[M\left(m + n\dfrac{\omega_v}{\omega_c}\right)\pi\right] \qquad (18\text{-}11)$$

in which the coefficient on the right is a Bessel function of the first kind with integer suffix and real argument.

In the case of uniform sampling the modulating wave is assumed to be instantaneously sampled at regular intervals T, and the pulses are subsequently position-modulated. To carry out this operation it is necessary to delay the sampling information by an interval greater than $MT/2$.

Natural Sampling

$$a_{mn} = k(-)^n \frac{\sin\left[m + n\frac{\omega_v}{\omega_c}\right]k\pi}{mk\pi} J_n(Mm\pi). \qquad (18\text{--}12)$$

In the case of natural sampling we produce PPM by making the displacement of successive pulses from their unmodulated positions proportional to the magnitudes of the modulating wave at the instants of sending the pulses. That is, the time of sampling coincides with what we may choose to regard as the time of appearance of the position-modulated pulse.

DEMODULATION METHODS

While deriving the preceding equations for the frequency spectrum of pulse-position modulated signals in 1942, J. O. Edson recognized an interesting fact. He noted that, when M was made moderately small, a delayed copy of the original signal with little distortion could be obtained by simply passing the PPM signal through a low-pass filter followed by an appropriate amplifier. This is true for either uniform or natural sampling. The amplifier gain falls 6 decibels for each two-to-one increase in frequency. An additional fact brought out by (18–11) and (18–12) is that, although this method of detection may produce little distortion regardless of the sampling method, there is less distortion in the case of natural sampling.

When the wanted signal is derived in the manner described and with uniform sampling, Fig. 18–1 displays the degree of linearity and higher-

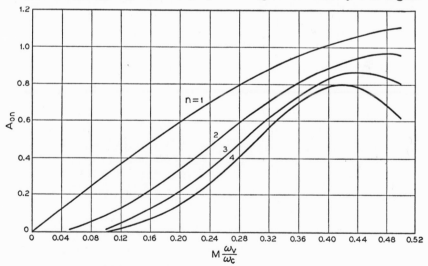

Fig. 18–1 Calculated linearity and distortion products of PPM assuming uniform sampling and demodulation by feeding the position-modulated pulses to a low-pass filter followed by an amplifier whose gain falls 6 decibels per octave

order products of distortion. For natural sampling, an error of less than one per cent is introduced by replacing the sine by its argument in (18–12), viz.,

$$a_{mn} \approx k(-)^n \left[1 + \frac{n\omega_v}{m\omega_{c_c}} \right] J_n(Mm\pi). \qquad (18\text{–}13)$$

Another way to demodulate position-modulated pulses is to convert them first to duration-modulated pulses. This may be done by means of a double-stability circuit that is thrown to its "on" position by regularly spaced pulses from the synchronizer, and to its "off" position by the received position-modulated pulses. The circuit switches to the "off" position whenever the voltage of one edge of the position-modulated pulse passes through a pre-assigned value. Either the leading or trailing edge may be made to control the operation. The duration-modulated pulses at the output of the double-stability circuit are all of the same magnitude. The duration-modulated pulses may be demodulated by any of the methods described in Chapter 17.

SIGNAL–TO-NOISE RATIO

Small Noise

Noise will modify the times at which the incoming pulses reach the slicing level. Figure 18–2 shows how a small noise voltage of root-mean-square value N', when superimposed on a video pulse of peak value S', acts to change the root-mean-square triggering time of the slicer by an amount ϵ. From the geometry of the figure,

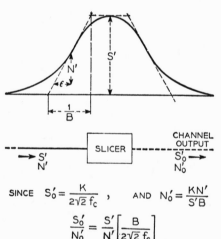

$$\frac{S'}{N'} = \frac{1}{B\epsilon}. \qquad (18\text{–}14)$$

After passing the intermediate-frequency amplifier of band width B and the second detector, the approximate slope of the leading edge of the pulse at the slicing level is $S'B$, and the corresponding "time of rise" is $1/B$. Another figure that is sometimes used is $2/\pi B$. In any event, the time of rise is inversely proportional to the band width, other factors being equal.

SINCE $S_0' = \dfrac{K}{2\sqrt{2}\, f_c}$, AND $N_0' = \dfrac{KN'}{S'B}$

$$\frac{S_0'}{N_0'} = \frac{S'}{N'}\left[\frac{B}{2\sqrt{2}\, f_c}\right]$$

FIG. 18–2   Equation for signal-to-noise improvement

The time of rise is about twice as long as for a typical low-pass filter. This follows since we are, in effect, concerned with the envelope detection of upper and lower sidebands around the mid-band frequency of the intermediate-frequency of the intermediate-frequency amplifier. A low-pass filter for an equivalent system would occupy half the band width of the intermediate-frequency amplifier.

When the output of the slicer is passed to the receiving multiplex, the error in timing, ϵ, will cause a noise voltage, N_0', in the output of the low-pass filter individual to each channel.

Single Channel. Assume a one-channel system as in Fig. 18–3, and assume that the maximum permissible excursion of a pulse is the limiting value of plus or minus $1/2f_c$. This implies B is so much larger than f_c that the duration of the pulse is negligible in relation to half the frame time. Consequently, it may be ignored. Then, plus or minus $1/2f_c$ represents the peak mod-

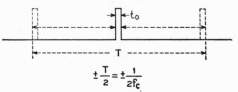

$$\pm \frac{T}{2} = \pm \frac{1}{2f_c}$$

FIG. 18–3   Single-channel pulse-position modulation system

ulation of a pulse, or the maximum displacement in time from its unmodulated position. When the pulses are modulated fully by a single-frequency test tone, the corresponding root-mean-square displacement approaches $\dfrac{1}{2\sqrt{2}f_c}$. If S_0' denotes the corresponding root-mean-square signal voltage in the output of a low-pass filter individual to the channel,

$$S_0' = \frac{K}{2\sqrt{2}f_c} \tag{18–15}$$

where K is a constant factor of proportionality.

In Fig. 18–2, N' may be regarded, for the moment, as the voltage of an instantaneous noise sample taken at the time of triggering and ϵ as the corresponding error in timing caused by the noise sample. N' would normally vary from sample to sample. The root-mean-square value of ϵ is the root-mean-square value of N' divided by the slope which is approximately $S'B$. This follows if we note that the root-mean-square value of the noise (Chapter 4, Theorems III and IV) will equal the root-mean-square value of the instantaneous noise samples, N'. Let N_0' denote the root-mean-square noise in the output of a low-pass filter individual to the channel. Since

$$S_0' = \frac{K}{2\sqrt{2}f_c} \tag{18–15}$$

and since

$$N_0' = \frac{KN'}{S'B}, \tag{18–16}$$

we have,

$$\frac{S_0'}{N_0'} = \frac{S'}{N'}\left[\frac{B}{2\sqrt{2}f_c}\right]. \tag{18–17}$$

Improvement Threshold

Common to all systems that exchange band width for noise improvement, PPM has a well-defined improvement threshold. As a result, the greater the noise improvement, the larger the increase in noise once the threshold is exceeded. For example, in the case of PPM–AM, if the PPM is recovered by envelope detection of the upper and lower sidebands of the position-modulated pulses, the threshold is half the peak signal.

Present concern will be with signal-to-noise ratio just at the threshold. This is usually set by specifying the probability that the threshold will be violated. Next, the peak factor of the noise is evaluated. Peak factor is the ratio of peak to root-mean-square value and may depend upon the above-mentioned probability. In the case of resistance noise, Table 7–1 in Chapter 7 indicates the decibel equivalent of the ratio associated with probabilities in the range of interest. This figure added to the improvement threshold expressed in decibels specifies the ratio of the peak value of the pulse to the root-mean-square noise at the slicer input. This in turn implies the signal-to-noise ratio at the output of each channel.

For example, if the threshold is 6 decibels and we specify that the root-mean-square noise should be 12 decibels below the threshold, then the root-mean-square noise should be 18 decibels below the improvement threshold at the input to the slicer. In this instance, $S'/N' = 8$, approximately.

If $\left[\dfrac{S_0'}{N_0'}\right]_T$ designates the corresponding ratio of root-mean-square signal to root-mean-square noise at output of the channel low-pass filter, equation (18–17) at threshold becomes

$$\left[\frac{S_0'}{N_0'}\right]_T = \frac{2\sqrt{2}B}{f_c} \tag{18–18}$$

where, it will be recalled, $2B \gg f_v$.

J Channels. To extend the foregoing results to a multichannel system, let J equal the number of like channels while retaining the nomenclature and symbols of this and the previous section. With like channels, the part of the frame time allocated to each channel will be $1/Jf_c$. Even though we assume that pulses in adjacent channels just touch when all channels are fully modulated, only part of the allocated time is available for modulation. The part of the frame time occupied by the pulse itself is not available for time modulation. With B as the band width of the intermediate amplifier, it is reasonable to assume the significant pulse duration to be $2/B$.

On this basis, the maximum excursion of a pulse becomes plus or minus $\left[\frac{1}{2Jf_c} - \frac{1}{B}\right]$. When this is inserted in place of $1/2f_c$ in (18–17), we have

$$\frac{S_0'}{N_0'} = \frac{S'}{N'} \frac{1}{\sqrt{2}} \left[\frac{B}{2Jf_c} - 1\right]. \tag{18–19}$$

Again suppose that peak noise four times its root-mean-square value would probably be exceeded rarely enough to make this value acceptable as a limit. This would set the noise peak at $S'/2$, which is the assumed improvement threshold with no allowance for margins. Then $S'/N' = 8$ as before and

$$\left[\frac{S_0'}{N_0'}\right]_T = 4\sqrt{2} \left[\frac{B}{2Jf_c} - 1\right]. \tag{18–20}$$

If, for example, the so-called rise time is assumed to be $2/\pi B$ instead of $1/B$, (18–19) and (18–20) become

$$\frac{S_0'}{N_0'} = \frac{S'}{N'} \frac{\pi}{2\sqrt{2}} \left[\frac{B}{2Jf_c} - 1\right] \tag{18–19a}$$

and

$$\left[\frac{S_0'}{N_0'}\right]_T = 2\sqrt{2}\pi \left[\frac{B}{2Jf_c} - 1\right], \tag{18–20a}$$

respectively.

The relationships illustrate a general principle common to all pulse systems, namely, that the ratio of root-mean-square signal to root-mean-square noise at the output of each like channel is approximately proportional to the ratio of total band width gainfully used to the sum of the channel bands.

DESCRIPTION OF A WORKING SYSTEM

To illustrate the application of some of the principles discussed in this and the three preceding chapters, the following is a brief description (Ref. 22) of an early portable multichannel microwave radio relay system.

Equipment and Operating Features

The system provides eight high-grade telephone channels between points separated by an unobstructed line-of-sight transmission path. Message channels are multiplexed by time division, and pulse-position modulation serves to minimize interchannel crosstalk and improve signal-to-noise ratio. Simultaneous two-way communication is achieved by the use of different radio frequencies confined to nonoverlapping bands, one for each direction of transmission. That is, the two directions of transmission are over different microwave channels separated by frequency division.

The position-modulated pulses are caused to key a microwave oscillator that generates a frequency of nearly five billion cycles per second. At

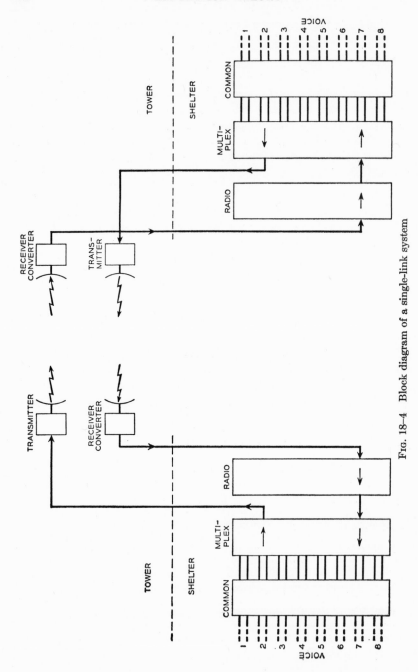

Fig. 18-4 Block diagram of a single-link system

this extremely high frequency, static and most man-made interference are absent. Spurts of microwave power from the oscillator go to an antenna that radiates a highly directive and sharply focused microwave beam. Because the antennas are highly directional, the transmitter power is made only one four-millionth as great as would be required were the antennas omnidirectional. For these reasons peak power of a few watts serves for distances as great as one hundred miles. Since transmission is along a line-of-sight path, the distance between stations is limited by the curvature of the earth. Communications may be extended by using pairs of intermediate sets as repeaters.

The frontispiece depicts one arrangement used in field operations. The arrangement shown is a portable microwave radio set and, as indicated in Fig. 18–4, takes the form of a combined radio transmitter and receiver with multiplex arrangements for modulating and demodulating the eight channels. Pulses are synchronized on a start-stop basis by a 4-microsecond synchronizing pulse called a marker. Eight thousand times a second a 4-microsecond burst of microwave power is followed by eight 1-microsecond bursts corresponding to the eight position-modulated channel pulses. Each spurt of microwave power is substantially constant in magnitude and frequency.

At the receiving end, attenuated microwave spurts from the distant transmitter go to a converter as shown in Fig. 18–4. The converter changes microwave pulses to intermediate-frequency pulses which are further amplified and detected by the "radio receiver." The position-modulated pulses produced by the second detector go to the receiving multiplex.

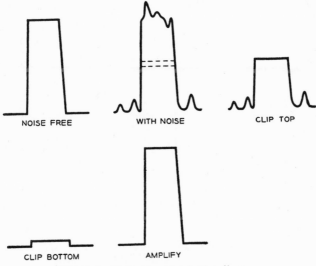

NOISE FREE   WITH NOISE   CLIP TOP

CLIP BOTTOM   AMPLIFY

Fig. 18–5   Reduction of noise by slicer

The radio receiver has automatic tuning to correct for unwanted frequency drifts originating in the transmitting oscillator. The receiver also has automatic volume control to compensate for fading in order that the signals fed to the slicer will be of constant magnitude. The slicer (Fig. 18–5) carves out a narrow slice amounting to about 5 per cent from each video pulse and, as explained in the preceding section, thereby substantially frees the pulses of noise.

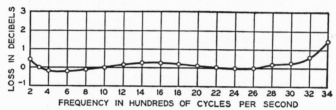

FIG. 18–6   Typical transmission-frequency characteristic

Transmission Performance

The telephone channels which the system provides are high-quality message circuits and meet commercial standards for long-distance telephone transmission. Each channel is capable of transmitting signaling, dialing, facsimile, pictures, or multichannel voice-frequency telegraph.

As shown by the typical transmission-frequency characteristic plotted in Fig. 18–6, the over-all transmission varies less than one decibel as the signal frequency varies from 300 to 3,000 cycles per second.

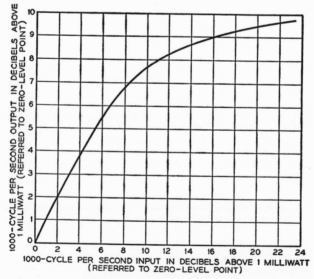

FIG. 18–7   Typical load performance

Load-carrying capacity is indicated by the typical characteristic shown in Fig. 18–7. The sinusoidal input to a channel may vary up to plus 8 decibels above a milliwatt without appreciable overloading. The "zero-

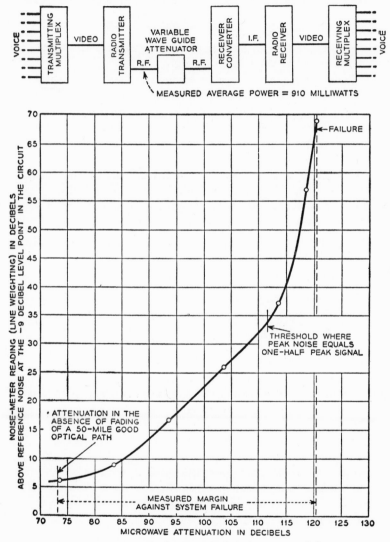

FIG. 18–8 Message-circuit noise for a single link versus path loss

level point" of reference used in Figs. 18–7 and 18–8 refers to the point where the multiplex connects to an external two-wire telephone circuit.

As indicated by the analytical treatment of noise and as clearly shown in Fig. 18–8, the circuit noise contributed by a single link depends primarily upon the radio-frequency attenuation of the path. For a many-link system the total noise power is the sum of the noise powers contributed by the individual links. Even so, under normal conditions of use each message channel is unusually quiet. Over a typical 50-mile path, if it is assumed that the signal is 8 decibels above a milliwatt at the zero level point, the root-mean-square, signal-to-noise ratio is 75 decibels. Moreover, as indicated by Fig. 18–8, an additional increase in path loss of 48 decibels can be encountered before the system fails.

In the nonsynchronous system to be described in Chapter 20, our concern will be with pulses that are intentionally caused to jitter with respect to their unmodulated positions. Accordingly, it will be of interest at this point to note the order of magnitude of the intervals of time that are significant in determining the exact position in time of a channel pulse in a conventional PPM system. For example, in Fig. 18–8, assuming a typical 50-mile path, if the relative average random jitter of the trailing edges of the channel pulses had been as great as one billionth of a second, the average power of the background noise present in the output of each message channel would have been doubled.

Although the path attenuation may vary by substantial amounts due to meteorological conditions, the over-all transmission stability of the eight

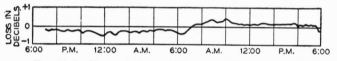

FIG. 18–9   Transmission stability of a 3,200-mile circuit

channels is unusually good. This, of course, might be surmised since the amplitudes of the pulses do not convey the specification of the message. The over-all transmission stability of a 3,200-mile circuit is illustrated by a typical 24-hour recording (reproduced in Fig. 18–9) of the received level of a 1,000-cycle-per-second test tone. The maximum variation is less than plus or minus half a decibel. In this instance a long circuit was obtained by operating ten sets so as to form five two-way, eight-channel systems, each operating simultaneously over the same 40-mile air path. By connecting in tandem the five systems, the eight channels, and both directions of transmission, the resulting one-way transmission was over an air path 3,200 miles long.

References*

1. C. J. H. A. Stall, "An Installation for Multiplex-Pulse Modulation," *Phillips Technical Review*, Eindhoven, Netherlands, Vol. 11, November 1949, pp. 133–144.

* Some of the references cited are not limited to pulse-position-modulation.

2. Arnold E. Ross, "A Type of Nonlinear Random Distortion (Noise) in Pulse Communication," *Physical Review*, New York, Vol. 73, 2nd Series, 1948, p. 1126.
3. Sidney Moskowitz and Donald D. Grieg, "Noise-Suppression Characteristics of Pulse-Time Modulation," *Proceedings of the Institute of Radio Engineers*, New York, Vol. 36, 1948, pp. 446–450.
4. Vernon D. Landon, "Theoretical Analysis of Various Systems of Multiplex Transmission," *RCA Review*, New York, Vol. 9, 1948, pp. 287–351 and 433–482.
5. M. M. Levy, "A Technique for the Design of Pulse-Time Multichannel Radio Systems," *Journal of the British Institution of Radio Engineers*, London, Vol. 9, 1949, pp. 386–411.
6. R. R. Long, "The Application of Pulse Modulation to Multiplex Communication Systems," *Proceedings of the Institution of Radio Engineers*, Sydney, Australia, Vol. 10, 1949, pp. 10–17.
7. D. D. Grieg and H. Gallay, "Pulse-Time-Modulated Multiplex Radio-Relay System-Radio-Frequency Equipment," *Electrical Communication*, New York, Vol. 24, 1947, pp. 141–158.
8. Britton Chance, "Time Modulation," *Proceedings of the Institute of Radio Engineers*, New York, Vol. 35, 1947, pp. 1039–1044.
9. Britton Chance, "Time Demodulation," *Proceedings of the Institute of Radio Engineers*, New York, Vol. 35, 1947, pp. 1045–1049.
10. F. Altman and J. H. Dyer, "Multiplex Broadcasting," *Electrical Engineering*, New York, Vol. 66, 1947, pp. 372–380.
11. Bertram Trevor, Orville E. Dow, and William D. Houghton, "Pulse-Time-Division Radio Relay," *RCA Review*, New York, Vol. 7, 1946, pp. 561–575.
12. John J. Kelleher, "Pulse-Modulated Radio-Relay Equipment," *Electronics*, New York, Vol. 19, May 1946, pp. 124–129.
13. Harold Goldberg and Carl C. Bath, "Multiplex Employing Pulse-Time and Pulsed-Frequency Modulation," *Proceedings of the Institute of Radio Engineers*, New York, Vol. 37, 1949, pp. 22–28.
14. F. L. H. M. Stumpers, "Noise in a Pulse-Frequency-Modulation System," *Phillips Research Reports*, Eindhoven, Netherlands, Vol. 3, 1948, pp. 241–254.
15. Arnold E. Ross, "Theoretical Study of Pulse-Frequency Modulation," *Proceedings of the Institute of Radio Engineers*, New York, Vol. 37, 1949, pp. 1277–1286.
16. D. D. Grieg and A. M. Levine, "Pulse-Time-Modulated Multiplex Radio-Relay System-Terminal Equipment," *Electrical Communication*, New York, Vol. 23, 1946, pp. 159–178.
17. Sidney Moskowitz and Donald D. Grieg, "Noise-Suppression Characteristics of Pulse-Time Modulation," *Electrical Communication*, New York, Vol. 26, 1949, pp. 46–51.
18. J. H. McGuire and P. J. Nowacki, "A Common-Wave Duplex Pulse Communication System," *The Journal of the Institution of Electrical Engineers*, London, Vol. 94, Part 3A, 1947, pp. 528–532.
19. Z. Jelonek, "Noise Problems in Pulse Communications," *The Journal of the Institution of Electrical Engineers*, London, Vol. 94, Part 3A, 1947, pp. 533–545.
20. M. M. Levy, "Some Theoretical and Practical Considerations of Pulse Modulation," *The Journal of the Institution of Electrical Engineers*, London, Vol. 94, Part 3A, 1947, pp. 565–572.

21. D. G. Reid, "A 60–CM Multichannel System Employing Pulse-Phase Modulation," *The Journal of the Institution of Electrical Engineers*, London, Vol. 94, Part 3A, 1947, pp. 573–583.
22. H. S. Black, J. W. Beyer, T. J. Grieser, and F. A. Polkinghorn, "A Multichannel Microwave Radio-Relay System," *Transactions of the American Institute of Electrical Engineers*, New York, Vol. 65, 1946, pp. 798–806.
23. Gordon L. Fredendall, Kurt Schlesinger, and A. C. Schroeder, "Transmission of Television Sound on the Picture Carrier," *Proceedings of the Institute of Radio Engineers*, New York, Vol. 34, 1946, pp. 49P–61P.
24. C. B. Feldman and W. R. Bennett, "Band Width and Transmission Performance," *The Bell System Technical Journal*, New York, Vol. 28, No. 3, July 1949, pp. 490–595.

Problems

1. Derive an expression for the spectra of the instantaneous samples of $V(t)$, assuming (a) regular sampling and (b) natural sampling.
2. Derive an expression for the spectra of clamped samples of $V(t)$, assuming (a) regular sampling and (b) natural sampling.
3. Solve Problem 2(a) under the condition that the stored samples decay (a) linearly and (b) exponentially.
4. Binary digits are transmitted over a PAM–FM radio system. Theoretically, what is the minimum peak signal-to-peak noise ratio at threshold in the radio-frequency system and at the output of the final detector?

CHAPTER 19

PULSE–CODE MODULATION

When called upon to communicate messages by electric signals, engineers have used, in the past, either amplitude modulation or frequency modulation. In both cases, the process is continuous and the application of a continuously varying message wave causes amplitude or frequency variations of a sinusoidal carrier with time. For some purposes, frequency modulation (Chapters 12 to 14) is better than amplitude modulation (Chapters 9 to 11), although it does require a greater use of frequency space, which is valuable, and it calls for somewhat more complicated transmitter and receiver techniques.

Pulse modulation (Chapters 15 to 18) now joins these older methods to give engineers a new* tool for improving communication systems. In pulse modulation, the message is not projected continuously, as in other modulation methods, but as discrete signal elements, for example, short spurts or pulses. These discrete signal elements represent samples defining the specification of the message. However, the samples are of continuous variation; that is, they are not quantized.

More recently, communication engineers have shown considerable interest in pulse-code modulation. This is a new method of transmitting continuous signals in which the signal is sampled and the magnitude of each sample is rounded off to the nearest one of a finite set of permitted values. This allows the signal to be transmitted by codes such as have been used in all telegraph systems, with all the advantages these systems have over the ordinary methods of transmission.

The development of modern pulse-code modulation stems from two factors: one, a recognition that quantized samples may closely approximate an exact specification of a continuously varying wave; the other, the availability of improved techniques whereby quantized samples may be generated and translated into more complex codes at the enormous speeds corresponding to our present-day broad-band systems of communication. Although it is too early to predict to what extent code modulation will dis-

---

* Pulse modulation is not entirely new. Pulse-amplitude modulation goes back many generations. Pulse-duration modulation was suggested in an invention by R. A. Heising filed on April 18, 1924. Pulse-position modulation was described in a patent by R. D. Kell which was filed on September 29, 1934.

place or supplement other established methods, it seems likely that pulse-code modulation will be a strong competitor in many communication areas.

Although a pulse-code modulation (PCM) system inherently is capable of transmitting discrete messages, the term is usually understood to mean a system that permits the conversion of a continuously varying wave into quantized samples that normally can be and often are translated into a more appropriate code for transmission over the medium. The treatment to follow will be confined to PCM systems that transmit code characters to represent the quantized instantaneous samples of the continuously varying wave to be conveyed.

Compared with conventional systems of modulation, PCM is reasonably attractive as a way of communicating efficiently (as brought out in Chapters 6, 7, and 8) and it places minimum restrictions upon the type of message that may be transmitted. It has the advantage that, through the use of regenerative repeaters, transmission in which the signal-to-noise ratio is substantially independent of the number of repeaters becomes possible. To obtain this advantage the only requirement is that noise, interference, and other disturbances add up to less than half a quantum step at each regenerative repeater.

SAMPLING AND QUANTIZATION

As mentioned in Chapter 5, application of the sampling principle permits the reduction of a continuously varying wave to a limited number of discrete values per second, and application of the quantizing principle permits the value of each sample to be represented with sufficient accuracy by an appropriate code character. The code characters use various combinations of a specified number of code elements. Each code element is quantized and hence may be a binary, ternary, or in general an n'ary code element. Systems using binary code elements require extra band width for a given information capacity, but in return they are more tolerant to interference. Band width is conserved by using many quantum steps per code element, but only at the expense of increased susceptibility to interference. These relationships are discussed in Chapters 6, 7, and 8.

NUMBER AND SIZE OF QUANTUM STEPS

Since quantization is a method for representing a continuously varying function by a set of discrete values, the representation is necessarily approximate, although the accuracy always can be improved by using smaller steps. Consequently, the number of quantum steps and the size of each step, if the steps are tapered, are matters of keeping the granularity noise

(Ref. 1)* due to quantization (Chap. 5) within acceptable limits. Clearly, the optimum design will depend entirely upon the characteristics of the message.

In ordinary telephony, 64 to 128 steps that are logarithmically tapered result in a high degree of fidelity as judged by experienced observers. On the other hand, if the message wave is derived from the output of a multi-channel, frequency-division, carrier telephone system or represents a high-quality sound program, nearly uniform steps are needed because in this instance the quantization noise is required to be substantially independent of the magnitude of the message wave. High-speed facsimile, television, and other types of messages could be expected to impose still different requirements. In any event, the general principle is to use enough steps to make the effects due to granularity unimportant. The steps may be equal, unequal with logarithmic variation, or unequal with any other law of variation, depending upon the type of message.

METHOD OF ESTABLISHING A CODE AND THE RESULTING NUMBER OF CODE ELEMENTS

When the principles that are described in Chapter 6 are followed, the proper number of code elements becomes a matter of trading band width for noise reduction and, therefore, will depend upon the particular application. However, when the number of code elements and the number of quantum steps per element have been selected, the transmitter power is indicated and needs to be enough to over-ride noise, usually to the extent implied by half a quantum step. In addition, extra power is required for a variety of practical reasons including margins and tolerances.

If q is the number of code elements comprising each code character and s the number of quanta per code element, $(s^q)!$ represents the available number of different codes. In other words, the factorial of the number of values into which the samples are quantized represents the number of different ways in which the possible values of a sample may be correlated with the code values. Usually the choice of code will be controlled entirely by the problem of how to simplify the instrumentation. This point will be illustrated by examples in a later section of this chapter dealing with the instrumentation of coders and decoders.

PCM TIME–DIVISION SYSTEMS

In applications using PCM, it is natural to multiplex channels by time division. This has advantages which will be mentioned. However, listing the advantages of PCM is not intended to give the impression that it

* The references cited are listed at the end of each chapter according to the number used in the text.

is preferable.   In practical applications, preference as to the over-all choice depends upon many other factors which we are not considering.

From a theoretical point of view, time division affords a degree of flexibility and other features not obtainable in a frequency-division system. For example, problems of adding and dropping channels at intermediate repeater points are simplified substantially.   In a time-division system, it is particularly convenient to multiplex widely different types of channels. In frequency division, this may impose hardships.   For example, in cable carrier systems, the requirement that any voice channel be capable of handling voice-frequency telegraph leads to composite requirements for repeaters and terminals that are more difficult to meet than corresponding requirements imposed by a system in which the channels are either all telephone channels or all telegraph channels.   Similarly, a broad-band, carrier-telephone system capable of handling television channels is also faced with composite terminal and repeater requirements of a complicated nature.   Finally, time division may prove to be flexible and economical from the standpoint of coordination with switching, signaling, nationwide dialing, and other related operations.

In time division, each channel keeps its individuality throughout the journey from the first transmitter to the last receiver; whereas in frequency division, economic considerations usually lead to a definite grouping of the channels.   This individuality accounts for the comparative ease with which channels may be dropped or reinserted at any repeater point in a time-division system.   To drop channels, we merely remove every Kth pulse or group of pulses following the synchronizing pulse, and to reinsert channels we merely reinsert pulses.   By contrast, in present types of frequency-division systems, these same operations require a formidable array of modulating and filtering equipment.

To illustrate the application of time division to switching, let us envision a group of N channels in which each channel is sampled simultaneously; next, these samples could be multiplexed in any time sequence by the insertion of suitable delays; time-scanning of the group would connect the individual incoming channels to outgoing paths in an order determined by the value of the individual channel delay; and finally, by changing the delay encountered by individual channels, channels could be switched between incoming and outgoing paths in any desired manner.

Time division implies switching at precisely fixed times.   To avoid crosstalk in a time-division system, operations in group equipment common to a number of channels must proceed without memory of the signals from preceding channels.   This requires that the build-up and decay times be small, and it implies a sufficiently wide pass band together with sufficient phase linearity.

As the number of similar channels is increased, the time interval that can be allotted to each channel must be reduced, since all of them must be fitted into a period of time corresponding to the reciprocal of the sampling rate. This means that the allowable duration of a code character representing an individual sample is shortened as the number of time-division channels in a group is increased. Then too, pulses or signal elements tend to become more difficult to generate and to transmit as their duration decreases. Moreover, if the pulses become short enough, phase linearity and other imperfections of the transmitting medium may begin to interfere with the proper operation of the system. For these reasons, it inevitably becomes necessary eventually to restrict the number of channels that can be included within a time-division group. For larger numbers of channels, frequency division may be used to keep each time-division group within practical limits.

METHOD OF SYNCHRONIZATION

If the system of communication is to be efficient, the connection of a transmitting channel to its proper receiving circuit in a time-division part of a PCM system requires that the two terminals be synchronized. This means that the timing operations at the receiver, except for the time lost in propagation and repeatering, must follow closely those at the transmitter. In a general way this amounts to getting a local clock to keep the same time as a distant standard clock except as the local clock is slow by an amount corresponding to the time required to transport the signals. Here, the criterion of good time-keeping might be regarded as extremely precise by some standards. For example, in a 10,000-channel telephone system, we cannot work with a discrepancy as long as 1/500 of a microsecond, for the very good reason that incorrect routing of pulses would occur and this would produce intolerably large decoding errors. To avoid this, the system of synchronization usually provides means whereby: *first*, the synchronization is monitored continuously; *second*, if the system is out of frame (as it may be after transmission has been interrupted temporarily), the monitoring circuit hunts for and establishes synchronism; and *third*, whenever the system is not synchronized and properly framed, all messages on all channels are interruped so as to avoid unnecessary noise and crosstalk.

One possible procedure is to set aside a code element or pulse within the frame and to transmit this pulse only every other frame. For example, if the channels are ordinary telephone channels, the time allocated to a frame would be the reciprocal of the sampling rate, for example, 125 microseconds. The fundamental frequency that the synchronizing pulse generates is selected by a band filter, and the effects of modulation and noise on the frequency selected are made unimportant by using a sufficiently narrow band filter. That is, sidebands produced by other modulated code elements are attenuated to negligible proportions, as is the background noise. It is the output of this filter that serves to control the receiving clock.

Once the transmission is interrupted, it is highly improbable that the two clocks (transmitting and receiving) will indicate the same time. Accordingly, in carrying out a synchronizing process, an orderly procedure is set up for locating the synchronizing pulse. This consists of examining the code elements one by one until the synchronizing pulse is reached and identified. After any one element is viewed long enough to establish the absence of the synchronizing pulse, the receiving clock is set back one code element and the next code element is viewed. Hence, the time required to synchronize a repeater or the receiver varies, depending upon the epoch at which the system connection is re-established.

In order not to limit the usefulness of the PCM channels, it is customary to provide a system of synchronization that can tolerate values of noise and interference that would cause the message channels to fail. Apart from the fact that a failure of synchronization affects all channels, it also is reasonably easy to provide this feature.

Channels are not only dropped and added at intermediate repeater points, but it is usually necessary to transfer channels from one system to another. In a typical communication network, such branching and junction points would be encountered at a comparatively large number of the repeaters. If it is assumed that the channels are multiplexed by time division, this creates a synchronization problem at the branching and junction points. This, in turn, implies network synchronization.

Apparently, the most promising solution to this problem is to provide one master oscillator for the entire network of many systems throughout the country and to control a plurality of slave sources from this master source. The purpose of this is to insure that identical frame frequencies are generated at all branching, junction, and terminal points in every system. Suitable provision must be made so that when the master oscillator fails, or when the network is broken up into parts by failure in one or more repeater sections, the control function will be taken over temporarily by appropriate ones of the slave sources which automatically become master oscillators, in accordance with a pre-arranged order of succession. When the trouble condition has been cleared, the master oscillator regains control.

In addition to frame-frequency control, delay networks are required for bringing the frames into coincidence on the time axis at interconnecting points. In order to be able to interconnect successfully, variations in delay from point to point must be held to within a small fraction (perhaps 10 per cent) of the interval assigned to a code element. For example, for a 10,000-channel telephone system using binary code elements, this would mean variations in delay of less than about 1/5,600 microsecond.

ESSENTIALS OF REGENERATIVE REPEATERING

One of the major problems in communication systems design has been the reduction of noise and distortion that is picked up along the way or introduced by equipment. Until recently, noise and distortion have been controlling factors in long-distance transmission. This is principally because of the cumulative building-up of noise and other transmission impairments with each of the many amplifications necessary over long distances.

In fact, in all of the conventional or nonquantized systems, the repeaters must have exceptionally low distortion so that a signal may be propagated through a large number of them (say 1,333 repeaters for a 4,000-mile cable circuit made up of 3-mile repeater spans) without too much deformation. In spite of good repeater design, a signal passing through such a large number of repeaters will accumulate considerable noise, considerable interference from other systems, and considerable linear and nonlinear distortion inherent to each repeater. In nonquantized systems there is no escaping accumulations of this sort.

By transmitting quantized signals, it is possible to remove noise and distortion as a limiting factor. When the total perturbation from all causes is less than half a quantum step, the quantized signal element can be identified. Next, if regenerative repeatering is assumed, a new-pulse generator is caused to produce a new signal element of the correct magnitude and correct wave form, occurring at the correct time. By this means, it has been found practical in actual installations to transmit through as many repeaters in tandem as may be desired, with no apparent impairment of the quantized message.

On the other hand, one of the characteristics of a regenerative PCM system is that attenuation in any one span in excess of the threshold limit will cause the system to fail. This means that, in engineering a system, the noise margins must be large enough to make the likelihood of a failure due to this cause sufficiently remote.

It should also be noted that regenerative repeatering entails additional delay. At each regenerative repeater there will be a delay corresponding to the time lost in identifying a code element, plus the time required to regenerate the element, plus the time required to put the signal back on the transmitting medium. When the first and last of these three operations include filtering, as is commonly the case, the delay corresponding to the time of transmission through each filter is unescapable.

METHODS OF INSTRUMENTATION OF THE CODER AND DECODER

Although there are many different ways of instrumenting a coder or decoder, they can be divided into three categories according to the way in which they evaluate the magnitude of the samples. This classification is independent of whether the code elements are binary, ternary, or in general n'ary. In the first category, the magnitude is measured by comparison with one code element value after another, proceeding from the most significant element value to the least, and subtracting the code element value in question each time that value is found to be smaller than the magnitude (or its residue from the previous subtraction). In the second category, a magnitude is measured by counting out the number of units contained in it one by one, until less than one unit remains. In the third category, magnitude is measured in a single operation by comparison with a set of scaled values. The number of operations and the time required for coding tend to be least in the third category. Obviously, rapid coding is highly desirable since it allows more channels to be handled by common equipment.

Feedback Subtraction (Ref. 2)

To illustrate the subtraction process associated with the first category, we will assume a multichannel, voice-frequency, time-division system in which each quantized speech sample is represented by a code character composed of five binary code elements.

Coder. Each voice wave is sampled at regular intervals to produce amplitude-modulated pulses. These pulse samples (Fig. 19–1) have an average value when the signal is zero and may have any value between zero and twice average when a signal is present.

Each pulse sample in turn is stored as a charge on a capacitor. Let it be assumed that the average stored charge in the absence of modulation is 16 units and the maximum possible charge is just less than 32 units. A comparison circuit measures the stored charge (that is, the sample) and compares it with a reference voltage of 16 units. If the stored charge exceeds 16 units, the first code element is transmitted and 16 units of the stored charge are removed from the storage capacitor. If the stored charge does not exceed 16 units, the first code element is not transmitted and the stored charge is left unchanged. In either case the charge remaining on the capacitor is less than 16 units.

Next, the stored charge is compared with 8 units. The second code element is sent if the charge exceeds 8 units and suppressed if it is less than 8 units. Again, if the charge exceeds 8 units, the subtraction circuit operates and removes 8 units of charge. The residual charge must now be less than 8 units.

Repetitions of the process with successive reference voltages of 4, 2, and 1 units, respectively, reduce the stored charge to less than 1 unit and result in the successive transmission or suppression of the corresponding code elements (Fig. 19–2). Finally, the storage capacitor is discharged completely and stands ready to receive the next signal sample and to transmit the next code character in a similar manner.

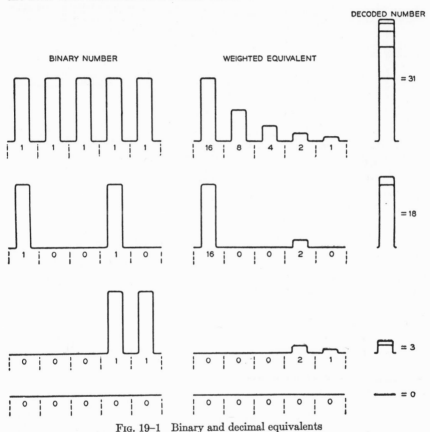

FIG. 19–1   Binary and decimal equivalents

Decoder. Synchronization and gating are performed in the usual way. At the instant preceding the reception of each code character, a storage capacitor is charged to a standard reference voltage. Next, as the five successive binary code elements that comprise a code character arrive, a subtraction circuit similar to that used at the transmitter removes charge at the rate of 16 units for the first pulse, 8 units for the second, and so on. Thus, the total charge removed is the same as that required to discharge the storage capacitor at the transmitter. The total charge removed is delivered to the input of a low-pass filter. The result of a sequence of such operations is to reproduce the original wave, except, of course, for granularity (Fig. 19-2).

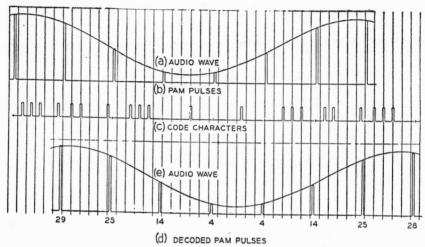

(d) DECODED PAM PULSES

FIG. 19-2 Pulse-amplitude modulation (PAM) and pulse-code modulation (PCM) transmitting and receiving wave forms

Pulse Counting (Refs. 3 and 4)

The following sequence of events, presently to be described in more detail, result in the automatic conversion of speech to code (Fig. 19-3), and is an example of the counting method classified under the second category. The method, of course, is not limited to a speech wave; a speech wave is merely taken for purposes of illustration. It will be assumed that the

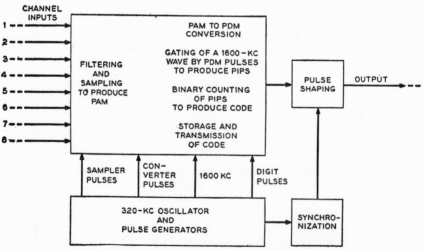

FIG. 19-3 Functional diagram of PCM transmitter

voice-frequency channels are multiplexed by time division, and an eight-channel system will be described.   The quantized samples will be represented by code characters consisting of five binary code elements.

Fundamentally, the functional operation of the coder as indicated in Fig. 19–3 centers around the use of a binary counter (Refs. 5 and 6).   At the transmitting end, preliminary to the production of a code character, the binary counter counts the number of pulses passing through a "gate" that, in turn, is opened for an interval of time proportional to the magnitude of a logarithmically compressed sample of the speech wave.   The condition of the binary counter at the end of each count will be found to display and will be utilized to produce the particular code character, that is, the desired pattern of pulses for transmission over the high-frequency medium.

At the receiving end, as depicted by Fig. 19–4, the primary function of the PCM receiver is to perform the same sequence of operations, but in

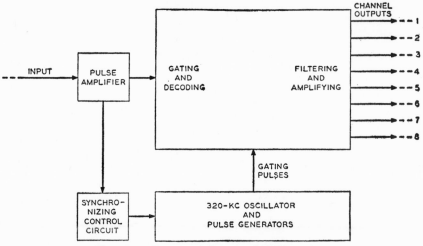

FIG. 19–4   Functional diagram of PCM receiver

the reverse order, and not necessarily by the same methods.   The message delivered will be a delayed copy of the original modulating wave.   It is possible to arrange the design so that the accuracy of the delivered message depends primarily upon the granularity of the quantized samples of the modulating wave, that is, upon the degree of fineness of the quantum steps.

PCM Transmitter.   As indicated in Fig. 19–3, all of the operations in the PCM transmitter are accurately timed by a 320-kilocycle-per-second, crystal-controlled oscillator.   This control is exercised, first, by a variety of pulses produced by circuits known as "ring counters" (Ref. 7) and, second, by a 1,600,000-cycle-per-second sinusoidal timing wave obtained by generating the fifth harmonic of the 320-kilocycle oscillations.   In the diagram of Fig. 19–3, these control circuits are included in the block marked "oscillator and pulse generators." The output of the 320-kilocycle oscillator drives a five-stage ring counter. Each stage of this ring counter divides the input frequency by five so that 64,000 pulses per second appear in the output of each stage. Pulses in the output of a particular stage are coupled to the input of an eight-stage ring counter with the result that 8,000 pulses per second are produced in the output of each stage. These pulses occur at 125-microsecond intervals and have a duration of 15 5/8 microseconds. Also, at any particular instant, one and only one stage is producing a pulse.

As indicated on the left of Fig. 19–3, the input to each channel is filtered by passing through a low-pass filter with a cutoff frequency of less than 4,000 cycles per second. Each channel is sampled 8,000 times a second by a sampler, individual to the channel. A particular channel sampler is activated by pulses from a particular stage of the eight-stage ring. The outputs of all of the samplers are combined to produce an array of amplitude-modulated pulses multiplexed by time division.

The amplitude-modulated pulses go to a common-channel converter and are changed to duration-modulated pulses, compression being introduced so that the duration of each pulse is logarithmically related to the magnitude of the corresponding sample. These duration- or length-modulated pulses are used to enable an amplifier which is referred to as a gate. Thus, the amplifier is active during intervals of time corresponding to the duration of each pulse.

The grids of this amplifier are driven in a push-pull relationship by a 1,600-kilocycle timing wave. The plates connect to the input of the binary counter (Fig. 19–5) and deliver short pulses or "pips" at the rate of 3,200,000 per second for the duration of each of the duration-modulated pulses. Each group of pips is counted. Counts from 0 to 31 are possible. With no input to a channel, a count of 15 or 16 is equally probable.

The binary counter (Fig. 19–5) has five stages, and each stage has two tubes which will be designated A and B. Each stage is designed so that when A conducts, B does not, and vice versa. If a pulse is applied to the input of a stage, the stage reverses its position and assumes the opposite state regardless of which state it was in. For example, if A is conducting and B is not, the next pulse makes A nonconducting and B conducting. Stages are so connected that a pulse is applied to the next stage only when B of the previous stage is conducting. Knowledge of the condition of either A or B tells whether the stage has counted an even or odd number of pulses.

Thus, at the end of a counting interval, to determine how many pulses were counted, it is sufficient to look at the A tubes. If the A tube of the first stage is conducting, we write 1, and, if nonconducting, we write zero.

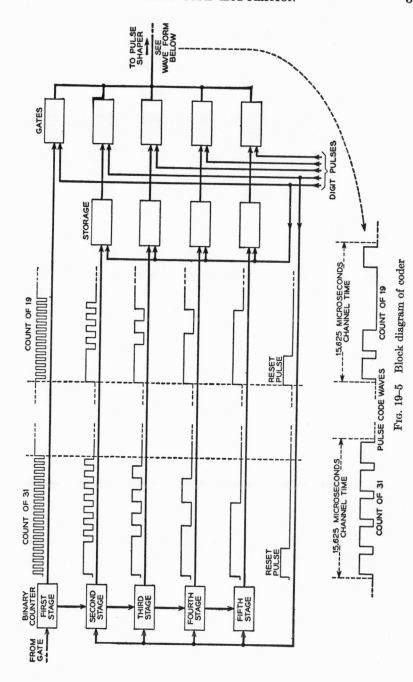

Fig. 19-5 Block diagram of coder

If the A tube of the second stage is conducting, the number we write is 2, and, if nonconducting, 0. For the remaining three stages, we write 4 or 0, 8 or 0, and 16 or 0 respectively. The sum of the five numbers equals the number of pulses counted.

The counter has provision whereby the application of a reset pulse forces all of the B tubes to conduct. Removal of the reset pulse leaves the counter in a condition to register the count of the next series of pulses. For purposes of illustration, Fig. 19–5 depicts particular, idealized wave forms as a function of time in the output of the different stages of the binary counter.

At the end of each counting period and preceding the reset pulse, information describing the count that has been registered is transmitted over the high-frequency medium to the PCM receiver by sending in succession a binary digit for each counter stage to describe whether its A tube is conducting or nonconducting. The first digit is transmitted directly under the control of the A tube. The remaining data are stored. This is accomplished by charging, under the control of the A tubes, storage capacitors. Gates coupled to the storage capacitors are turned on by control pulses in successive intervals and do or do not deliver pulses according as the A tube of each counter stage is or is not conducting. Since the storage tubes reverse the polarity, the output of the first counter stage is reversed relative to the other stages.

Pulses derived from the coder are not of uniform duration or shape and, hence, are applied to a new-pulse generator. The new-pulse generator consists of a gate, opened or closed by the coder output and fed by short pulses from the synchronizer that are of constant amplitude and recur uniformly at a 320-kilocycle rate. By this means, the transmitted pulses are of uniform shape, amplitude, and duration.

PCM Receiver. Since the channels are multiplexed by time division, the channels are separated (Fig. 19–4) by pulsed amplifiers serving as gates that are opened sequentially by pulses from the receiving synchronizer. By a process of decoding that is the reverse of the coding process, amplitude-modulated pulses are obtained and are applied to a low-pass filter. The output of the filter is amplified to the desired signal power for transmission to the subscriber.

Electron Beam Coders and Decoders (Refs. 8 to 10)

Although high-speed beam coders and decoders are a comparatively new suggestion they would seem to offer attractive possibilities for creating simpler, better, and more flexible systems of pulse-code modulation. Recently these possibilities have been explored by producing a twelve-channel transmitter and receiver. A specially developed beam deflection tube was used for coding and electronic circuits for decoding.

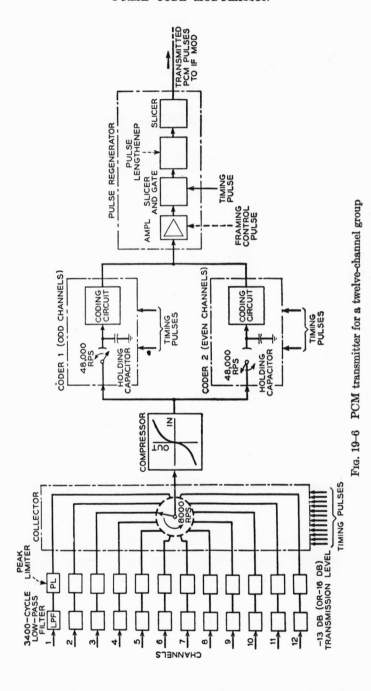

Fig. 19–6   PCM transmitter for a twelve-channel group

Twelve-Channel Transmitter. Again using multichannel speech waves for purposes of illustration, each audio input (Fig. 19–6) is passed through a low-pass filter with a cutoff comfortably below 4,000 cycles per second, and then through a limiter that chops off the positive and negative peak of any signal exceeding a prescribed maximum absolute value. The inputs then enter a "collector" circuit, that assembles samples of the channels on a common lead. The result is an array of amplitude-modulated pulses multiplexed by time division. Although the collector circuit functions electronically under the control of pulses derived from a master oscillator that clocks the PCM transmitter, the resulting switching operations are analogous to the operation of a mechanical commutator. The "contact arm" rotates 8,000 times a second, and provides a conducting path to a common multiplex lead from each channel circuit in turn for an interval of 1/12 of a revolution. This implies a group of twelve channels.

It should be noted that one of the advantages of a time-division system is that certain functions may be performed by circuits common to a plurality of channels. In this instance, for example, the time-divided, amplitude-modulated pulses go to a *common-channel* instantaneous compressor (Refs. 11 to 13) having an input-output characteristic of the form depicted in Fig. 19–6. The general purpose of this type of circuit was discussed in Chapter 5 where it was pointed out that there are substantial advantages if the quantized samples vary logarithmically. Steps that are approximately logarithmic mean that a considerable number of small steps are devoted to the treatment of low-level signals.

After compression, the multiplex signal goes to the input of two coders. The function of the coder is to convert a sample to an appropriate code character composed of seven binary code elements. As indicated in Fig. 19–6, the samples are stored on "holding capacitors" in order that they do not change during the operation of coding. In Fig. 19–6 the analogy of a rotating switch is again called upon to illustrate the routing of alternate samples to separate six-channel coders. Each compressed channel sample is connected to a holding capacitor for 5 microseconds and is held for about 16 microseconds.

Simplified Description of the Coder and Decoder. The general principles of electron beam coders and electronic circuits for decoding are illustrated by Fig. 19–7, which indicates the successive functional operations starting with the incoming voice wave of one channel, at the upper left, and ending with the corresponding outgoing reproduced wave at the lower right. In Fig. 19–7, five instead of seven binary digits are shown for ease of illustration. This beam coder utilizes a new electronic beam tube wherein a beam sweeps across a checkered mask as shown in the upper part of Fig. 19–7. In effect, the checkered mask is used as a scale for the measurement of each sample. The five columns of the scale are divided into fractions of

A SPEECH WAVE 120-MILLISECONDS LONG
FREQUENCY RANGE 0-4000 CPS

Each sample may be considered as measured by the checkered scale whose five columns are divided into fractions of the total magnitude (1/2, 1/4, 1/8, 1/16, and 1/32). If the sampled magnitude as projected on this scale cuts the unshaded portion of any column, a pulse is placed in the corresponding position of the pulse code group. The sum of the position values of all the pulses appearing in a five-position group represents the value of the sample.

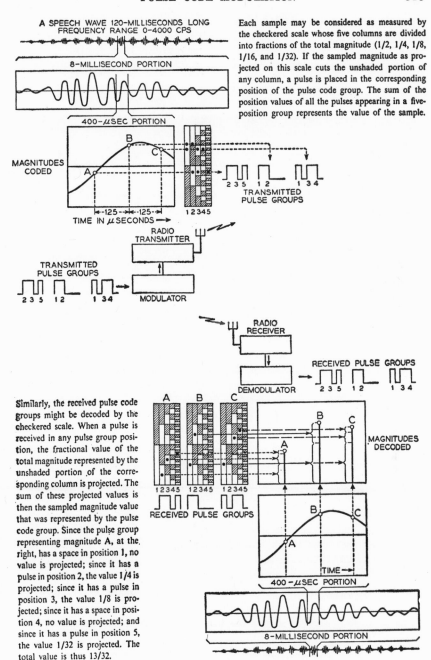

Similarly, the received pulse code groups might be decoded by the checkered scale. When a pulse is received in any pulse group position, the fractional value of the total magnitude represented by the unshaded portion of the corresponding column is projected. The sum of these projected values is then the sampled magnitude value that was represented by the pulse code group. Since the pulse group representing magnitude A, at the right, has a space in position 1, no value is projected; since it has a pulse in position 2, the value 1/4 is projected; since it has a pulse in position 3, the value 1/8 is projected; since it has a space in position 4, no value is projected; and since it has a pulse in position 5, the value 1/32 is projected. The total value is thus 13/32.

FIG. 19-7   Simplified drawing of the coding and decoding processes

its total range, namely, 1/2, 1/4, 1/8, 1/16, and 1/32. If the sample, as projected on this scale, encounters the unshaded portion of any column, a pulse is placed in the corresponding digital position of the code character that specifies the magnitude of the sample. For example, consider sample A. Since A is less than 1/2, the code element in digital position 1 appears as a space, that is, no pulse. Since A is greater than 1/4, the code element in digital position 2 appears as a mark, that is, as a pulse. Since A is more than 3/8, digital position 3 is occupied by a mark. Since A is smaller than 7/16, position 4 is a space, and since A is greater than 12/32, position 5 is a mark. This process is repeated for other samples, for example, samples B and C. Code-modulated signals are transmitted and received as indicated by the diagram in the center of the figure.

A similar mask or checkered scale shown in the lower part of Fig. 19–7 might serve to decode the message at the receiver. Actually electronic circuits are used that associate the proper values with the various digital positions and add them. After decoding, the reconstructed samples are distributed to their respective channels. The wanted message wave is obtained by passing the expanded samples through a low-pass filter.

Coder. As shown in Fig. 19–8, an input voltage representing a compressed sample may be converted into a code character by means of the electron beam deflection tube shown in (a) of Fig. 19–8. The code masking plate (sometimes referred to as an aperture plate) is at the focal point and perpendicular to the axis of the electron gun. The deflection axis of the X and Y deflector plate pairs are aligned with the coordinates of the code masking plate. Whenever the electron beam passes through an opening in the code masking plate, it strikes the output plate.

When an input voltage of appropriate value is applied to the Y deflector plates, the beam is deflected to point a of the code masking plate as indicated in (a) of Fig. 19–8. With a fixed voltage on the Y deflector plates, if a linear-sweep voltage is applied to the X deflector plates, the electron beam sweeps across the code masking plate along the line a–b. When the beam passes through the openings of the code masking plate along the line a–b, a series of pulses is produced in the output of the coder.

In order to simplify the instrumentation of the coder, the code masking plate shown in Fig. 19–8 is laid out in accordance with the binary number system. For purposes of simplifying the illustration, the code masking plate shown in Fig. 19–8 is a four-digit code plate and, therefore, provides only sixteen discrete magnitude values.

The uniform spacing between the horizontal dashed lines in (b) of Fig. 19–8 means that the code characters are separated by equal increments of input voltage on the Y deflector plates. If the electron beam were infinitely small, input voltages corresponding to the range from 0 to y_1 would produce the same code character. Similarly, input voltages or samples corresponding to the range from y_1 to y_2 would produce another, although always the same code character.

Thus, the method as described divides the total input range into sub-ranges and is so arranged that input voltages within a particular subrange produce one and only one code character. Under these conditions the input samples would, in effect, be quantized in the process of encoding.

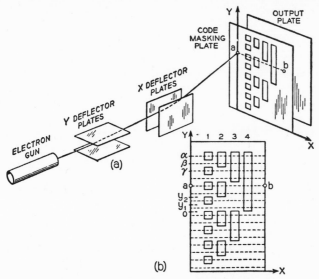

FIG. 19–8   Electron beam deflection tube for coding

However, the tube of Fig. 19–8 will quantize successfully if and only if the axis of the X deflection plates and the code masking plate are aligned exactly, and if and only if the electron beam is infinitely small. Reasonably accurate quantization and correct code characters are required. These problems have been solved by the use of a quantizing grid located in front of the code masking plate. On some of the figures, the code masking plate will be referred to as the aperture plate.

The quantizing grid consists of horizontal wires parallel to the X-axis so placed that one wire as viewed by the beam lies between each adjacent pair of code characters. By means of a feedback path to the Y deflection plates, which is shown schematically in Fig. 19–9, the desired result is obtained. A detailed description of this instrumentation is included in the source articles by R. W. Sears (Refs. 9 and 10). By the use of this arrangement, quantization is accomplished in a fraction of a microsecond. The feedback circuit functions to counteract unwanted changes that, without feedback, would move the beam as much as two grid wires in either direction.

As shown schematically in Fig. 19–10, the coder includes, in addition to the coding tube, a sampling and holding circuit that sorts out the odd (or even) channels from the input multiplex signal, push-pull amplifiers for vertical and horizontal beam deflection plates, and simple arrangements for blanking, focusing, and centering.

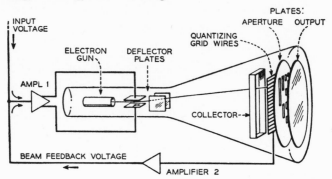

FIG. 19–9   Coding tube with quantizing grid and circuit schematic

Plate II pictures an experimental model of an electron beam tube that transforms speech samples into patterns of code characters, each code character consisting of seven binary code elements.   The tube is about 11 1/4 inches long and 2 1/4 inches in diameter.

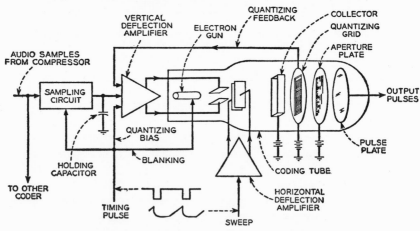

FIG. 19–10   Functional schematic of the coder

The four electrodes of the assembled target, secondary collector, quantizing grid, aperture plate (that is, code masking plate), and outer plate are shown in Plate III from bottom to top respectively.   The target end of the tube as viewed from a point near the gun is shown in Plate IV.   Behind the parallel wires of the quantizing grid, we see the code-element

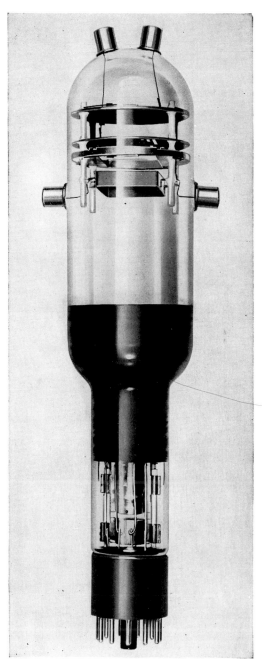

PLATE II Coding tube: this new electronic device transforms speech samples into
seven-digit codes

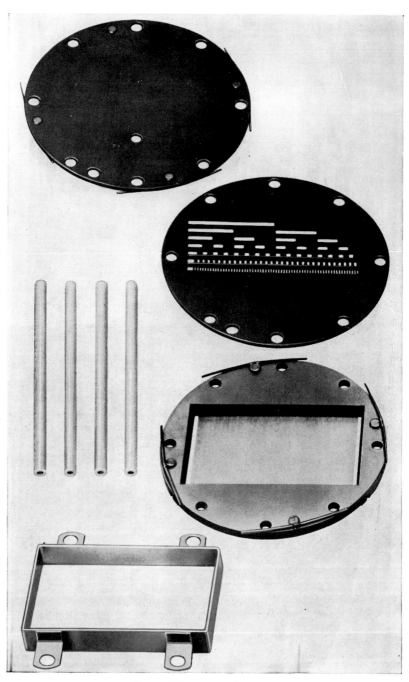

PLATE III   Target electrodes

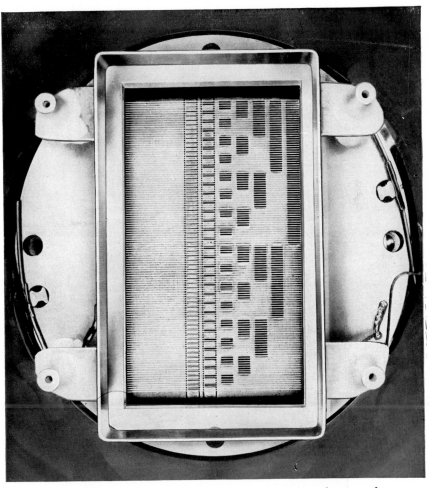

PLATE IV   Interior of the coder tube, viewed from the gun end

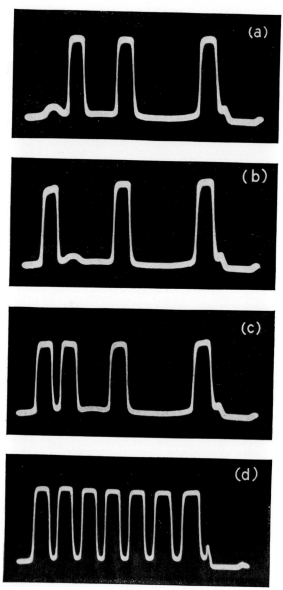

PLATE V   Typical pulse-code outputs

openings or "digit holes" in the code masking plate, laid out in accordance with the binary number system. One may count 64 holes in the vertical column on the left, 32 holes in the next column, 16 in the next, and so on. The 129 grid wires mask the upper and lower edges of every one of these holes when viewed from the point of origin of the beam.

Plate V illustrates the performance of the tube. Successive pulse positions occur from left to right. As indicated in Fig. 19–6, small imperfections in the wave forms of the pulses delivered by the coder are minimized by passing the output of the coder through a slicer.

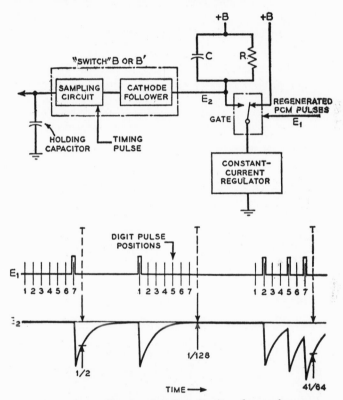

Fig. 19–11 Shannon decoding circuit and wave forms

Decoder. The method of decoding (Ref. 14) is a very simple one originally proposed by C. E. Shannon. In its basic form it uses a resistance-capacitor circuit as illustrated in Fig. 19–11. Upon the arrival of each code element, an identical increment of charge is placed upon the capacitor. The time constant RC is such that any charge on the capacitor decays precisely 50 per cent during the interval of time allocated to a code element. Thus, at any designated time following the arrival of a complete code character, the total charge remaining on the capacitor is the sum of the contributions of the seven on-or-off pulses weighted in a binary manner. For example, suppose the contribution of a pulse in the last digital position is regarded as 1/2. Then the contributions of pulses in successively earlier digital positions will be 1/4, 1/8, 1/16, 1/32, 1/64, and 1/128 respectively. Any value from 0 to 127/128, in steps of 1/128, might be produced. Of course, the openings in the code masking plate of the coding tube are arranged to make this simple method of decoding workable.

Three typical code characters are depicted in Fig. 19–11. In the first, a mark in the last digital position produces a decoded value of 1/2; in the second, a mark in position 1 produces 1/128; and in the third, marks in positions 2, 5, and 7 give a decoded value of 41/64. By the alternate use of two decoders, there is an idle interval (corresponding to the time allotted to seven code elements) between successive code characters that are to be decoded by a particular decoder. This allows sufficient time for the result of one decoding operation to decay to negligible proportions before another code character has to be decoded.

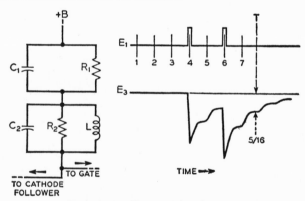

Fig. 19–12   Shannon-Rack decoder

Clearly, precise timing (Ref. 15) is required for the Shannon decoder. Although sufficient accuracy can be obtained without impracticable difficulty, a modification has been introduced that greatly eases the requirements. This modification, suggested and developed by A. J. Rack, utilizes a damped resonant circuit in combination with a resistor-capacitor as shown in Fig. 19–12. The damped resonant circuit resonates at the pulse rate, and the time constant of its damped oscillation ($2R_2C_2$) matches that of the resistor-capacitor, R_1C_1. By properly choosing C_1 and C_2, the magnitudes of the damped waves may be so proportioned that the derivative of their combined potential equals zero at successive points one pulse period apart. In fact, it is worth while to make both the first and second derivatives simultaneously equal zero at such points.

As a result of this modification, both the time of occurrence of a code element and the subsequent time of sampling the accumulated charge are made much less critical. Figure 19–12 depicts the response to a typical pair of code elements, and Plate VI is a presentation of the wave forms of a full set of the 128 possible code characters in sequence as delivered by the cathode-follower of a Shannon-Rack decoder and superimposed on an oscilloscope screen. It can be noticed that, in each successive time interval, the number of possible values is doubled. In the last two intervals, the number of lines is so great that the individual lines cannot be distinguished.

Twelve-Channel Receiver. Figure 19–13 shows in diagrammatic form a PCM receiver for a twelve-channel group. The detected signals appear at the input to the PCM receiver. Here they are sliced at the half-amplitude level to minimize the effects of noise. Code characters, each composed of seven binary code elements, are routed alternately to two Shannon-Rack decoders, that handle even and odd channels respectively. Alternate routing to two decoders is indicated in Fig. 19–13 by a two-segment commutator designated A and rotating at 48,000 revolutions per second. Before entering the decoder, the pulses are again sliced to secure better uniformity and more exact timing. Immediately after the arrival of the last code element of each code character of these standardized pulses, the decoder delivers a voltage proportional to the quantized value represented by the code character.

Because the quantized samples produced by the decoder are available only momentarily, each is sampled at the proper time and stored as a charge on a holding capacitor. This process is represented symbolically by switches B and B', one for each decoder. Each switch closure lasts 2 microseconds, and the stored sample is held for about 19 microseconds.

The next operation is to collect the six samples from the odd-numbered channels stored successively on one holding capacitor and the six from the even-numbered channels stored on the other and combine them into a twelve-channel, time-divided pulse array. Switch C carries out this operation.

This twelve-channel multiplex signal goes to a common-channel instantaneous expander. The compressor and expander use identical silicon units. In the expander, the nonlinear silicon unit is in the feedback path of a wide-band negative feedback amplifier rather than in the direct transmission path, thus providing an accurate inverse characteristic.

Except for a constant factor of proportionality, the wave form at the output of the expander is essentially the same as that at the input to the twelve-channel compressor (Fig. 19–6) in the PCM transmitter. As shown in Fig. 19–13, the channels are routed to their respective channel destinations by distributor D which rotates at the rate of 8,000 revolutions per second. It will be recalled, as mentioned previously, that electronic circuits are used to achieve these results.

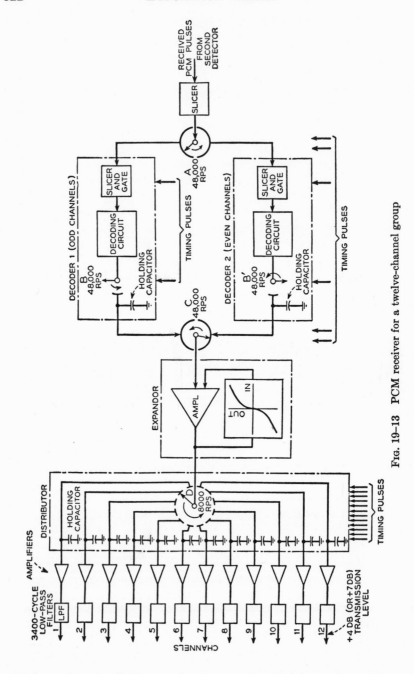

Fig. 19–13 PCM receiver for a twelve-channel group

PLATE VI Output of Shannon-Rack decoder for a signal giving 100 per cent modulation

PCM RECEIVER   PCM TRANSMITTER

PLATE VII   Terminal apparatus for an eight-channel PCM system using a five-pulse
binary code

TRANSMISSION PERFORMANCE OF WORKING SYSTEMS

Plate VII pictures the terminal apparatus for an eight-channel PCM system housed in portable units suitable for field use.   The five-pulse, binary-code characters generated by the PCM transmitter may be propagated by radio, coaxial cable, nonloaded cable pair, open-wire line, or any

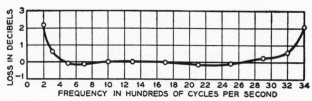

FIG. 19–14   Typical transmission-frequency characteristic

other path capable of propagating 320,000 on-or-off pulses per second to the PCM receiver.

The eight telephone circuits which the system provides give acceptable performance, as indicated by the transmission-frequency and load per-

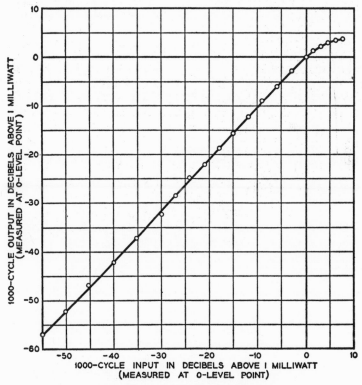

FIG. 19–15   Typical load performance

formance characteristics of Figs. 19–14 and 19–15. Characteristic of code-modulation systems, the over-all transmission stability is outstanding. Fig. 19–16 is a typical record and shows that the over-all variation in transmission is less than 0.3 decibel. The 160-mile circuit mentioned in Fig. 19–16 was obtained by connecting the eight-channel PCM system to a

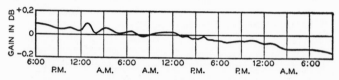

FIG. 19–16   Transmission stability of 160-mile circuit

160-mile, microwave, radio-relay system that included three intermediate repeaters.

An experimental 96-channel, pulse-code modulation system has been described by C. B. Feldman (Ref. 16). Tests were made utilizing terminal equipment for twelve channels plus power-supply equipment for ninety-six channels. This system was set up to evaluate experimentally the

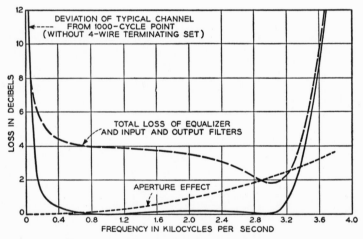

FIG. 19–17   Equalization for the aperture effect

problems involved in providing multichannel facilities of toll-system quality. Figure 19–17 shows the over-all transmission and illustrates the aperture effect (Chap. 4) and its subsequent equalization. The aperture effect comes about because at the receiver the reconstructed samples are prolonged as a means of conserving voice-frequency amplification and thereby simplifying instrumentation. Figure 19–18 shows a typical, over-all, input-output characteristic for the case of a single channel and for

five channels connected in tandem.   The latter simulates a circuit layout
that involves decoding to voice-frequencies at four junction points as well
as at the final terminal.   This should not be confused with tandem repeatering wherein the PCM pulses are successively regenerated without

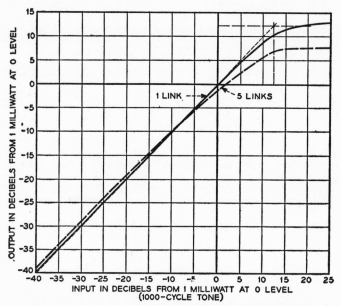

FIG. 19–18   Input-output characteristics of PCM channels

decoding.   In the latter case, of course, the over-all performance is virtually independent of the number of spans.

In a properly designed PCM system, quantization is the only significant
source of noise in the reconstructed message in the output of the final receiver.   Values of noise measured in the absence of speech are shown in
Fig. 19–19.   These measurements are for various numbers of channels
from one to ten, connected in tandem.   Figure 19–19 shows two scales of
ordinates.   One is the reference scale of weighted noise commonly used in
evaluating the noise performance of a telephone circuit.   The other on
the right relates the corresponding, unweighted, root-mean-square noise
to the maximum, undistorted, single-frequency output of the system.
With five links in tandem the noise is 8 decibels less than the accepted
limit for a 4,000-mile circuit.   The average noise power due to quantization is proportional to the number of links.

Experience with the transmission performance of working systems dem-
onstrates that the service provided by well-designed multichannel PCM
systems compares favorably with regular wire service.   The user is entirely unaware that his words are being transported by discrete code sym-

bols. It has been found that the over-all quality more than meets the requirements generally imposed upon such systems with respect to such

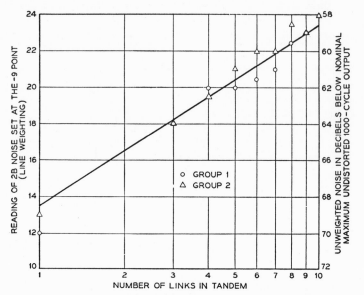

FIG. 19–19 Noise measurements on idle PCM channels

factors as band width, volume range, fidelity of reproduction, noise, and crosstalk.

References

1. W. R. Bennett, "Noise in PCM Systems," *Bell Laboratories Record*, New York, Vol. 26, No. 12, December 1948, pp. 495–499.
2. W. M. Goodall, "Telephony by Pulse-Code Modulation," *The Bell System Technical Journal*, New York, Vol. 26, No. 3, July 1947, pp. 395–409.
3. A. H. Reeves, United States Patent 2,272,070, February 3, 1942, assigned to International Standard Electric Corporation. Also French Patent 852,185, October 23, 1939.
4. H. S. Black and J. O. Edson, "Pulse-Code Modulation," *Transactions of the American Institute of Electrical Engineers*, New York, Vol. 66, 1947, pp. 895–899.
5. C. E. Wynn-Williams, "Electrical Method of Counting," *Report on Progress in Physics*, London, Vol. 3, 1936, pp. 239–261.
6. Herbert J. Reich, "New Vacuum-Tube Counting Circuits," *Review of Scientific Instruments*, New York, Vol. 9, July 1938, pp. 222–223.
7. C. E. Wynn-Williams, "The Use of Thyratrons for High-Speed Automatic Counting of Physical Phenomena," *Proceedings of the Royal Society of London*, London, Series A, Vol. 132, July 1931, pp. 295–310.
8. L. A. Meacham and E. Peterson, "An Experimental Multichannel Pulse-Code Modulation System of Toll Quality," *The Bell System Technical Journal*, New York, Vol. 27, No. 1, January 1948, pp. 1–43.

9. R. W. Sears, "Electron-Beam Deflection Tube for Pulse-Code Modulation," *The Bell System Technical Journal*, New York, Vol. 27, No. 1, January 1948, pp. 44–57.
10. R. W. Sears, "Beam-Deflection Tube for Coding in PCM," *Bell Laboratories Record*, New York, Vol. 26, No. 10, October 1948, pp. 411–415.
11. P. A. Reiling, "Companding in PCM," *Bell Laboratories Record*, New York, Vol. 26, No. 12, December 1948, pp. 487–490.
12. C. O. Mallinckrodt, "Instantaneous Compandors," *The Bell System Technical Journal*, New York, Vol. 30, No. 3, July 1951, pp. 706–720.
13. J. C. Lozier, "Instantaneous Compandors on Narrow-Band Speech Channels," *The Bell System Technical Journal*, New York, Vol. 30, No. 4, Part II, October 1951, pp. 1214–1220.
14. R. L. Carbrey, "Decoding in PCM," *Bell Laboratories Record*, New York, Vol. 26, No. 11, November 1948, pp. 451–455.
15. A. E. Johanson, "Timing Control for PCM," *Bell Laboratories Record*, New York, Vol. 27, No. 1, January 1949, pp. 10–15.
16. C. B. Feldman, "A 96-Channel Pulse-Code Modulation System," *Bell Laboratories Record*, New York, Vol. 26, No. 9, September 1948, pp. 364–370.

CHAPTER 20

MOBILE PULSE–MODULATION SYSTEMS

Time-divided channels may be either *distributed* or *grouped*. Mobile pulse-modulation systems deal with *distributed* channels. *Distributed* channels are encountered in a system wherein each of many transmitters has access over a common transmitting medium of limited band width to any of many receivers. All multichannel pulse-modulation systems that have been discussed previously transmitted *groups* of channels between specified points.

Regardless of whether channels are grouped or distributed, they may be multiplexed either by orthogonal functions or by nearly orthogonal functions. When the channels are divided in time: orthogonal functions imply synchronous transmission; almost orthogonal functions permit nonsynchronous transmission.

In a point-to-point pulse system, groups of channels may be multiplexed in time by orthogonal functions and synchronously transmitted. This is advantageous because the signal-to-noise ratio is very much better for a given band width, as compared with multiplexing by almost orthogonal functions and nonsynchronous transmission. Even though the problems of synchronizing a complete communication network become fairly involved, the advantages offset the disadvantages. Synchronized networks of this type were treated in Chapter 19.

DISTRIBUTED CHANNELS

When channels are distributed, it is more difficult to estimate the relative advantages and disadvantages of synchronous versus nonsynchronous transmission. Synchronous transmission may be realized in a straightforward manner. Nonsynchronous systems are intriguing from a theoretical point of view, but have not been studied sufficiently to permit an appraisal of their practical potentialities.

An example of each type will be described to indicate the important theoretical advantages and disadvantages of each. First, however, the distributed-channel case and its two solutions will be described in more general terms. Although the philosophy is with reference to mobile systems, the results are equally applicable when the terminals are stationary.

Typical Mobile System

Consideration will be limited to a system that provides individual two-way channels for simultaneous communication between a main station, called the control station, and each of a plurality of independently located substations. As indicated by Fig. 20–1, one end of each of N two-way

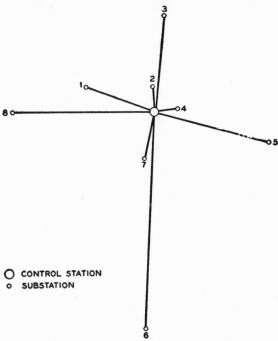

Fig. 20–1 Typical multichannel system layout for providing two-way communication between a control station and a plurality of substations

channels terminates at a control station. The other ends of the N two-way channels terminate at N other stations at distinct (and, in general, different) distances and directions from the control station.

All of the stations may be in relative motion. Although not indicated by Fig. 20–1, the stations may move in N different arbitrary directions at unrelated and diverse speeds. The stations might be airplanes, ships, automobiles, or trains.

The medium might be radio. Either time or frequency division might separate the two directions of transmission. With frequency division, communication to and from the control station would be carried over different frequency bands, and time division would serve to multiplex channels in each direction. Pulse systems of this type might find application to fixed and mobile distributed-channel communications generally. Typical examples would be navigation, traffic control, control of manufacturing and farming operations, field maneuvers, fire-fighting operations, and so on.

Multiplexing by Orthogonal Functions

Theoretical considerations (Refs. 1 to 8)* confirm and justify our natural, intuitive feelings that there must exist a great many different ways of multiplexing channels. By far the commonest and best-known methods of multiplexing are frequency division, time division, and phase discrimination. In theory and under idealized conditions, all three utilize orthogonal functions of time. That is, each channel transmits only signals that are orthogonal to any signals that may be transmitted by any other channel. For example, in frequency division, to the extent that the frequencies transmitted by different channels are confined to nonoverlapping bands, the integral over all time of the product of the signals transmitted by any two channels each expressed as a function of time is zero. In general, whenever true orthogonality exists, complete separation is possible, at least in principle.

For purpose of appraisal and comparison with other alternatives, an important consideration is the minimum band width for complete separation. We note that different channel messages cannot be represented by the same signal at the same time. Consequently, if messages individual to each channel are not quantized; if at the sending end, messages are transmitted as fast as they are received except for a fixed delay encountered in the process of transforming the messages to their desired signal representation for multiplex transmission over the medium; and if in the absence of significant noise, only correct messages are delivered: then it is a fundamental principle that the total band width of the multiplexed signal shall be at least as great as the sum of the individual channels.

Frequency division is a good illustration. Here the signal output from a particular channel may consist of any one of all signals that do not contain significant frequency components outside the frequency range allotted to that particular channel. A similar description applies to any other channel in the group of channels being multiplexed. Also, no significant frequency component shall be common to two or more channels. Accordingly, the total band is the sum of the channel bands.

Similarly, in time division, the total time is the sum of the channel times. As explained in Chapter 16, in a time-division system the total band is never less than and usually exceeds the sum of the channel bands. This conclusion was the result of assuming complete channel separation, nonquantized signals, no avoidable delay in getting the correct messages through, and synchronous transmission.

* The references cited are listed at the end of each chapter according to the number used in the text.

Multiplexing by Approximately Orthogonal Functions

The difficulty with truly orthogonal functions is that, if a broad-band channel is divided into N channels, there is no convenient opportunity to accommodate an additional channel. A standard, frequency-division, twelve-channel bank, as described in Chapter 11 on page 170, divides 48 kilocycles per second into twelve, pre-assigned, 4-kilocycle-per-second bands, and there is nothing left to assign to a thirteenth talker.

In essence, this is a lack of flexibility. Any system has a definite capacity; and the more efficiently it is used, the sharper will be its threshold if it is over-loaded. It is fundamental that if an efficient system is over-loaded by adding more channels, the system will deliver less information per channel, and at best the reduced rate per channel multiplied by the number of channels cannot be higher than the theoretical capacity (that is, information rate) of the system.

However, as pointed out in many of the references (Reference 8, for example), there would seem to be many advantages in the kind of a system in which channels are assigned approximately orthogonal functions of time. The use of approximately orthogonal functions would have the disadvantage of introducing a certain amount of crosstalk. The deleterious effects of this crosstalk cannot be overcome merely by using more signal power.

The system would have the following features: Each modulating wave is acted upon by its associated coder. Different coders are not synchronized in any way. The outputs of the different coders go to a common transmitting medium. The medium is coupled to each decoder. Decoders are not synchronized in any way. A particular decoder is associated with a particular coder. Each wanted modulating wave is recovered at the output of its corresponding channel decoder.

It should be noted that in this system the coders and decoders take the place of conventional switching.

This type of system has one outstanding advantage. As many channels as desired (a thousand, for example) may be connected to the common medium. Although it is true that the system has only a limited capacity, say fifty, depending on the capacity of the broad-band channel of the transmitting medium, nevertheless any fifty out of the thousand may use the medium at any one time, without any switching. In practice, when the number of channels is large, it usually works out that we do not have to provide appreciably more capacity than corresponds to average usage.

A definite disadvantage of this type of system, however, is that the previously-mentioned inherent crosstalk or noise is reduced only 3 decibels per octave instead of 6 as we increase the band width to reduce the intrinsic interference. This disadvantage may be serious if it becomes necessary to resort to considerable reduction in order to obtain satisfactory quality.

The nonsynchronous mobile system described at the end of the chapter is a good example of a system of this type.

MOBILE SYSTEM WITH SYNCHRONOUS TRANSMISSION

Little has been published to indicate that mobile time-division systems may be readily synchronized. A practical scheme for achieving this desirable result was invented and described by J. O. Edson (Ref. 9). The scheme is not limited to pulse-position modulation. It is, for example, equally applicable to pulse-code modulation.

General Description

As a specific illustration, consider the eight-channel PPM system described at the end of Chapter 18. Assume a control station designated 0, and eight substations designated 1 to 8 variously located and communicating by radio. At the control station, the transmitting and receiving antenna systems are nondirective. The antenna at a substation is either nondirective or directive. When it is directive, it is at all times caused to point to the control station. Channels 1 to 8 are assigned to the eight control stations.

Obviously, even though the nine stations may be in relative motion with respect to one another, there is no new problem in communicating from the control station to any one of the eight substations. Synchronization is achieved as usual. The 4-microsecond marker pulse precedes the eight 1-microsecond, position-modulated channel pulses and is identified at each substation because of its longer length. Identification of the marker pulse would ordinarily cause eight gates to open sequentially and admit the position-modulated pulses one by one to independent, pre-assigned receiving circuits. In this instance, at each substation, seven of the eight receiving circuits are not required. Even with only one receiving circuit, the channel assigned to a particular substation may be readily changed by varying the adjustment of the channel gate.

Transmission in the opposite direction obviously creates a new problem. Assume, for practical reasons, that the two directions of transmission are separated by frequency division. The problem that confronts us is to arrange to transmit each pulse from each substation at just such a time that the eight pulses in a particular frame arrive at the control station not only in proper sequence but also each at just the right time. In the case of moving stations, this timing must be continuously regulated. The control station, however, is in a unique position of being able to determine the extent to which the incoming pulses are early or late and, moreover, may transmit information at all times to each substation at the expense of using band width. Therefore, a solution to the problem exists.

The control station is called upon to communicate to each substation information relative to the time that modulated pulses from that particular substation arrived at the control station.   According to whether the pulses received by the control station arrive early or late, this information is received and utilized by each substation to correct and control the timing of its transmitted pulses.

In Fig. 20–2, the position-modulated pulses associated with a particular voice frequency channel are simultaneously position-modulated at the

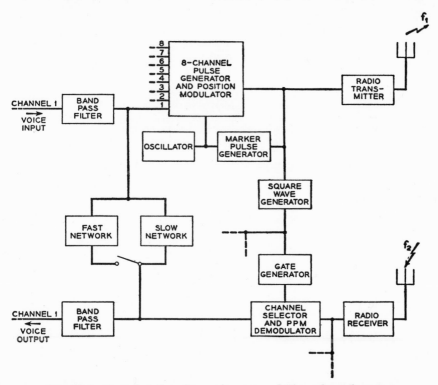

Fig. 20–2   Control station of a synchronous multichannel mobile system

control station by a pilot current that is proportional to the time of arrival of the position-modulated pulses coming from the corresponding substation. The times of arrival of modulated pulses from a particular substation are measured relative to their assigned times.   At each substation, as indicated in Fig. 20–3, as a result of demodulating the received position-modulated pulses, the pilot current is recovered and is utilized to vary the phase and frequency of an oscillator.   It is the output of this oscillator that controls the transmission of position-modulated pulses in the reverse direction. These operations will be explained in more detail presently.

Differences

Compared with the grouped-channel case (as, for example, in a conventional point-to-point system with fixed stations) the equipment differences are relatively small. At the control station (Fig. 20–2) the usual low-pass filters in the incoming and outgoing voice-circuits are replaced by band-pass filters. Each band filter has a pass band that extends from 200 to

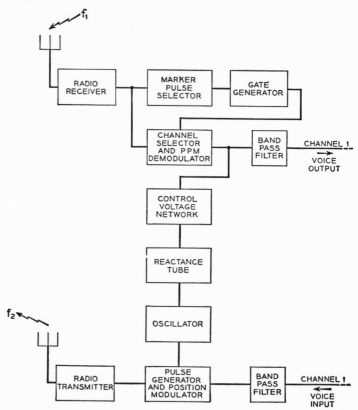

Fɪɢ. 20–3   Substation of a synchronous multichannel mobile system

3,500 cycles per second. By this means the low-frequency channel used for synchronization control is separated from its associated voice frequency channel and vice versa. Also, as shown in Fig. 20–2, an oscillator clocks, or times, the operations of the receiving multiplex in addition to controlling the transmitting multiplex. The use of a single oscillator to synchronize both multiplexes simplifies some of the control circuits.

The general objective at the control station is to frame the receiving gates with reference to the transmitted marker pulse. At a control station, the received signals do not contain any marker pulse. In each receiving channel, as indicated in Fig. 20–2, provision is made for obtaining a d-c current that is a measure of the mean position of the channel pulses. This current is passed through the slow or fast nets, as shown in Fig. 20–2, and the voice or other signal frequencies are adequately filtered out.

At a substation, as depicted by Fig. 20–3, the low-pass filters are similarly replaced by band-pass filters. The receiver is synchronized by the incoming marker pulse, and a pre-assigned channel is demodulated in the usual way. The output contains two wanted signals. One is the usual audio signal which is selected by the band-pass filter. The other is the pilot-current control, and it is selected by a low-frequency net. After selection, the pilot control is applied to a reactance tube and thereby varies the phase and frequency of the transmitting oscillator and hence the timing of the transmitted pulses. Thus, the transmitter at each substation is synchronized by remote control in response to signals received from the control station.

Operation

The method of operation can best be understood by referring (Fig. 20–4) to the frame diagrams that depict the relative positioning of the pulses at

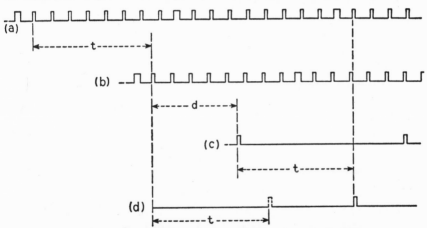

Fig. 20–4   Generated and received pulses at the control station

various points in the system. Figure 20–4 shows the pulse array transmitted by the control station. In each frame a 4-microsecond marker is followed by eight 1-microsecond channel pulses. Assume that the time of transmission to substation 1 is t. Then the pulses arriving at substation 1 are depicted by (b) of Fig. 20–4.

If the substation transmitter were operated in synchronism with the received pulses, the channel-1 pulse received by the control station would arrive at a time indicated by the dotted pulse on (d) of Fig. 20–4. By comparing this with (a) of Fig. 20–4, the pulse is seen not to fall in the time allotted to channel 1, but elsewhere so as to interfere with pulses from another substation. Moreover, as the two stations move relative to one another, the relative position of the channel-1 pulse at the control station moves. The same sort of result would be produced by the pulses from other substations, and the combined result would be a disordered array.

Now, if the pulse transmitted from substation 1 is delayed by an amount d as shown in (c) of Fig. 20–4, the channel-1 pulse arriving at the main station will be the solid-line pulse in (d) of Fig. 20–4, and this falls in its assigned position and passes the channel-1 gate. Clearly, if the delay d is regulated as the distance between stations varies, synchronization of channel 1 is maintained. Other channels can be similarly synchronized.

As explained, at each station the receiver gives out a d-c current, depending on the mean position of the channel pulse. At the control station, this d-c current position-modulates the transmitted pulses. At the substation, this d-c current is recovered, and it varies the oscillator that controls the timing of the transmitted pulses. If the mean position of the channel pulses received at the control station is late, the corresponding outgoing channel pulses will be late, and late pulses at the corresponding substation will cause the pulses transmitted therefrom to be earlier. The control circuit is a closed loop. The problem of its stable operation, when viewed in terms of its envelope response, is identical in principle to the problem of stability in a feedback amplifier.

Suppose the transmitter at the substation were turned on and varied in frequency so as to sweep the channel pulse until contact was established. The pulses generated would pass through time periods assigned to other channels. This would affect the pilot-current controls of these other channels and would throw their transmitters out of correct timing. If the responses of the different nets to an impulse were identical, established channels would be thrown out of synchronization before the searching pulse had traversed that channel interval.

This difficulty is avoided by providing the control circuit of each channel with filter networks of widely varying constants. During search, a comparatively wide-band network is used and the searching pulse sweeps rapidly across the channels. Once contact is established, the wide-band network is replaced by a narrow-band network having a band width that is limited to a few cycles per second.

Stations already synchronized are operating with a control channel the band width of which might be of the order of 2 cycles per second. Then pulse-sweeping during search at the rate of, say, 100 cycles per second will not affect sufficiently the control circuits of operating stations to throw them out of synchronism. The only effect of a sweeping pulse will be to cause a burst of noise lasting for about one millisecond as it passes through the time period of such a station.

Automatic Seizure

Figure 20–5 indicates a modification of Fig. 20–2 whereby the above-mentioned change from a condition for establishing contact to one for communication is carried out automatically. The resistor and capacitor designated *RC* are the equivalent of the fast network in Fig. 20–2, provided

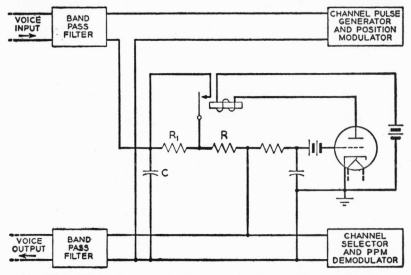

FIG. 20–5   Circuit that provides for automatic seizure at the control station

R_1 is short-circuited by operation of the relay. When the relay is not operated, the time constant is longer and is equivalent to the slow network in Fig. 20–2.

In the absence of any received pulse in the demodulator output, the vacuum tube shown in Fig. 20–5 is conducting and the relay is in its operated position. When a signal pulse appears, the grid is driven sufficiently negative to block space current so that the relay is released, thereby introducing the slow network. Another resistor-capacitor network in the grid circuit serves to slow the release of the relay, thus preventing a large transient on the opening of the relay contacts.

With automatic seizure and in the absence of a channel pulse, the control circuit will always be in the fast operating condition required for searching. When, during searching, the pulse finds its proper position in time, the control circuit is automatically shifted to the condition for communication; that is, it is connected to the network having a long time constant.

The system as described transmits pulses without regard to whether a channel is busy or idle. It would be a comparatively simple matter to transmit pulses only when a channel was "busy," "busy" in the sense that the two-way voice channel was being used for talking, supervision, or signaling and not in the sense that it was active for a short talk spurt.

Advantages

The advantages are the very important transmission improvements that are made possible by synchronous transmission. These include conservation of signal power and band-width occupancy coupled with high-quality reception and liberal operating margins. The value of these improvements is offset by the cost of the synchronizing system with its many two-way control channels, one for each substation.

MOBILE SYSTEM WITH NONSYNCHRONOUS TRANSMISSION

In principle, the type of nonsynchronous system mentioned earlier would be applicable to either mobile or fixed communications and would provide the required two-way channels from a control station to each of a plurality of substations. References 10 to 13 deal with certain aspects of nonsynchronous operation.

J. R. Pierce originally proposed and analyzed a pulse-modulation system for achieving this type of performance. A system of this type was developed by A. L. Hopper and is described in References 8 and 10. The description to follow is abstracted from these references and includes the results of laboratory tests. It represents an example of the second type of solution to the problem of distributed channels multiplexed by time division.

Description

Each modulating wave is sampled at somewhat irregular intervals. This irregularity is introduced by means of a statistical source so that there is a lack of exact coherence between the instants of sampling for the different channels. The average sampling rate is about the same for all channels and is somewhat in excess of the Nyquist rate. Channel samplers are not synchronized in any way.

The magnitude of each sample is conveyed by a group of pulses. The group also carries information identifying the channel to which the pulses belong. For example, in the system tested, the group was a pair of pulses of equal but opposite amplitudes, and the spacing between pulses identified the channel.

Each receiver responds only to pulse groups associated with a particular channel. The amplitude of the pulses that compose a group is proportional to the magnitude of a sample. When a pulse group is accepted, the magnitude of the sample is stored as a voltage on a capacitor. This voltage is amplified and then goes to the usual low-pass filter. When another pulse group is accepted, the voltage on the capacitor is changed to correspond to the magnitude of the new sample. By this means the magnitude of this new sample is held. The method of operation is to hold each sample until a new sample is accepted. As a result, when a sample is lost due to interchannel crosstalk, the previous value is used and amplified and is then sent to the low-pass filter.

If interchannel crosstalk overlaps the wanted pulse group sufficiently, the deformed group is rejected and a sample is lost. If the overlap is slight, the group is accepted, but the sample is in error to the extent that the magnitude is wrong. Accidental production of the wanted code group by interchannel crosstalk will also cause error in the accepted group. By precise timing and by making the requirements for accepting or rejecting a group very precise, errors in accepted groups can be reduced at the expense of increasing the number of samples lost.

When different channels use almost the same average sampling rate but without a small amount of superimposed random jitter, interchannel crosstalk will cause the loss of a series of successive samples. Experiments have demonstrated that this is more objectionable than random loss of samples.

Advantages

When band width is not at a premium and is available, the signal-to-noise ratio (with due allowance for interchannel crosstalk) can be made as large as required by using a wide enough band. The average power introduced by interchannel crosstalk is proportional to the number of active channels so that more channels can be accommodated at the expense of more crosstalk. Interchannel crosstalk is unintelligible. For some types of service including ordinary telephony, holding the previous sample when a sample is lost reduces interchannel crosstalk. Pulses are not transmitted when a channel is idle, that is, in the absence of talk spurts. This conserves power and minimizes interchannel crosstalk. There is no limit to the number of assignments if essentially the same mean sampling rate is used for each channel. Accordingly, a system of this type might be attractive for relatively light traffic use where many stations must have continuous access to the medium.

Operation

The operation of the channel coder is depicted by Fig. 20–6. The modulating wave is filtered by the usual low-pass filter in order to attenuate frequency components equal to or higher than half the sampling rate. Whenever the modulating wave exceeds a predetermined value, it operates the "voice-operated relay." This connects the random pulse generator to the sampler, and samples of the modulating wave are produced at somewhat irregular intervals as previously described. The paired pulses or code group is produced by a delay line and combining amplifier. The delay line governs the exact spacing between the two pulses of a group.

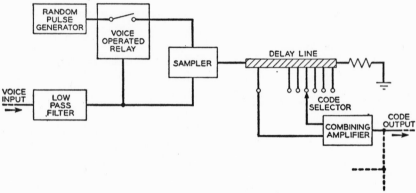

Fɪɢ. 20–6 Simplified diagram of channel coder for a nonsynchronous, time-division system with holding and random sampling

The random-pulse generator includes a thyratron noise source the output of which is amplified and goes to a blocking oscillator. The output of the oscillator goes to a one-shot multivibrator. The output of the multivibrator goes to a differentiator and then to a clipper. These tandem operations guarantee that the random-spaced pulses going to the sampler are of constant amplitude.

The delay line has a total delay of about 10 microseconds, taps are located at 1/4-microsecond intervals, phase is linear to about 1.4 megacycles per second, and loss rises to about 3 decibels at 1 megacycle per second. The approximate band width of the system measures about 0.5 megacycle per second, pulse shapes are approximately Gaussian, and pulses endure for about 2 microseconds.

The method of operation of a channel decoder is shown in Fig. 20–7. The decoder is called upon to recognize each desired pulse group unless it is deformed beyond recognition by interchannel interference; to store the magnitude of one of the recognized pulses on the storage capacitor; and to amplify and filter the voltage across the storage capacitor. By the use of a tapped delay line, a desired code group at a particular time would produce the voltages 1, 2, 3, and 4 as indicated at the top of Fig. 20–7 at taps 1, 2, 3, and 4, respectively. The "recognizer" checks that voltage 1 is equal and opposite to 3 and also to 4, and that 2 is equal and opposite to 3 and also to 4. This is done in such a way that, at all other times, x disables the gate. The fifth tap on the delay line provides an enabling pulse that is utilized to be sure that the four voltages which the recognizer checks are not all zero. If the checks are satisfied and the gate is enabled,

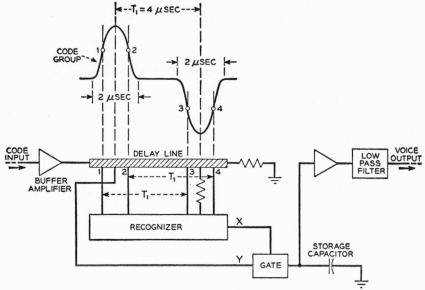

FIG. 20–7 Simplified diagram of channel decoder for a nonsynchronous, time-division system with holding and random sampling

the peak value of the pulse enters the gate by way of y and is stored as a voltage across the storage capacitor. The held samples are amplified and filtered to produce the desired output.

Transmission Performance

Inspection of Fig. 20–8 shows that, when a single channel is lightly loaded with a sinusoidal signal the frequency of which is 1,000 cycles per second, there is a background of noise. This noise is the result of filtering clamped samples irregularly spaced in time. With increased loading, distortion due to nonlinearity of the circuits becomes predominant and the ratio of signal to noise-plus-distortion becomes poorer in the region above reference level output. The two-channel characteristic shown in Fig. 20–8 indicates the increase in noise caused by crosstalk from the added channel and gives a measure of the effect of the lost samples. In Reference 8, this effect is calculated and it is demonstrated that the measurements agree with the calculations. The values of noise and distortion plotted in Fig. 20–8 were measured with a so-called "2B noise-measuring set" with "FIA" line weighting, a measuring device which takes into account the frequency characteristics of present telephone equipment and which is standard for the measurement of noise on message circuits.

Listening tests were also made, and it was found that, when a second channel was active, the intelligibility of the message received over the first channel was not interfered with at normal talking levels, although the channel was judged to be below toll quality. Lost samples produced a

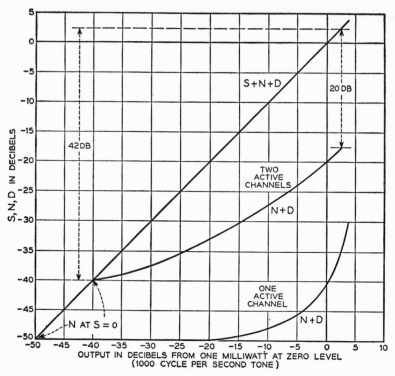

FIG. 20–8 Average signal, noise, and distortion powers expressed in decibels relative to the sinusoidal output designated zero decibels on the axis of abscissa

rasping effect, and by simulating the effect of more interfering channels, the distortion became progressively worse. It was concluded that speech intelligibility would be tolerable with between five and eight active, interfering channels. The band width of the system was about 500,000 cycles per second, the average sampling rate was about 8,000 cycles per second, and, as shown in Fig. 20–9, the over-all transmission of a typical channel was reasonably flat up to about 3,100 cycles per second.

Application to Rural Telephony

To indicate for what use a nonsynchronous pulse-multiplex system of this general type might be particularly well suited, we shall consider briefly its possible application to rural telephony as described in References 8 and 10. Figure 20–10 depicts a small subscriber's exchange in which each

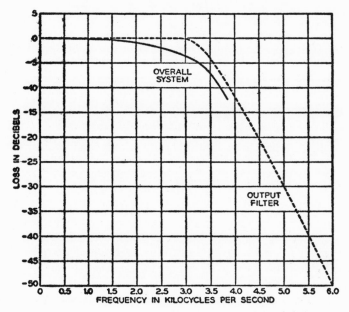

FIG. 20–9 Over-all transmission-frequency characteristic

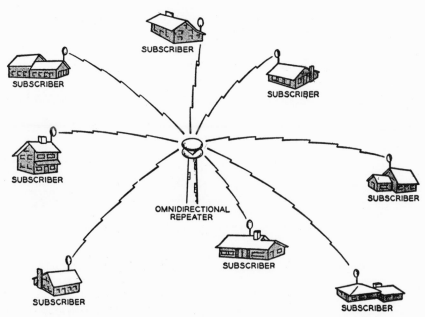

FIG. 20–10 Application of nonsynchronous, time-division pulse-modulation to rural telephony

substation has a directional antenna pointing to a central, nondirectional repeater. Each subscriber transmits on a common channel the center frequency of which is f_1, and each receives on f_2. The output from each subscriber's transmitter is so adjusted that the repeater inputs are equalized. The repeater is also a frequency changer. Received pulses are amplified, are changed in frequency from f_1 to f_2, and are reradiated in all directions.

Each subscriber is assigned a number and to that number corresponds a particular pulse group. By means of a dial, each subscriber may simultaneously set his transmitter and receiver to any allowable number. Whenever a subscriber's receiver is not in use, his transmitter and receiver automatically revert to the particular pulse group corresponding to his assigned number. Each subscriber's receiver is operating all the time, and, with the receiver down, whenever a pulse group is received corresponding to the subscriber's number, a bell rings. Each subscriber's transmitter radiates pulses whenever his "ring" button is operated or whenever the subscriber is talking and thereby producing talk spurts that operate the voice-operated relay shown in Fig. 20–6.

To make a call, A lifts his receiver, dials B's number, pushes his ring button, and thereby causes his transmitter to radiate B's pulse group; B's bell rings, and B lifts his receiver. A and B may now talk to each other, both using the pulse group corresponding to B's number. Numbers might also be assigned to one or more operators to provide connections to distant exchanges.

C may talk to A and B by calling B. C cannot reach A because A and B are talking on B's pulse group. Thus, eavesdropping is possible as it now is on rural party lines. Also, there is no busy signal. When a subscriber's phone is busy, the subscriber does not know he is being called.

References

1. L. A. Zadeh and K. S. Miller, "Fundamental Aspects of Linear Multiplexing," *Proceedings of the Institute of Radio Engineers*, New York, Vol. 40, No. 9, September 1952, pp. 1091–1097.
2. John P. Costas, "Coding with Linear Systems," *Proceedings of the Institute of Radio Engineers*, New York, Vol. 40, No. 9, September 1952, pp. 1101–1103.
3. N. Marchand, H. R. Holloway, and M. Leifer, "Analysis of Dot-Sequential Color Television," *Proceedings of the Institute of Radio Engineers*, New York, Vol. 39, No. 10, October 1951, pp. 1280–1287.
4. L. A. Zadeh, *Some Basic Problems in Communication of Information*, New York Academy of Sciences, New York, Vol. 14, March 1952, pp. 201–204.
5. L. A. Zadeh, "A General Theory of Linear Signal Transmission Systems," *Journal of the Franklin Institute*, Philadelphia, Vol. 253, April 1952, pp. 293–312.
6. L. A. Zadeh and K. S. Miller, "Generalized Ideal Filters," *Journal of Applied Physics*, New York, Vol. 23, February 1952, pp. 223–228.

7. W. D. White, "Theoretical Aspects of Asynchronous Multiplexing," *Proceedings of the Institute of Radio Engineers*, New York, Vol. 38, No. 3, March 1950, pp. 270–275.
8. J. R. Pierce and A. L. Hopper, "Nonsynchronous Time Division with Holding and with Random Sampling," *Proceedings of the Institute of Radio Engineers*, New York, Vol. 40, No. 9, September 1952, pp. 1079–1088.
9. J. O. Edson, United States Patent 2,457,986, January 4, 1949.
10. Andrew L. Hopper, "Nonsynchronous Pulse Multiplex System," *Electronics*, New York, Vol. 25, No. 8, August 1952, pp. 116–120.
11. J. A. Pierce, "An Introduction to Loran," *Proceedings of the Institute of Radio Engineers*, New York, Vol. 34, No. 5, May 1946, pp. 216–234.
12. J. A. Pierce, A. A. McKenzie, and R. H. Woodward, *Loran*, M.I.T. Radiation Laboratory Series, Vol. 4, McGraw-Hill Book Co., Inc., New York, 1948.
13. A. Roberts, *Radar Beacons*, M.I.T. Radiation Laboratory Series, McGraw-Hill Book Co., Inc., New York, Vol. 3, Chapter 5, 1947, pp. 83–103.

Problem

1. Given the known empirical properties of resistance noise waves, show that any two finite segments from independent noise sources are approximately orthogonal functions if the segments are sufficiently long.

APPENDIX

1. If the modulating wave is restricted essentially to a limited frequency range in which the essential frequency components range from zero to B cycles per second, and if the frequency of the carrier is sufficiently high:
   (a) Is the band width of an amplitude-modulated sinusoid independent of the carrier frequency?
   (b) What is the band width of a single sideband?
2. What happens to the essential information-carrying capacity of a conventional, double-sideband, amplitude-modulated sinusoid when:
   (a) One sideband is eliminated from the transmitted wave?
   (b) Both sidebands are eliminated from the transmitted wave?
   (c) The carrier is eliminated from the transmitted wave?
3. In a suppressed-carrier, single-sideband modulation system, what determines the frequency and phase requirements imposed upon the local oscillator at the receiver which supplies the missing carrier?
4. How might the pulses for a two-channel, time-division pulse-modulation system be distinguished from one another, assuming uniform sampling and no synchronizing circuits at the receiver?
5. For each of the three categories into which the instrumentation of coders has been classified, outline the principle of operation.
6. With reference to pulse-modulation theory, what is meant by the "aperture effect"? Is it possible to compensate for it?
7. Why do we sample the message wave at the transmitting terminal of a pulse-modulation system designed for voice transmission?
8. Does superposition hold in a frequency modulator?
9. Write a general expression for a frequency-modulated wave, assuming a sinusoidal carrier and a modulating wave $V(t)$.
10. What is the purpose of the marker pulses (or marker intervals) in a time-division pulse-modulation system using "start-stop" synchronization?
11. Name the two operations which permit the reduction of a continuously changing message wave to a finite number of discrete values per second.
12. Which type of sampling, "uniform" or "natural," employs uniformly spaced sampling intervals?
13. Describe one type of marker pulse that may be used in time-division PAM systems.
14. In the application of the double Fourier series to the spectrum analysis of a train of modulated pulses, what are the formulas that relate the variables x and y to time?
15. Draw a simple circuit diagram showing a carrier generator, a modulating-wave generator, and two nonlinear elements combined to produce a balanced modulator the output of which theoretically will contain no even-order distortion of the modulating wave.

16. Do the noise voltages that are received along with the marker pulses in a time-division PPM system affect the signal-to-noise ratio at the output of the system when synchronization is on a "start-stop" basis?

17. Write a general expression for a phase-modulated wave, assuming a sinusoidal carrier and a modulating wave $V(t)$.

18. In the three-dimensional configuration used in the double Fourier series method of spectrum analysis, how is the slope of the line OA (along which the section is taken) with respect to the X-axis (along which the carrier is represented) related to the angular frequencies ω_v and ω_c?

19. To which type of modulating wave is the double Fourier series method of spectrum analysis applicable, one in which the modulating wave is periodic with respect to time, or one in which the modulating wave is nonperiodic with respect to time?

20. How does the average power in a frequency-modulated wave vary with the modulating signal?

21. What is the purpose of the "gates" used at the receiving terminal of a time-division pulse-modulation system?

22. In a time-division pulse-modulation system using a "long-time" synchronizer, what is the requirement on the frequency of the sine wave that controls the operation of the synchronizer in order to eliminate the need for the hunting feature?

23. Describe one type of marker pulse that may be used in time-division pulse-position modulation (PPM) systems.

24. Theoretically, in a pulse-code modulation (PCM) system, what ordinarily is the only significant source of noise in the reconstructed message delivered by the final receiver?

25. Is the double Fourier series method of spectrum analysis applicable to waves other than pulses?

26. What is meant by the terms *pre-emphasis* and *de-emphasis?*

27. Distinguish between the maximum possible rate of generating information and the actual rate.

28. If a modulating wave occupies a frequency band almost B cycles per second wide, what is the minimum sampling rate that will allow the original wave to be precisely reconstructed from the sampled values?

29. What is meant by the "principle of superposition"?

30. Explain what is meant by "pulse-duration modulation" (PDM).

31. Which method is capable of giving the more favorable signal-to-noise ratio at the output of a time-division PPM system: "long-time" synchronization or "start-stop" synchronization?

32. Is it true that any system which transmits quantized messages and makes full use of the product of frequency range multiplied by the time during which it is available for use inevitably will suffer from a threshold effect with respect to noise?

33. Given a number, n, of quanta per code element and the number, m, of code elements comprising each code character, what is the number of different codes that might be used?

34. Let S be the average signal power, and suppose the noise is resistance noise of average power N in the band B occupied by the signal. Write the formula for the maximum information capacity of this system expressed in terms of binary digits per second, assuming a frequency of errors as arbitrarily small as may be desired and not precluding involved encoding and decoding and long delays at the transmitter and receiver.

35. In the three-dimensional configuration used in the double Fourier series method of spectrum analysis, how are the shapes of the portions of the surfaces (walls) that occupy the different elementary squares (with edges 2π radians long) related to one another?

36. In time-division pulse modulation systems using "start-stop" synchronization, how many marker pulses are transmitted per frame of message-bearing pulses?

37. Name two outstanding advantages of pulse-code modulation (PCM).

38. What property of a frequency-modulation system makes the use of de-emphasis in the receiver particularly advantageous?

39. Assume that a sinusoidal modulating wave is caused to phase-modulate a sine-wave carrier, and assume further that the peak phase deviation is φ_m radians. Write expressions for the amplitudes of the carrier and the various side frequencies which are present.

40. Which of the four arithmetical operations characterizes amplitude modulation (AM)?

41. Does a transmitted carrier AM telephone system that is limited to 100 per cent modulation utilize its available power capacity efficiently?

42. What is the precise definition of signal-to-noise ratio that is commonly used in developing formulas to depict the effects of noise and interference in frequency-modulation systems?

43. In a time-division PPM system using "long-time" synchronization, a sine wave is used to control the operation of the receiving synchronizer. How is this wave ordinarily obtained?

44. List three different classifications of PDM that are independent of the type of sampling.

45. Can the granularity due to quantization be eliminated from the output of a PCM receiver?

46. What is the purpose of the filter that is used at the output of the transmission medium (that is, the filter appearing in the input to the receiver or input to a repeater) in a time-division, pulse modulation system?

47. Describe very briefly time-division, frequency-division, and phase-discrimination multiplexing.

48. Can any measurement be made on a frequency-modulated or phase-modulated wave that will distinguish which of the two types of modulation the wave represents without a knowledge of the modulating wave? Explain.

49. When an envelope detector is used to recover the modulated wave from a double-sideband, amplitude-modulated wave, the modulation must be less than 100 per cent if substantially undistorted reproduction is desired. This limit is lowest when the frequency of the modulating wave is high. Give the physical reason for this limitation of percentage modulation.

50. Define the term *guard interval*, as applied to a train of PDM pulses.

51. What is the primary function of the synchronizing circuit that is used at the transmitting terminal of a time-division pulse-modulation system?

52. Why is it undesirable, in a time-division pulse-modulation system, to use marker pulses which are of shorter duration than the message-bearing pulses?

53. Compare the output waves of a low-index phase modulator and an amplitude modulator if both are modulated with the same modulating wave.

54. What similarities are there between the processes of modulation and demodulation?

55. Summarize the three basic steps in the procedure used in the double Fourier series method of spectrum analysis.

56. What is the expression for the advantage gained in signal-to-noise power ratio in a frequency-modulation system over a double-sideband amplitude-modulation system? Assume equal detector input noise-power density for both systems, assume that the noise-power density is independent of frequency and uncorrelated, and assume that the cutoff of the output low-pass filter is the same in each system. Also assume sinusoidal modulating waves in both systems, 100 per cent modulation in the amplitude-modulation system, and the same carrier power in both cases.

57. Name three types of unquantized pulse-modulation systems.

58. In the integrals that give the coefficients of the double Fourier series, is it necessary that the area of integration be a square?

59. Assume that a sinusoidal modulating wave is caused to phase-modulate a sine-wave carrier. What happens to the side frequencies as the phase deviation becomes very small? What are the amplitudes of the side frequencies when the deviation is very small? Assume the unmodulated carrier amplitude is unity.

60. Which gives the more compact expression for a double Fourier series: real or complex notation?

61. What happens to the output signal from a conventional frequency demodulator when the band width in the transmission medium is too restricted?

62. Are the in-phase and quadrature components of a modulated wave uniquely defined waves?

63. Define interference threshold.

64. In Chapter 15, a method of scaling was described whereby the properties of an N-channel time-division pulse-modulation system may be derived in terms of the properties of a one-channel system. Under the conditions assumed with this method, what is the ratio of the transmitted power in the N-channel system to the transmitted power in a one-channel system?

65. Draw a simple circuit diagram showing a carrier generator, a modulating-wave generator, and two nonlinear elements combined to produce a balanced modulator the output of which will contain no sidebands around even harmonics of the carrier.

66. As applied to time-division pulse-modulation systems, what is the purpose of the "hunting" circuit that is used in synchronizers operating on a "long-time" basis?

67. State the sampling principle either in its most general form or in one of its more common but restricted forms.

68. What factors are involved in determining the distortion produced by envelope detection of a vestigial sideband wave?

69. What is the ratio of power in the upper sideband to that in the lower sideband of an undistorted amplitude-modulated wave?

70. What is meant by an efficient coder?

71. Define quantization.

72. Is the multiplexing of channels usually performed on a time-division basis or on a frequency-division basis in a pulse-modulation system?

73. What is the function of the synchronizing circuit that is used at the receiving terminal of a time-division pulse-modulation system?

74. Define code, code element, code character, binary code, ternary code, N'ary code, and signal element.

75. How does the information-carrying capacity of a one-channel single-sideband system compare with the information-carrying capacity of the corresponding voice-frequency system occupying the same band?

76. What property of the modulating waves used in voice and program transmission allows pre-emphasis to be used to advantage?

77. Define regenerative repeatering.

78. At what rate can the signal-to-noise power ratio at the output of a frequency-modulation system improve as the allowed high-frequency band width is increased? Assume that the noise-power density over the high-frequency band is constant and uncorrelated and that in the absence of modulation the carrier power is large compared to the total noise power.

79. Define "Nyquist interval" and state its significance.

80. What is the central problem of information theory?

81. What is meant by information-bearing signals?

82. According to modern communication theory, what is the most efficient method for reducing the chance of error in transmission?

In the following exercises check the correct statements:

83. The three parts into which the spectrum of an amplitude-modulated wave naturally separates are called
    __ amplitude, phase, and frequency.
    __ upper sideband, lower sideband, and carrier.
    __ current, voltage, and power.
    __ attenuation, phase shift, and delay.

84. A spectrum of a real function of time that is an odd function of frequency must
    __ be pure imaginary.
    __ be real.
    __ represent an odd function of time.
    __ represent an even function of time.

85. In order for the spectrum in the output of a balanced modulator to contain no overlapping components, the carrier of an amplitude-modulated wave must be
    __ less than the lowest signal frequency.
    __ greater than the highest signal frequency.
    __ equal to the average signal frequency.
    __ greater than twice the highest signal frequency.

86. If the output of a binary pulse-code modulation system (in which the pulses are rectangular, completely fill their assigned time interval, and have equal probability of being positive or negative) is transmitted by double-sideband amplitude modulation and the carrier is 100 per cent modulated, the ratio of the average power in both sidebands to the average carrier power is
    __ two to one.
    __ one to one.
    __ one to two.
    __ one to four.

87. If in question 86 the pulses occupy only one-half of their allotted time interval, the ratio of average power in both sidebands to average carrier power is
    __ two to one.
    __ one to one.
    __ one to two.
    __ one to four.

88. An amplitude-modulated wave is
    __ the sum of the carrier and the modulating wave.
    __ the difference between the carrier and the modulating wave.

    — the product of the carrier and the modulating wave.

    — the ratio of the modulating wave to the carrier.

89. If an amplitude-modulated wave is passed through a network the transmission function of which has odd symmetry about the carrier,

    — the in-phase component is identical to the quadrature component.

    — the in-phase component is zero.

    — the quadrature component is zero.

    — nothing can be said about the quadrature component without more information.

90. If a resistance generator works into a network made up of an inductor, capacitor, and resistor in parallel,

    — the real part of the transmission function has approximately odd symmetry about the resonant frequency.

    — the imaginary part of the transmission function has approximately even symmetry about the resonant frequency.

    — neither part satisfies any symmetry relations even approximately.

    — the real part has approximately even symmetry and the imaginary part has approximately odd symmetry about the resonant frequency.

91. If in question 90 the generator voltage is an amplitude-modulated wave with its carrier component at the resonant frequency, the carrier frequency is high compared to the highest frequency component of the modulating wave, and the voltage across the output is resolved into its in-phase and quadrature components about the carrier, then the

    — in-phase component is negligible.

    — quadrature component is negligible.

    — quadrature component will have infinite peak value.

    — in-phase and quadrature components will have opposite signs.

92. Two product demodulators receive their inputs through perfect band filters, one for double-sideband reception, the other for single-sideband reception of the same signal, and their carriers are adjusted to give the same signal output. If the input is resistance noise, the ratio of the output noise power from the single-sideband system to that in the double-sideband system is

    — four to one.

    — two to one.

    — one to one.

    — one to two.

SUBJECT INDEX

353